Grant R. Fowles

UNIVERSITY OF UTAH

ANALYTICAL MECHANICS

Holt, Rinehart and Winston

New York

Preface

This textbook is written primarily for the junior course in analytical mechanics for students majoring in physics, physical science, or engineering science. It is presupposed that the student has taken a one-year course in general physics and that he has a thorough knowledge of differential and integral calculus. In addition, it is highly recommended that an introductory course in ordinary differential equations be taken prior to or concurrently with this course in mechanics.

Vectors are introduced at the beginning and are used throughout the text. The first two chapters comprise a short mathematical preparation in vector analysis. Rectilinear motion of a particle is presented in Chapter 3, and in Chapter 4 the motion of a particle in two and in three dimensions is studied. In the next chapter the effects of translation and rotation of the reference system are considered.

As a distinguishing feature of the book, a rather thorough treatment of celestial mechanics is given in Chapter 6. Celestial mechanics, as applied to space science, is a subject of recent revived interest and importance. Other applications to space science are found in Chapters 5 and 7.

The general theorems concerning motion of a system of many particles are proved in Chapter 7, and these are illustrated by studying collisions and rocket motion. The next two chapters are devoted to the study of rigid bodies. Statics is included only briefly as a part of rigid body motion in Chapter 8. (The student should already have had, in his previous courses in physics, considerable drill in solving problems in static equilibrium.) Elasticity and hydrodynamics have not been included. The author feels that these subjects are best postponed until the senior or graduate years when the student has acquired adequate mathematical preparation.

Lagrange's method is introduced in Chapter 10 and is used in the study of vibrating systems in Chapter 11. This chapter also includes a treatment of the stability of equilibrium.

The last chapter consists of a brief introduction to the special theory of relativity. It is highly desirable for physics majors to acquire early a working knowledge of special relativity as a part of their preparation for the study of atomic and nuclear physics in their senior and graduate years.

A list of problems is given at the end of each chapter. Some of these problems are important theorems for the student to prove, perhaps, in some cases, with a hint from the instructor. The author feels that the student should help develop the subject, rather than merely substitute numerical values into equations already developed in the book. Answers to the odd-numbered problems appear at the back of the text. Answers to the even-numbered problems are available to teachers on request.

A number of sections, or parts of sections, have been printed in *small type*, and are indicated by a star. These parts may be omitted in a short course without destroying the continuity of the text. These optional sections are, in any case, recommended reading for the better students.

Thanks are due Professor H. E. Duckworth of McMaster University for his many helpful suggestions during the preparation of the manuscript and Professor J. H. Wolfe of the Department of Mathematics of the University of Utah for his comments on the first four chapters. The author also wishes to thank his wife for her patience and for typing the final manuscript.

G.R.F.

Salt Lake City, Utah
February, 1962

Contents

v

12. The Special Theory of Relativity   257

Answers to Odd-numbered Problems   270

Index   275

Introduction

Mechanics, the science of motion, is basic to all other branches of physics. There is evidence of motion everywhere and on every scale of measurement — from the microscopic, for example, the atoms in a piece of matter, to the astronomical scale, the galaxies in the distant parts of the universe.

As a science, mechanics involves the application of the "scientific method"; that is, the use of observational data to form a theory which, in turn, can be used to predict the results of further observations. Although mechanics had its beginnings in antiquity — Archimedes formulated the principle of the lever in the third century B.C. — it was not until the seventeenth century A.D. that the *science* of mechanics was truly founded. It was at this time that Galileo, Huygens, and Newton showed that all things move in accordance with a few very definite rules.

It is important to realize that mechanics does not undertake to explain *why* bodies move; rather, it shows *how* bodies move in a given situation and how to describe the motions of bodies in the simplest manner. That branch of mechanics which is concerned with the purely geometric description of motion is called *kinematics*. In kinematics the concepts of position, velocity, and acceleration are treated. The larger part of mechanics, that which deals with the physical laws governing the actual motion of material bodies, is called *dynamics*. In dynamics the concepts of mass and force are introduced. A subdivision of dynamics, the study of bodies at rest, is known as *statics*.

In our study of mechanics at this level we shall be mainly concerned with *classical* or Newtonian mechanics, which, as the name implies, is essentially the study of the consequences of the laws of motion as formulated by Newton in his *Philosophiae Naturalis Principia Mathematica* (the Principia) published in 1686. This monumental work has been described by Sir James Jeans* as "certainly the greatest scientific work ever produced by the human intellect." Newtonian mechanics, until the beginning of the present century, was believed to represent the ultimate description of

*The Growth of Physical Science, Cambridge University Press, London, 1947.

the universe. Today we know that Newton's ideas need to be modified in at least two extreme cases: when the distances involved are of atomic dimensions, and when the speeds of the bodies become comparable to the speed of light. The modified mechanics (quantum theory and relativity, respectively) are nevertheless built upon the foundations laid down by Newton. In practically all of the vast applications of applied science and engineering, the classical laws are still valid.

1

Fundamental Concepts. Vectors

In any physical theory it is necessary to begin with certain undefined intuitive concepts and certain reasonable assumptions. Two of these intuitive concepts in mechanics are *space* and *time*. We assume that the *physical space* of experience is adequately described by the *three-dimensional mathematical space* of Euclidean geometry. We assume also that a sequence of events, one after another, can be defined in terms of a uniform absolute time scale.

In order to define the position of a body in space, it is necessary to have something for reference. In mechanics we use a *coordinate system*. The basic type of coordinate system for our purpose is the *Cartesian* or *rectangular* coordinate system, a set of three mutually perpendicular straight lines or *axes*. The position of a point in such a coordinate system is specified by three numbers or coordinates, x, y, and z. The coordinates of a *moving* point change with time; that is, they are functions of the quantity t as measured on our time scale.

A very useful concept in mechanics is the *particle* or mass point, an entity that has mass* but does not have spatial extension. Strictly speaking the particle is an idealization that does not exist — even an electron has a finite size — but the idea is useful as an approximation of a small body, or rather, one whose size is relatively unimportant in a particular discussion. The earth, for example, might be treated as a particle in celestial mechanics.

1.1. Physical Quantities and Units

The observational data of physics are expressed in terms of certain fundamental entities called *physical quantities* — for example, length, time, force, etc. A physical quantity is something that can be measured quantita-

*The concept of mass will be discussed in Chap. 3.

1

tively in relation to some chosen unit. When we say that the length of a
certain object is, say 7 in., we mean that the quantitative measure 7 is the
relation (ratio) of the length of that object to the length of the unit (1 in.).
It has been found that it is possible to define all of the *unit* physical quantities of mechanics in terms of just three basic ones. These are:

(1) The unit of *length*. The standard unit of length is the *meter*. The
meter was formerly the distance between two scratches on a
platinum bar kept at the International Bureau of Metric Standards,
Sevres, France. The meter is now defined as the distance occupied
by exactly 1,650,763.73 wavelengths of light of the orange spectrum
line of the isotope krypton 86.

(2) The unit of *mass*. The standard unit of mass is the *kilogram*. It is
the mass of a cylinder of platinum iridium also kept at the International Bureau.

(3) The unit of *time*. The earth is the standard timekeeper. The
standard unit of time, the *second* was formerly defined as 1/86,400th
of a mean solar day. The second is now more precisely defined as
exactly 1/31,556,925.9747th of the year 1900.

The above system of units is called the mks system. (In this system there is
a fourth unit, the *coulomb* of electric charge, which is used to define electrical
units.) Other sets of physical quantities can be employed to define units.
The so-called gravitational systems use length, *force*, and time. There are
two other systems in common use, the cgs (centimeter-gram-second) system, and the fps (foot-pound-second) system. These latter two systems
may be regarded as secondary systems, however, because these units are
certain defined fractions of the mks units (1 ft being 0.3048 m, and 1 lb
being 0.4536 kg).

1.2.   Scalar and Vector Quantities

A physical quantity that is specified by a single magnitude, or number,
in addition to units, is called a *scalar*. Density, volume, and temperature
are examples of scalars. Those physical quantities which require for their
complete specification a direction, as well as a magnitude are called *vector
quantities*, or simply *vectors*. Displacement, velocity, and force are three
familiar examples of vectors. The vector concept and the development of a
"mathematics" of vectors have greatly simplified the science of mechanics.
In the remainder of this chapter we shall study briefly the algebra of vectors.

1.3. Notation

Vector quantities are denoted in print by boldface type, for example, **A**, whereas ordinary italic type represents scalar quantities. In written work it is customary to use a distinguishing mark, such as an arrow, $\vec{A}$, to designate a vector.

A given vector **A** is specified by stating its magnitude and its direction relative to some chosen reference system. A vector is represented diagrammatically by a directed line segment, as shown in Fig. 1.1. A vector

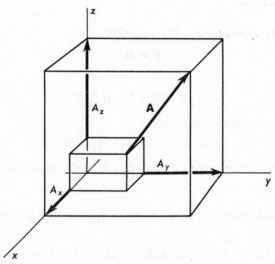

Fig. 1.1

can also be specified by listing its *components* or projections of the vector along the coordinate axes used for reference. The component symbol $[A_x, A_y, A_z]$ will be used as an alternate designation of a vector. The equation

$$\mathbf{A} = [A_x, A_y, A_z]$$

means that the vector **A** is expressed on the right in terms of its components in a particular coordinate system. (It will be assumed that a Cartesian coordinate system is meant, unless stated otherwise.) For example, if the vector **A** represents a *displacement* from a point $P_1(x_1, y_1, z_1)$ to the point $P_2(x_2, y_2, z_2)$, then $A_x = x_2 - x_1$, $A_y = y_2 - y_1$, $A_z = z_2 - z_1$. If **A** represents a *force*, then A_x is the x component of the force, etc. Clearly, the numerical values of the scalar components of a given vector depend on the choice of the coordinate axes.

If a particular discussion is limited to vectors in a plane, only two components are necessary. On the other hand, one can define a mathematical space of any number of dimensions. Thus the symbol $[A_1, A_2, A_3, \ldots A_n]$ denotes an n-dimensional vector. In this abstract sense a vector is an ordered set of numbers.

1.4.   Definitions

We begin the study of vector algebra with some formal definitions using component notation.

1. Equality of vectors.   The equation

$$\mathbf{A} = \mathbf{B}$$

or

$$[A_x, A_y, A_z] = [B_x, B_y, B_z]$$

is equivalent to the three equations

$$A_x = B_x \quad A_y = B_y \quad A_z = B_z$$

That is, two vectors are equal if, and only if, their respective components are equal.

2. Vector addition.   The addition of two vectors is defined by the equation

$$\mathbf{A} + \mathbf{B} = [A_x, A_y, A_z] + [B_x, B_y, B_z] = [A_x + B_x, A_y + B_y, A_z + B_z]$$

The sum of two vectors is a vector whose components are sums of the components of the given vectors.

3. Multiplication by a scalar.   If n is a scalar and A a vector,

$$n\mathbf{A} = n[A_x, A_y, A_z] = [nA_x, nA_y, nA_z] = \mathbf{A}n$$

The product $n\mathbf{A}$ is a vector whose components are n times those of $\mathbf{A}$.

4. Vector subtraction.

$$\mathbf{A} - \mathbf{B} = \mathbf{A} + (-1)\mathbf{B} = [A_x - B_x, A_y - B_y, A_z - B_z]$$

5. The null vector.   The vector $\mathbf{O} = [0,0,0]$ is called the *null* vector. The direction of the null vector is undefined. From (3) and (4) it follows that $\mathbf{A} - \mathbf{A} = \mathbf{O}$.

6. The commutative law of addition. This law holds for vectors; that is,

$$\mathbf{A} + \mathbf{B} = \mathbf{B} + \mathbf{A}$$

since $A_x + B_x = B_x + A_x$, etc.

7. The associative law. The associative law is also true, because

$$\begin{aligned}\mathbf{A} + (\mathbf{B} + \mathbf{C}) &= [A_x + (B_x + C_x), A_y + (B_y + C_y), A_z + (B_z + C_z)]\\ &= [(A_x + B_x) + C_x, (A_y + B_y) + C_y, (A_z + B_z) + C_z]\\ &= (\mathbf{A} + \mathbf{B}) + \mathbf{C}\end{aligned}$$

8. The distributive law. Under multiplication by a scalar the distributive law is valid, because, from (2) and (3),

$$\begin{aligned}n(\mathbf{A} + \mathbf{B}) &= n[A_x + B_x, A_y + B_y, A_z + B_z]\\ &= [n(A_x + B_x), n(A_y + B_y), n(A_z + B_z)]\\ &= [nA_x + nB_x, nA_y + nB_y, nA_z + nB_z]\\ &= n\mathbf{A} + n\mathbf{B}\end{aligned}$$

Thus vectors obey the rules of ordinary algebra as far as the above operations are concerned.

1.5. Magnitude of a Vector

The magnitude of a vector $\mathbf{A}$, denoted by $|\mathbf{A}|$ or by A, is defined as the square root of the sum of the squares of the components, namely,

$$A = |\mathbf{A}| = (A_x^2 + A_y^2 + A_z^2)^{1/2} \qquad (1.1)$$

where the positive root is understood. Geometrically, the magnitude of a vector is its length, that is, the length of the diagonal of the rectangular parallelopiped whose sides are A_x, A_y, and A_z.

1.6. Geometric Meaning of Vector Operations

If we consider a vector to be represented by a directed line segment, it is easily verified that the definitions stated above have the following simple interpretations:

(1) Equality of two vectors means that the vectors are parallel and have the same length, but they do not necessarily have the same

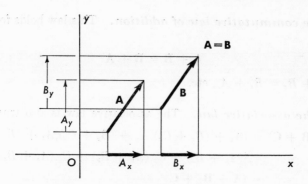

FIG. 1.2

position. Equal vectors are shown in Fig. 1.2, where only two components are drawn for clarity. Notice that the vectors form opposite sides of a parallelogram. (Equal vectors are not necessarily equivalent in all respects. Thus two vectorially equal forces acting at *different* points on an object may produce different mechanical effects.)

(2) The vector sum of two vectors is equal to the third side of a triangle, two sides of which are the given vectors. The vector sum is illustrated in Fig. 1.3. The sum is also given by the parallelogram rule, as shown in the figure. [The vector sum is defined, however, according to definition 1.4(2) even if the vectors do not have a common point.]

(3) The vector $n\mathbf{A}$ is parallel to $\mathbf{A}$ and is n times the length of $\mathbf{A}$. When $n = -1$, the vector $-\mathbf{A}$ is one whose direction is the reverse of that of $\mathbf{A}$, as shown in Fig. 1.4.

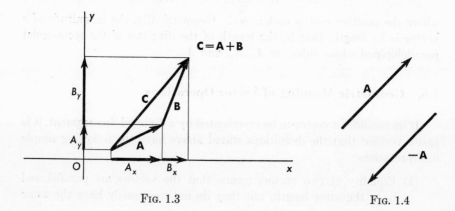

FIG. 1.3   FIG. 1.4

1.7.   Equilibrium of a Particle

Let a number of concurrent forces $\mathbf{F}_1, \mathbf{F}_2, \ldots \mathbf{F}_n$ act on a particle. Then the condition for *static equilibrium* of the particle, that is, the condition that the particle will not move under the action of those forces, is that their vector sum is null:

$$\mathbf{F}_1 + \mathbf{F}_2 + \cdots + \mathbf{F}_n = \Sigma\,\mathbf{F}_i = \mathbf{O}$$

If we denote the x component of $\mathbf{F}_1$ by X_1, etc., then the above equation of equilibrium is equivalent to the three equations:

$$\Sigma\,X_i = 0$$
$$\Sigma\,Y_i = 0$$
$$\Sigma\,Z_i = 0$$

as is evident from the definition of the vector sum given in Sec. 1.4(2) above. If all but one of the forces are given, the above equations of equilibrium allow us to solve for the components of the unknown force.

1.8.   The Scalar Product

Given two vectors $\mathbf{A}$ and $\mathbf{B}$, the scalar product or "dot" product, $\mathbf{A}\cdot\mathbf{B}$, is the scalar defined by the equation

$$\mathbf{A}\cdot\mathbf{B} = A_x B_x + A_y B_y + A_z B_z \qquad (1.2)$$

It follows from the above definition that

$$\mathbf{A}\cdot\mathbf{B} = \mathbf{B}\cdot\mathbf{A} \qquad (1.3)$$

since $A_x B_x = B_x A_x$, etc. It also follows that

$$\mathbf{A}\cdot(\mathbf{B} + \mathbf{C}) = \mathbf{A}\cdot\mathbf{B} + \mathbf{A}\cdot\mathbf{C} \qquad (1.4)$$

because if we apply the definition [(1.2)] in detail

$$\mathbf{A}\cdot(\mathbf{B} + \mathbf{C}) = A_x(B_x + C_x) + A_y(B_y + C_y) + A_z(B_z + C_z)$$
$$= A_x B_x + A_y B_y + A_z B_z + A_x C_x + A_y C_y + A_z C_z$$
$$= \mathbf{A}\cdot\mathbf{B} + \mathbf{A}\cdot\mathbf{C}$$

From analytical geometry we recall the formula for the cosine of the angle between two line segments

$$\cos\theta = \frac{A_x B_x + A_y B_y + A_z B_z}{(A_x^2 + A_y^2 + A_z^2)^{1/2}(B_x^2 + B_y^2 + B_z^2)^{1/2}}$$

Using Eqs. (1.1) and (1.2), the above formula may be written

$$\cos \theta = \frac{\mathbf{A} \cdot \mathbf{B}}{AB} \qquad (1.5)$$

The above equation may be regarded as an alternate definition of the dot product. Geometrically, $\mathbf{A} \cdot \mathbf{B}$ is equal to the length of the projection of $\mathbf{A}$ on $\mathbf{B}$, times the length of $\mathbf{B}$.

If the dot product $\mathbf{A} \cdot \mathbf{B}$ is equal to zero, then $\mathbf{A}$ is perpendicular to $\mathbf{B}$, provided neither $\mathbf{A}$ nor $\mathbf{B}$ is null.

The square of the magnitude of a vector $\mathbf{A}$ is given by the dot product of $\mathbf{A}$ with itself,

$$A^2 = |\mathbf{A}|^2 = \mathbf{A} \cdot \mathbf{A}$$

1.9.   Some Applications of the Dot Product

1. Work.   Suppose an object under the action of a constant force $\mathbf{F}$ undergoes a linear displacement $\Delta \mathbf{s}$, as shown in Fig. 1.5. By definition, the *work* ΔW done by the force is given by the product of the component of $\mathbf{F}$ in the direction of $\Delta \mathbf{s}$, multiplied by the magnitude Δs of the displacement, that is

$$\Delta W = (F \cos \theta) \, \Delta s$$

where θ is the angle between $\mathbf{F}$ and $\Delta \mathbf{s}$. But the expression on the right is just the dot product of $\mathbf{F}$ and $\Delta \mathbf{s}$, that is,

$$\Delta W = \mathbf{F} \cdot \Delta \mathbf{s}$$

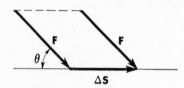 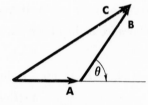

Fɪɢ. 1.5   Fɪɢ. 1.6

2. Law of cosines.   Given the triangle whose sides are $\mathbf{A}$, $\mathbf{B}$, and $\mathbf{C} = \mathbf{A} + \mathbf{B}$, as shown in Fig. 1.6. Take the dot product of $\mathbf{C}$ with itself

$$\mathbf{C} \cdot \mathbf{C} = (\mathbf{A} + \mathbf{B}) \cdot (\mathbf{A} + \mathbf{B})$$
$$= \mathbf{A} \cdot \mathbf{A} + 2\mathbf{A} \cdot \mathbf{B} + \mathbf{B} \cdot \mathbf{B}$$

The second step follows from the application of the rules in Eqs. (1.3) and (1.4). Replace $\mathbf{A} \cdot \mathbf{B}$ by $AB \cos \theta$ to obtain

$$C^2 = A^2 + 2AB \cos \theta + B^2$$

which is the familiar law of cosines.

1.10. The Vector Product

Given two vectors **A** and **B**, the vector product or "cross product," **A** × **B**, is defined as the vector whose components are given by the equation

$$\mathbf{A} \times \mathbf{B} = [A_y B_z - A_z B_y, \quad A_z B_x - A_x B_z, \quad A_x B_y - A_y B_x] \quad (1.6)$$

The geometric interpretation of the cross product is given in Sec. 1.12. It can be shown that the following rules hold for cross multiplication.

$$\mathbf{A} \times \mathbf{B} = -\mathbf{B} \times \mathbf{A} \quad (1.7)$$

$$\mathbf{A} \times (\mathbf{B} + \mathbf{C}) = \mathbf{A} \times \mathbf{B} + \mathbf{A} \times \mathbf{C} \quad (1.8)$$

$$n(\mathbf{A} \times \mathbf{B}) = (n\mathbf{A}) \times \mathbf{B} = \mathbf{A} \times (n\mathbf{B}) \quad (1.9)$$

The proofs of these follow directly from the definition [Eq. (1.6)], and are left as an exercise.

1.11. Unit Coordinate Vectors

A *unit vector* is one whose magnitude is unity. The three unit vectors

$$\mathbf{i} = [1,0,0] \quad \mathbf{j} = [0,1,0] \quad \mathbf{k} = [0,0,1] \quad (1.10)$$

are called *unit coordinate vectors*. In terms of these vectors, any vector can be expressed as a sum as follows:

$$\begin{aligned}
\mathbf{A} = [A_x, A_y, A_z] &= [A_x,0,0] + [0,A_y,0] + [0,0,A_z] \\
&= A_x[1,0,0] + A_y[0,1,0] + A_z[0,0,1] \\
&= \mathbf{i}A_x + \mathbf{j}A_y + \mathbf{k}A_z \quad (1.11)
\end{aligned}$$

The "sum" notation is convenient for many purposes and will often be used; we shall call it the **ijk** form of representing a vector.

The directions of the unit coordinate vectors are defined by the coordinate axes (Fig. 1.7). They form a right-handed or a left-handed triad, depending on which type of coordinate system is used. It is customary to use right-handed coordinate systems. The system shown in Fig. 1.7 is right handed.

From the definitions of the dot and the cross products, Eqs. (1.2) and (1.6), together with the definition [Eq. (1.10)] of the unit vectors **i**, **j**, and **k**, it follows that

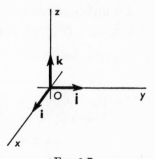

Fig. 1.7

$$\mathbf{i \cdot i = j \cdot j = k \cdot k} = 1 \qquad \mathbf{i \cdot j = i \cdot k = j \cdot k} = 0$$
$$\mathbf{i \times i = j \times j = k \times k} = 0 \qquad \mathbf{i \times j = k = -j \times i}$$
$$\mathbf{j \times k = i = -k \times j} \qquad \mathbf{k \times i = j = -i \times j}$$

For example,

$$\mathbf{i \cdot i} = [1,0,0] \cdot [1,0,0] = 1 + 0 + 0 = 1$$
$$\mathbf{i \times j} = [0 - 0, 0 - 0, 1 - 0] = [0,0,1] = \mathbf{k}$$

The remaining equations are easily proved in a similar manner.

1.12.   Geometric Interpretation of the Cross Product

The cross product expressed in **ijk** form is

$$\mathbf{A \times B} = \mathbf{i}(A_y B_z - A_z B_y) + \mathbf{j}(A_z B_x - A_x B_z) + \mathbf{k}(A_x B_y - A_y B_x)$$

Each term in parentheses is equal to a determinant

$$\mathbf{A \times B} = \mathbf{i}\begin{vmatrix} A_y A_z \\ B_y B_z \end{vmatrix} + \mathbf{j}\begin{vmatrix} A_z A_x \\ B_z B_x \end{vmatrix} + \mathbf{k}\begin{vmatrix} A_x A_y \\ B_x B_y \end{vmatrix}$$

and finally

$$\mathbf{A \times B} = \begin{vmatrix} \mathbf{i} & \mathbf{j} & \mathbf{k} \\ A_x A_y A_z \\ B_x B_y B_z \end{vmatrix} \tag{1.12}$$

which is readily verified by expansion. The determinant in Eq. (1.12) is a convenient aid for remembering the definition of the cross product. From the properties of determinants, it can be seen at once that if **A** is parallel to **B**, that is, if $\mathbf{A} = n\mathbf{B}$, then the two lower rows of the determinant are proportional and so the determinant is null. Thus the cross product of two parallel vectors is null.

Let us calculate the magnitude of the cross product. We have

$$|\mathbf{A \times B}|^2 = (A_y B_z - A_z B_y)^2 + (A_z B_x - A_x B_z)^2 + (A_x B_y - A_y B_x)^2$$

With a little patience this can be reduced to

$$|\mathbf{A \times B}|^2 = (A_x^2 + A_y^2 + A_z^2)(B_x^2 + B_y^2 + B_z^2) - (A_x B_x + A_y B_y + A_z B_z)^2$$

or, from the definitions [Eqs. (1.1) and (1.2)],

$$|\mathbf{A \times B}|^2 = A^2 B^2 - (\mathbf{A \cdot B})^2$$

Taking the square root of both sides of the above equation and using Eq. (1.5), we can express the magnitude of the cross product as

$$|\mathbf{A \times B}| = AB(1 - \cos^2 \theta)^{1/2} = AB \sin \theta \tag{1.13}$$

where θ is the angle between **A** and **B**.

To interpret the cross product geometrically, we observe that the vector $\mathbf{C} = \mathbf{A} \times \mathbf{B}$ is perpendicular to both $\mathbf{A}$ and to $\mathbf{B}$, because

$$\mathbf{A} \cdot \mathbf{C} = A_x C_x + A_y C_y + A_z C_z$$
$$= A_x(A_y B_z - A_z B_y) + A_y(A_z B_x - A_x B_z) + A_z(A_x B_y - A_y B_x)$$
$$= 0$$

Similarly, $\mathbf{B} \cdot \mathbf{C} = 0$. Thus the vector $\mathbf{C}$ is perpendicular to the plane containing the vectors $\mathbf{A}$ and $\mathbf{B}$.

The sense of the vector $\mathbf{C} = \mathbf{A} \times \mathbf{B}$ is determined from the requirement that the three vectors $\mathbf{A}$, $\mathbf{B}$, and $\mathbf{C}$ form a right-handed triad, as shown in Fig. 1.8. (This is consistent with the previously established result that in

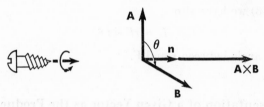

FIG. 1.8

the right-handed triad $\mathbf{ijk}$ we have $\mathbf{i} \times \mathbf{j} = \mathbf{k}$.) Therefore, from Eq. (1.13) we see that we can write

$$\mathbf{A} \times \mathbf{B} = (AB \sin \theta)\mathbf{n} \qquad (1.14)$$

where $\mathbf{n}$ is a unit vector normal to the plane of the two vectors $\mathbf{A}$ and $\mathbf{B}$. The sense of $\mathbf{n}$ is given by the *right-hand rule*, that is, the direction of advancement of a right-handed screw rotated from the positive direction of $\mathbf{A}$ to that of $\mathbf{B}$ through the angle between them, as illustrated in Fig. 1.8. Equation (1.14) may be regarded as an alternate definition of the cross product.

1.13. Moment of a Force

A particularly useful application of the cross product is the representation of moments. Let a force $\mathbf{F}$ act at a point $P(x,y,z)$, as shown in Fig. 1.9, and let the vector $\overrightarrow{OP}$ be designated by $\mathbf{r}$, that is,

$$\overrightarrow{OP} = \mathbf{r} = \mathbf{i}x + \mathbf{j}y + \mathbf{k}z$$

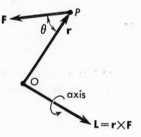

FIG. 1.9

The moment **L** of the force **F**, or the *torque*, about the point O is defined as the cross product of **r** and **F**:

$$L = r \times F \tag{1.15}$$

It should be emphasized that the moment of a force about a point is a vector quantity. To illustrate, suppose the force **F** is applied at a point P on an object which is free to turn (as a pivot) about the point O. Then the body will tend to rotate, and the axis of the resulting rotation will be perpendicular to **F** and also to $\overrightarrow{OP}$; that is, the axis will be in the direction of **L**. The magnitude of **L** is

$$L = |L| = |r \times F| \tag{1.15(a)}$$

From Eq. (1.13) we have also

$$L = rF \sin \theta \tag{1.15(b)}$$

where θ is the angle between **r** and **F**.

1.14. Representation of a Given Vector as the Product of a Scalar and a Single Unit Vector

Consider the equation

$$A = iA_x + jA_y + kA_z$$

Multiply and divide on the right by the magnitude of **A**

$$A = A\left(i\frac{A_x}{A} + j\frac{A_y}{A} + k\frac{A_z}{A}\right)$$

Now $A_x/A = l$, $A_y/A = m$ $A_z/A = n$ where l, m, and n are the direction cosines of the vector A. Thus we can write

$$A = A(il + jy + kz) = A[l,m,n]$$

or

$$A = A\lambda \tag{1.16}$$

where λ is a unit vector whose components are l, m, and n. Consider any other vector **B**. Clearly, the projection of **A** on **B** is just

$$B \cos \theta = \frac{B \cdot A}{A} = B \cdot \lambda \tag{1.17}$$

where θ is the angle between **A** and **B**.

★1.15.   Change of Coordinate System

Consider the vector **A** expressed relative to the triad **ijk**

$$\mathbf{A} = \mathbf{i}A_x + \mathbf{j}A_y + \mathbf{k}A_z$$

Relative to a new triad **i′j′k′** having a different orientation from that of **ijk**, the *same* vector **A** is expressed as

$$\mathbf{A} = \mathbf{i}'A_{x'} + \mathbf{j}'A_{y'} + \mathbf{k}'A_{z'}$$

Now the dot product **A·i′** is just $A_{x'}$, that is, the projection of **A** on the unit vector **i′**. Thus we may write

$$A_{x'} = \mathbf{A \cdot i'} = (\mathbf{i \cdot i'})A_x + (\mathbf{j \cdot i'})A_y + (\mathbf{k \cdot i'})A_z$$
$$A_{y'} = \mathbf{A \cdot j'} = (\mathbf{i \cdot j'})A_x + (\mathbf{j \cdot j'})A_y + (\mathbf{k \cdot j'})A_z \qquad (1.18)$$
$$A_{z'} = \mathbf{A \cdot k'} = (\mathbf{i \cdot k'})A_x + (\mathbf{j \cdot k'})A_y + (\mathbf{k \cdot k'})A_z$$

The scalar products $(\mathbf{i \cdot i'})$, $(\mathbf{i \cdot j'})$, etc., are called the *coefficients of transformation*. They are equal to the direction cosines of the axes of the primed coordinate system relative to the unprimed system. The unprimed components are similarly expressed as

$$A_x = \mathbf{A \cdot i} = (\mathbf{i' \cdot i})A_{x'} + (\mathbf{j' \cdot i})A_{y'} + (\mathbf{k' \cdot i})A_{z'}$$
$$A_y = \mathbf{A \cdot j} = (\mathbf{i' \cdot j})A_{x'} + (\mathbf{j' \cdot j})A_{y'} + (\mathbf{k' \cdot j})A_{z'} \qquad (1.19)$$
$$A_z = \mathbf{A \cdot k} = (\mathbf{i' \cdot k})A_{x'} + (\mathbf{j' \cdot k})A_{y'} + (\mathbf{k' \cdot k})A_{z'}$$

All of the coefficients of transformation in Eq. (1.19) also appear in Eq. (1.18), because $\mathbf{i \cdot i'} = \mathbf{i' \cdot i}$, etc., but those in the rows (equations) of Eq. (1.19) appear in the columns of terms in Eq. (1.18), and conversely. The transformation rules expressed in these two sets of equations constitute a general property of vectors.

EXAMPLE

Express the vector $A = 3\mathbf{i} + 2\mathbf{j} + \mathbf{k}$ in terms of the triad **i′j′k′** where the $x'y'$ axes are rotated 45° around the z axis, the z and the z' axes coinciding, as shown in Fig. 1.10. Referring to the figure, we have for the coefficients of transformation,

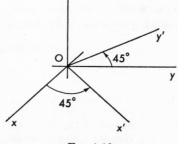

$$\mathbf{i \cdot i'} = 1/\sqrt{2} \qquad \mathbf{j \cdot i'} = 1/\sqrt{2} \qquad \mathbf{k \cdot i'} = 0$$
$$\mathbf{i \cdot j'} = -1/\sqrt{2} \qquad \mathbf{j \cdot j'} = 1/\sqrt{2} \qquad \mathbf{k \cdot j'} = 0$$
$$\mathbf{i \cdot k'} = 0 \qquad \mathbf{j \cdot k'} = 0 \qquad \mathbf{k \cdot k'} = 1$$

FIG. 1.10

These give

$$A_{x'} = \frac{3}{\sqrt{2}} + \frac{2}{\sqrt{2}} = \frac{5}{\sqrt{2}} \qquad A_{y'} = \frac{-3}{\sqrt{2}} + \frac{2}{\sqrt{2}} = \frac{-1}{\sqrt{2}} \qquad A_{z'} = 1$$

so that, in the primed system, the vector **A** is given by

$$\mathbf{A} = \frac{5}{\sqrt{2}}\,\mathbf{i'} - \frac{1}{\sqrt{2}}\,\mathbf{j'} + \mathbf{k'}$$

1.16.   Triple Products

The expression

$$\mathbf{A}\cdot(\mathbf{B}\times\mathbf{C})$$

is called the *triple scalar product* of **A**, **B**, and **C**. It is a scalar since it is the dot product of two vectors. Referring to the determinant expression for the cross product, Eq. (1.12), we see that the triple scalar product may be written

$$\mathbf{A}\cdot(\mathbf{B}\times\mathbf{C}) = \begin{vmatrix} A_x A_y A_z \\ B_x B_y B_z \\ C_x C_y C_z \end{vmatrix} \tag{1.20}$$

From the well-known property of determinants that the exchange of the terms of two rows or of two columns changes the sign but does not change the absolute value of the determinant, we can easily derive the following useful equation:

$$\mathbf{A}\cdot(\mathbf{B}\times\mathbf{C}) = (\mathbf{A}\times\mathbf{B})\cdot\mathbf{C} \tag{1.21}$$

Thus the dot and the cross may be interchanged in the triple scalar product.

The expression

$$\mathbf{A}\times(\mathbf{B}\times\mathbf{C})$$

is called the *triple vector product*. It is left for the student to prove that the following equation holds for the triple vector product:

$$\mathbf{A}\times(\mathbf{B}\times\mathbf{C}) = (\mathbf{A}\cdot\mathbf{C})\mathbf{B} - (\mathbf{A}\cdot\mathbf{B})\mathbf{C} \tag{1.22}$$

PROBLEMS

1. Given two vectors $\mathbf{A} = 3\mathbf{i} + 4\mathbf{j} + \mathbf{k}$ and $\mathbf{B} = \mathbf{i} + \mathbf{j} + 2\mathbf{k}$.
    (a) Find the value of $\mathbf{A}\cdot\mathbf{B}$.
    (b) Express in **ijk** form: $\mathbf{A} + \mathbf{B}$, $\mathbf{A} - 2\mathbf{B}$, $\mathbf{A}\times\mathbf{B}$.
    (c) Without calculating the angle between **A** and **B**, find the length of the projection of **A** on **B**.
    (d) Find the angle between **A** and **B**.

2. The vector $\mathbf{A} = q\mathbf{i} + 3\mathbf{j} + 2\mathbf{k}$ is perpendicular to the vector $\mathbf{B} = \mathbf{i} - \mathbf{j} + 4\mathbf{k}$. What is the value of q?

3. Show that Eqs. (1.7), (1.8), and (1.9) follow from the definition [Eq. (1.6)].

4. Two vectors **A** and **B** represent concurrent sides of a parallelogram. Show that the area of the parallelogram is equal to $|\mathbf{A} \times \mathbf{B}|$.

5. Prove the law of sines using vector methods.

6. Three forces acting on a particle are in equilibrium. Show that the lines of action lie in a single plane, and that the three forces may be represented by the sides of a triangle.

7. A force $\mathbf{F} = 2\mathbf{i} + 3\mathbf{j}$ is applied at the point P where the vector $\overrightarrow{OP} = \mathbf{r} = \mathbf{i} - \mathbf{j} + \mathbf{k}$. Find the moment $\mathbf{L}$ and the magnitude of $\mathbf{L}$ about the origin O.

8. Three vectors **A**, **B**, and **C** represent concurrent sides of a parallelepiped. Show that the volume of the parallelepiped is equal to the absolute value of the triple scalar product of the three vectors.

9. Express the vector $\mathbf{i} - \mathbf{j} + 3\mathbf{k}$ in terms of the triad $\mathbf{i'j'k'}$ where the $x'z'$ axes are rotated 30° around the y axis (which coincides with the y' axis). Verify that the magnitude of the vector is unchanged by this transformation of axes.

10. Prove Eq. (1.22).

2

Vector Calculus and Kinematics of a Particle

In this chapter we shall develop the formalism for the kinematic description of the motion of a particle. The treatment is greatly simplified by the use of the calculus applied to vector quantities.

2.1. Derivative of a Vector

Consider a vector $\mathbf{A}$, the components of which are functions of a single variable u. The vector may represent position, velocity, etc. The parameter u is usually the time t, but it can be any quantity which determines the components of $\mathbf{A}$:

$$\mathbf{A}(u) = \mathbf{i}A_x(u) + \mathbf{j}A_y(u) + \mathbf{k}A_z(u)$$

The derivative of $\mathbf{A}$ with respect to u is defined, quite analogously to the ordinary derivative of a scalar function, by the limit

$$\frac{d\mathbf{A}}{du} = \lim_{\Delta u \to 0} \frac{\Delta \mathbf{A}}{\Delta u} = \lim_{\Delta u \to 0} \left(\mathbf{i}\frac{\Delta A_x}{\Delta u} + \mathbf{j}\frac{\Delta A_y}{\Delta u} + \mathbf{k}\frac{\Delta A_z}{\Delta u} \right)$$

where $\Delta A_x = A_x(u + \Delta u) - A_x(u)$, etc. Hence

$$\frac{d\mathbf{A}}{du} = \mathbf{i}\frac{dA_x}{du} + \mathbf{j}\frac{dA_y}{du} + \mathbf{k}\frac{dA_z}{du} \tag{2.1}$$

The derivative of a vector, therefore, is a vector whose components are ordinary derivatives.

2.2. Position Vector of a Particle

In a given reference system the position of a particle can be specified by a single vector, namely, the displacement of the particle relative to the origin of the coordinate system. This vector is called the position vector of the particle. In rectangular coordinates, Fig. 2.1, the position vector is simply

$$\mathbf{r} = \mathbf{i}x + \mathbf{j}y + \mathbf{k}z$$

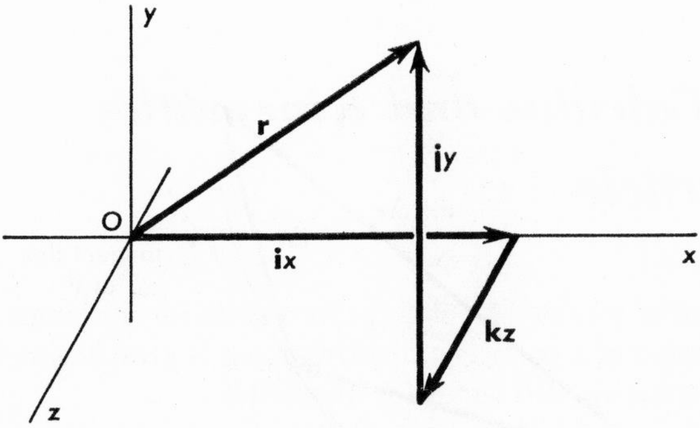

Fig. 2.1

The components of the position vector of a moving particle are functions of the time, namely,

$$x = x(t) \quad y = y(t) \quad z = z(t)$$

2.3. The Velocity Vector

In Sec. 2.1 we gave the formal definition of the derivative of any vector with respect to some parameter. In particular, if the vector is the position vector $\mathbf{r}$ of a moving particle and the parameter is the time t, the derivative of $\mathbf{r}$ with respect to t is called the *velocity*, which we shall denote by $\mathbf{v}$. Hence

$$\mathbf{v} = \frac{d\mathbf{r}}{dt} = \mathbf{i}\dot{x} + \mathbf{j}\dot{y} + \mathbf{k}\dot{z} \tag{2.2}$$

where the dots indicate differentiation with respect to t. (This convention is standard and will be used throughout the book.) Let us examine the geometric significance of the velocity vector. Suppose a particle is at a certain position at time t. At a time Δt later the particle will have moved from the position $\mathbf{r}(t)$ to the position $\mathbf{r}(t + \Delta t)$. The vector displacement during the time interval Δt is

$$\Delta \mathbf{r} = \mathbf{r}(t + \Delta t) - \mathbf{r}(t)$$

so the quotient $\Delta \mathbf{r}/\Delta t$ is a *vector* which is parallel to the displacement. As we consider smaller and smaller time intervals, the quotient $\Delta \mathbf{r}/\Delta t$ approaches a limit $d\mathbf{r}/dt$ which we call the velocity. The vector $d\mathbf{r}/dt$ expresses both the direction of motion and the rate. This is shown graphically in Fig. 2.2. In

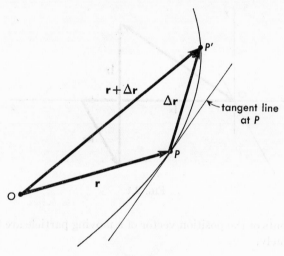

FIG. 2.2

the time interval Δt the particle moves along the path from P to P'. As Δt approaches zero, the point P' approaches P, and the direction of the vector $\Delta \mathbf{r}/\Delta t$ approaches the direction of the tangent to the path at P. The velocity vector, therefore, is always tangent to the path of motion.

The magnitude of the velocity is called the *speed*. In rectangular components the speed is just

$$v = |\mathbf{v}| = (\dot{x}^2 + \dot{y}^2 + \dot{z}^2)^{1/2} \tag{2.3}$$

If we denote the scalar distance along the path by s, then we can alternately express the speed as

$$v = \frac{ds}{dt} = \lim_{\Delta t \to 0} \frac{\Delta s}{\Delta t} = \lim_{\Delta t \to 0} \frac{[(\Delta x)^2 + (\Delta y)^2 + (\Delta z)^2]^{1/2}}{\Delta t} \tag{2.4}$$

which reduces to the expression on the right of Eq. (2.3).

2.4. Acceleration Vector

The time derivative of the velocity is called the *acceleration*. Denoting the acceleration by **a**,

$$\mathbf{a} = \frac{d\mathbf{v}}{dt} = \frac{d^2\mathbf{r}}{dt^2} \tag{2.5}$$

In rectangular components we have, therefore,

$$\mathbf{a} = \mathbf{i}\ddot{x} + \mathbf{j}\ddot{y} + \mathbf{k}\ddot{z} \tag{2.6}$$

Examples

1. Let us examine the motion represented by the equation

$$\mathbf{r}(t) = \mathbf{i}bt + \mathbf{j}\left(ct - \frac{gt^2}{2}\right) + \mathbf{0}\mathbf{k}$$

This represents motion in the xy plane, since the z component is constant and equal to zero. The velocity **v** is obtained by differentiating with respect to t, namely,

$$\mathbf{v} = \frac{d\mathbf{r}}{dt} = \mathbf{i}b + \mathbf{j}(c - gt)$$

The acceleration, likewise, is given by

$$\mathbf{a} = \frac{d\mathbf{v}}{dt} = -\mathbf{j}g$$

Thus **a** is in the negative y direction and has the constant magnitude g. The path of motion is a parabola, as shown in Fig. 2.3. (This equation actually

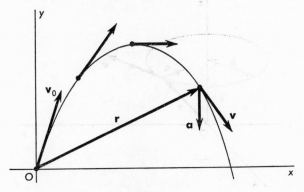

Fig. 2.3

represents the motion of a projectile.) The speed v varies with t according to the equation

$$v = (b^2 + g^2 t^2)^{1/2}$$

2. Suppose the position vector of a particle is given by

$$\mathbf{r} = \mathbf{i}b \sin \omega t + \mathbf{j}b \cos \omega t + \mathbf{k}c$$

Let us analyze the motion. The distance from the origin remains constant

$$|\mathbf{r}| = r = (b^2 \sin^2 \omega t + b^2 \cos^2 \omega t + c^2)^{1/2} = (b^2 + c^2)^{1/2}$$

Differentiating $\mathbf{r}$, we find

$$\mathbf{v} = \frac{d\mathbf{r}}{dt} = \mathbf{i}b\omega \cos \omega t - \mathbf{j}b\omega \sin \omega t + \mathbf{k}0$$

Since the z component of $\mathbf{v}$ is zero, the velocity vector is parallel to the xy plane. The particle traverses its path with constant speed

$$v = |\mathbf{v}| = (b^2\omega^2 \cos^2 \omega t + b^2\omega^2 \sin^2 \omega t)^{1/2} = b\omega$$

The acceleration

$$\mathbf{a} = \frac{d\mathbf{v}}{dt} = -\mathbf{i}b\omega^2 \sin \omega t - \mathbf{j}b\omega^2 \cos \omega t$$

which is perpendicular to the velocity, since the dot product of $\mathbf{v}$ and $\mathbf{a}$ vanishes, thus

$$\mathbf{v} \cdot \mathbf{a} = (b\omega \cos \omega t)(-b\omega^2 \sin \omega t) + (-b\omega \sin \omega t)(-b\omega^2 \cos \omega t) = 0$$

Further, the acceleration is perpendicular to the z axis, as shown in the figure, because $\mathbf{a} \cdot \mathbf{k} = 0$. The actual path is a circle of radius b, the plane of the circle being in the plane $z = c$. The motion is illustrated in Fig. 2.4.

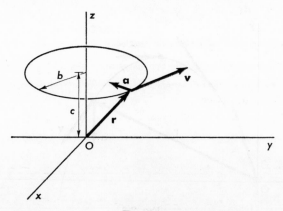

FIG. 2.4

2.5. Relative Velocity

Suppose we have two particles whose position vectors are $\mathbf{r}_1$ and $\mathbf{r}_2$, respectively, as shown in Fig. 2.5(a). The displacement of the second particle relative to the first is the difference $\mathbf{r}_2 - \mathbf{r}_1$ which we shall call $\mathbf{r}_{12}$. The velocity of the second particle relative to the first is therefore

$$\mathbf{v}_{rel} = \frac{d\mathbf{r}_{12}}{dt} = \frac{d\mathbf{r}_2}{dt} - \frac{d\mathbf{r}_1}{dt} = \mathbf{v}_2 - \mathbf{v}_1 \qquad (2.7)$$

which we shall call the relative velocity. The above vector equation is illustrated graphically in Fig. 2.5(b). The concept of relative velocity as a vector is very useful.

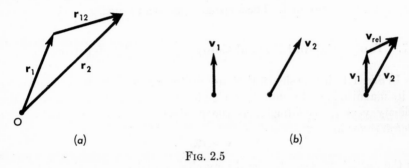

(a)   (b)

FIG. 2.5

EXAMPLE

Suppose an airplane is flying with a certain heading and a certain air speed; that is, this is the velocity of the airplane relative to the air, which we shall call $\mathbf{v}_{air}$. If the wind velocity is $\mathbf{v}_w$ and the *true* velocity of the airplane (relative to the ground) is $\mathbf{v}$, then

$$\mathbf{v} = \mathbf{v}_{air} + \mathbf{v}_w$$

2.6. Derivatives of Products of Vectors

It is often necessary to deal with derivatives of the products $n\mathbf{A}$, $\mathbf{A} \cdot \mathbf{B}$, and $\mathbf{A} \times \mathbf{B}$ where the scalar n and the vectors $\mathbf{A}$ and $\mathbf{B}$ are functions of a single parameter u, as in Sec. 2.1. From the general definition of the derivative, we have

$$\frac{d(n\mathbf{A})}{du} = \lim_{\Delta u \to 0} \frac{n(u + \Delta u)\mathbf{A}(u + \Delta u) - n(u)\mathbf{A}(u)}{\Delta u}$$

$$\frac{d(\mathbf{A} \cdot \mathbf{B})}{du} = \lim_{\Delta u \to 0} \frac{\mathbf{A}(u + \Delta u) \cdot \mathbf{B}(u + \Delta u) - \mathbf{A}(u) \cdot \mathbf{B}(u)}{\Delta u}$$

$$\frac{d(\mathbf{A} \times \mathbf{B})}{du} = \lim_{\Delta u \to 0} \frac{\mathbf{A}(u + \Delta u) \times \mathbf{B}(u + \Delta u) - \mathbf{A}(u) \times B(u)}{\Delta u}$$

By adding and subtracting expressions like $n(u + \Delta u)\mathbf{A}(u)$ in the numerators, we obtain the following rules:

$$\frac{d(n\mathbf{A})}{du} = \frac{dn}{du}\mathbf{A} + n\frac{d\mathbf{A}}{du} \tag{2.8}$$

$$\frac{d(\mathbf{A} \cdot \mathbf{B})}{du} = \frac{d\mathbf{A}}{du} \cdot \mathbf{B} + \mathbf{A} \cdot \frac{d\mathbf{B}}{du} \tag{2.9}$$

$$\frac{d(\mathbf{A} \times \mathbf{B})}{du} = \frac{d\mathbf{A}}{du} \times \mathbf{B} + \mathbf{A} \times \frac{d\mathbf{B}}{du} \tag{2.10}$$

Notice that it is necessary to preserve the order of the terms in the derivative of the cross product. The steps are left as an exercise for the student.

2.7. Tangential and Normal Components of Acceleration

In Sec. 1.13 it was shown that any vector can be written as the product of its magnitude and a unit vector giving its direction. We can write the velocity vector, accordingly, as the product of the speed v and a *unit tangent vector* λ_t

$$\mathbf{v} = v\lambda_t$$

As the particle moves, the speed may change and the direction of λ_t may change. Let us use the rule [Eq. (2.8)] and differentiate with respect to t to obtain the acceleration in the form

$$\mathbf{a} = \frac{d\mathbf{v}}{dt} = \frac{d(v\lambda_t)}{dt} = \dot{v}\lambda_t + v\frac{d\lambda_t}{dt} \tag{2.11}$$

Now, since the unit vector λ_t is of constant magnitude, the derivative $d\lambda_t/dt$ can mean only a change in the direction of λ_t with respect to time. This is shown in Fig. 2.6(a). The particle is initially at some point P, and in the time interval Δt it moves to another point P' a distance Δs along the path. Let us designate the unit tangent vectors at P and P' as λ_t and λ_t', respectively. The directions of λ_t and λ_t' differ by a certain angle $\Delta\psi$, as shown in Fig. 2.6(b). From the figure we see that the *magnitude* of the vector difference $|\Delta\lambda_t'|$ is equal to $2\sin\Delta\psi/2$ which approaches $\Delta\psi$ for small values of the latter. Hence $\lim_{\Delta\psi\to 0} |\Delta\lambda_t'|/\Delta\psi = 1$. Furthermore, the *direction* of $\Delta\lambda_t$ becomes perpendicular to that of λ_t in the limit. Therefore, $d\lambda_t/d\psi$ is a unit vector which is perpendicular to λ_t. We shall call it the *unit normal vector* λ_n, that is,

$$\frac{d\lambda_t}{d\psi} = \lambda_n \tag{2.12}$$

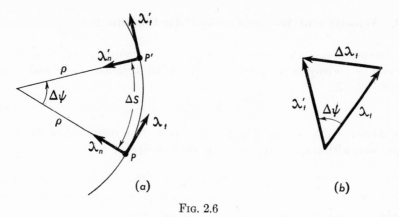

Fig. 2.6

We can now write, using the chain rule for differentiation,

$$\frac{d\lambda_t}{dt} = \lambda_n \frac{d\psi}{dt} = \lambda_n \frac{d\psi}{ds}\frac{ds}{dt} = \lambda_n \frac{v}{\rho} \qquad (2.13)$$

where $\rho = ds/d\psi$ is the radius of curvature of the path. The above value of $d\lambda_t/dt$ inserted into Eq. (2.11) yields

$$\mathbf{a} = \dot{v}\lambda_t + \frac{v^2}{\rho}\lambda_n \qquad (2.14)$$

Thus the acceleration of the particle has the component $\dot{v} = d^2s/dt^2$ in the direction of motion (the *tangential* component) and the component v^2/ρ normal to the path (the *normal* component). The normal component is always directed toward the concave side of the path, that is, toward the center of curvature, hence it is called the *centripetal acceleration*.

It should be noted that the magnitude of the acceleration, $|d\mathbf{v}/dt|$, is *not* $\dot{v}$, but, from Eq. (2.14),

$$\left|\frac{d\mathbf{v}}{dt}\right| = |\mathbf{a}| = (\dot{v}^2 + v^4/\rho^2)^{1/2}$$

EXAMPLE

If a particle moves on a circle with constant speed v, the acceleration vector is of magnitude v^2/ρ where ρ is the radius of the circle, and is directed toward the center of the circle. If the speed is not constant but is increasing at a certain rate $\dot{v}$ (the tangential component of $\mathbf{a}$), then the acceleration vector is directed forward, as shown in Fig. 2.7.

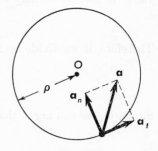

Fig. 2.7

2.8. Velocity and Acceleration in Polar Coordinates

The position of a particle having plane polar coordinates r, θ can be expressed vectorially as the product of the radial distance $r = |\mathbf{r}|$ and a *unit radial vector* $\boldsymbol{\lambda}_r$

$$\mathbf{r} = r\boldsymbol{\lambda}_r \tag{2.15}$$

The direction of $\boldsymbol{\lambda}_r$ is defined by the value of θ. Now differentiate the above expression with respect to t to obtain the velocity as

$$\mathbf{v} = \frac{d(r\boldsymbol{\lambda}_r)}{dt} = \dot{r}\boldsymbol{\lambda}_r + r\frac{d\boldsymbol{\lambda}_r}{dt} \tag{2.16}$$

Again, as in Sec. 2.7, the derivative of the unit vector $\boldsymbol{\lambda}_r$ is perpendicular to $\boldsymbol{\lambda}_r$ itself. We shall let $\boldsymbol{\lambda}_\theta$ (the *unit transverse vector*) denote a unit vector perpendicular to $\mathbf{r}$. The vectors are shown in Fig. 2.8. A study of the figure

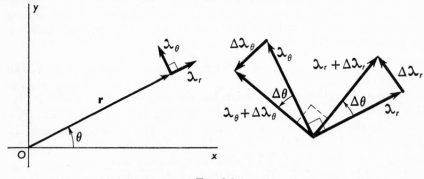

Fig. 2.8

will show that, for an increment $\Delta\theta$, the magnitude of $\Delta\boldsymbol{\lambda}_r$ approaches the value $\Delta\theta$, and so we may write the approximate equation

$$\Delta\boldsymbol{\lambda}_r \simeq \boldsymbol{\lambda}_\theta\Delta\theta$$

Therefore, if we divide by Δt and take the limit, we have

$$\frac{d\boldsymbol{\lambda}_r}{dt} = \boldsymbol{\lambda}_\theta\frac{d\theta}{dt} \tag{2.17}$$

Similarly, we can argue that $\Delta\boldsymbol{\lambda}_\theta \simeq -\boldsymbol{\lambda}_r\,\Delta\theta$, so that

$$\frac{d\boldsymbol{\lambda}_\theta}{dt} = -\boldsymbol{\lambda}_r\frac{d\theta}{dt} \tag{2.18}$$

Inserting the value of $d\lambda_r/dt$ from Eq. (2.17) into Eq. (2.16), we obtain the following expression for the velocity:

$$\mathbf{v} = \dot{r}\lambda_r + r\dot{\theta}\lambda_\theta \tag{2.19}$$

The above equation means that $\dot{r}$ is the *radial* component of the velocity, and $r\dot{\theta}$ is the *transverse* component.

Upon differentiating Eq. (2.19) with respect to t, we obtain the acceleration, namely,

$$\mathbf{a} = \frac{d\mathbf{v}}{dt} = \ddot{r}\lambda_r + \dot{r}\frac{d\lambda_r}{dt} + \frac{d(r\dot{\theta})}{dt}\lambda_\theta + r\dot{\theta}\frac{d\lambda_\theta}{dt} \tag{2.20}$$

The use of Eqs. (2.17) and (2.18) for the values of $d\lambda_r/dt$ and $d\lambda_\theta/dt$ yields

$$\vec{a} = (\ddot{r} - r\dot{\theta}^2)\lambda_r + (2\dot{r}\dot{\theta} + r\ddot{\theta})\lambda_\theta \tag{2.21}$$

for the acceleration in terms of its radial and transverse components. The radial component of the acceleration contains the term $-r\dot{\theta}^2$ in addition to the second time derivative of r, which means that there is a radial component of acceleration (inward) even if the radial distance r is constant.

EXAMPLES

1. Let a particle move on a circle of constant radius b. Then the magnitude of the radial component of acceleration is $b\dot{\theta}^2$. The magnitude of the transverse component is $b\ddot{\theta}$.

2. A bug crawls outward with constant speed v_o along the spoke of a wheel which is rotating with constant angular speed ω. Find the radial and transverse components of the acceleration as functions of time. We have $\dot{r} = v_o$ and $\dot{\theta} = \omega = $ constant, so $\ddot{r} = \ddot{\theta} = 0$. Taking $r = 0$ at time $t = 0$, we can write $r = v_o t$. From Eq. (2.21) we then have $a_r = -v_o t\omega^2$ for the radial component of $\mathbf{a}$, and $a_\theta = 2v_o\omega$ for the transverse component.

★2.9.   Velocity and Acceleration in Spherical Coordinates

In the general three-dimensional case the same expression for the position vector obtains as in the previous section, namely,

$$\mathbf{r} = r\lambda_r$$

The direction of the unit vector λ_r is defined in spherical coordinates by *two* angles θ and φ. We define two additional unit vectors λ_θ and λ_φ, as shown in Fig. 2.9, such that λ_r, λ_θ, and λ_φ form a right-handed triad. Now

$$\mathbf{v} = \frac{d\mathbf{r}}{dt} = \dot{r}\lambda_r + r\frac{d\lambda_r}{dt} \tag{2.22}$$

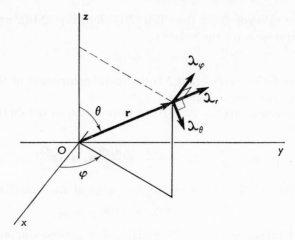

Fig. 2.9

Our problem is how to express the derivative $d\lambda_r/dt$ in terms of the other unit vectors.

From the diagram we have

$$\lambda_r = \mathbf{i} \sin\theta \cos\varphi + \mathbf{j} \sin\theta \sin\varphi + \mathbf{k} \cos\theta \qquad (2.23)$$

$$\lambda_\theta = \mathbf{i} \cos\theta \cos\varphi + \mathbf{j} \cos\theta \sin\varphi - \mathbf{k} \sin\theta \qquad (2.24)$$

$$\lambda_\varphi = -\mathbf{i} \sin\varphi + \mathbf{j} \cos\varphi \qquad (2.25)$$

where $\mathbf{i}$, $\mathbf{j}$, and $\mathbf{k}$ are the unit coordinate vectors along the $Oxyz$ axes, as shown. Differentiating Eq. (2.23) gives

$$\frac{d\lambda_r}{dt} = \mathbf{i}(\cos\theta \cos\varphi\dot\theta - \sin\theta \sin\varphi\dot\varphi) + \mathbf{j}(\cos\theta \sin\varphi\dot\theta + \sin\theta \cos\varphi\dot\varphi) - \mathbf{k}\sin\theta\dot\theta$$

which, upon using Eqs. (2.24) and (2.25), reduces to

$$\frac{d\lambda_r}{dt} = \lambda_\theta\dot\theta + \lambda_\varphi \sin\theta\dot\varphi \qquad (2.26)$$

Accordingly, Eq. (2.22) becomes

$$\mathbf{v} = \dot r\lambda_r + r\dot\theta\lambda_\theta + r \sin\theta\dot\varphi\lambda_\varphi \qquad (2.27)$$

which expresses the velocity $\mathbf{v}$ in terms of its components in the triad λ_r, λ_θ, λ_φ.

Let us differentiate again with respect to t in the above equation. We have

$$\mathbf{a} = \frac{d\mathbf{v}}{dt} = \ddot r\lambda_r + \dot r\frac{d\lambda_r}{dt} + \frac{d(r\dot\theta)}{dt}\lambda_\theta + r\dot\theta\frac{d\lambda_\theta}{dt} + \frac{d(r \sin\theta\dot\varphi)}{dt}\lambda_\varphi + r\sin\theta\dot\varphi\frac{d\lambda_\varphi}{dt}$$
$$(2.28)$$

The derivatives $d\lambda_\theta/dt$ and $d\lambda_\varphi/dt$ can be found by differentiating Eqs. (2.24) and (2.25). The results, after a little manipulation, are

$$\frac{d\lambda_\theta}{dt} = -\lambda_r\dot\theta + \lambda_\varphi \cos\theta\dot\varphi \tag{2.29}$$

$$\frac{d\lambda_\varphi}{dt} = -\lambda_r \sin\theta\dot\varphi - \lambda_\theta \cos\theta\dot\varphi \tag{2.30}$$

The steps are left as an exercise. Using Eqs. (2.26), (2.29), and (2.30), our expression [Eq. (2.28)] for the acceleration finally reduces to

$$\mathbf{a} = \frac{d\mathbf{v}}{dt} = (\ddot r - r\dot\varphi^2 \sin^2\theta - r\dot\theta^2)\lambda_r$$
$$+ (2\dot r\dot\theta - r\dot\varphi^2 \sin\theta \cos\theta + r\ddot\theta)\lambda_\theta$$
$$+ (2\dot r\dot\varphi \sin\theta + r\ddot\varphi \sin\theta + 2r\dot\theta\dot\varphi \cos\theta)\lambda_\varphi \tag{2.31}$$

PROBLEMS

1. Show that $(d/du)(\mathbf{A} + \mathbf{B}) = d\mathbf{A}/du + d\mathbf{B}/du$.
2. Find the velocity, speed, and acceleration, and interpret geometrically the motion represented by the following equations:

   (a) $\mathbf{r} = \mathbf{i}ct - \mathbf{j}\dfrac{g}{2}t^2$

   (b) $\mathbf{r} = \mathbf{i}ct + \mathbf{j}\,A\sin\omega t$

   (c) $\mathbf{r} = \mathbf{i}A\sin\omega t + \mathbf{j}B\cos\omega t$

   (d) $\mathbf{r} = \mathbf{i}ct + \mathbf{j}b\sin\omega t + \mathbf{k}b\cos\omega t$

   (e) $\mathbf{r} = \lambda_r e^{kt}$ $\quad\theta = bt$ (polar coordinates)

   (f) $\mathbf{r} = \lambda_r a$ $\quad\theta = b\sin\omega t \quad\varphi = ct$ (spherical coordinates)

3. The *hodograph* of a moving particle is the curve traced out by the velocity vector when the latter is drawn from a single fixed origin. What is the form of the hodograph of a particle (a) moving in a circle with constant speed, and (b) moving in a circle with constant tangential acceleration?
4. Verify Eqs. (2.19) and (2.21) by differentiating

   $$\mathbf{r} = \mathbf{i}\,r\cos\theta + \mathbf{j}r\sin\theta$$

   (NOTE: $\mathbf{i}$ and $\mathbf{j}$ are constant, $\lambda_r = \mathbf{i}\cos\theta + \mathbf{j}\sin\theta$, and $\lambda_\theta = -\mathbf{i}\sin\theta + \mathbf{j}\cos\theta$.)
5. A particle moves with constant speed but with a continually changing direction. Show that the acceleration vector is always perpendicular to the velocity vector.
6. Verify Eqs. (2.29) and (2.30).

3

Dynamics of a Particle.
Rectilinear Motion

3.1. Newton's Laws of Motion

As stated in the introduction, the study of mechanics at the intermediate level is largely based on Newton's laws of motion:
  (1) Every body continues in its state of rest or of uniform motion in a straight line, unless it is compelled by a force to change that state.
  (2) Change of motion is proportional to the force and takes place in the direction of the force.
  (3) To every action there is always an equal and opposite reaction; or, the mutual actions of two bodies are always equal and oppositely directed.
Let us examine these laws in some detail.

3.2. Newton's First Law and Inertial Reference Systems

The first law of motion describes a common property shared by all matter, that of *inertia*. This law states that a moving body travels in a straight line unless some influence, called *force*, prevents the body from pursuing such a course. We shall say more about this point later; suffice it to say here that whether a body moves in a straight line or not depends not only upon outside influences (forces) but also upon the particular reference system that is used to describe the motion. The first law actually *defines* a particular kind of reference system, called an *inertial* or Newtonian system, such a system being one in which Newton's first law holds! For all practical purposes, the background of the so-called "fixed" stars forms a basis for a fundamental inertial system.

3.3. Mass and Force. Newton's Second and Third Laws

We are all familiar with the fact that a big stone is not only hard to lift, but that such an object is more difficult to set in motion (or to stop) than, say, a small piece of wood. We say that the stone has more inertia than the wood. The quantitative measure of inertia is called *mass*. Suppose we have two bodies A and B. How do we determine the measure of inertia of one relative to the other? There are many experiments that can be devised to answer this question. If the two bodies can be made to interact with one another, say by a spring connecting them, then it is found, by all experiments that have ever been made in such cases, that the accelerations of the two bodies are always opposite in direction and have a *constant ratio*. (It is assumed that the accelerations are given in an inertial reference system and that only the *mutual* influence of the two bodies A and B is under consideration.) We can express this very important and fundamental fact by the equation

$$\frac{d\mathbf{v}_A}{dt} = -\frac{d\mathbf{v}_B}{dt}\, \mu_{BA} \qquad (3.1)$$

The constant μ_{BA} is, in fact, the measure of relative inertia of B with respect to A. From Eq. (3.1) it follows that $\mu_{BA} = 1/\mu_{AB}$. Thus we might express μ_{BA} as a ratio

$$\mu_{BA} = \frac{m_B}{m_A}$$

and use some standard body as a unit of inertia. Now the ratio m_B/m_A ought to be independent of the choice of the unit. This will be the case if, for any third body C,

$$\mu_{BC}/\mu_{AC} = \mu_{BA}$$

This is indeed found to be true. We call the quantity m the *mass*.* We may then write Eq. (3.1) in the form

$$m_A \frac{d\mathbf{v}_A}{dt} = -m_B \frac{d\mathbf{v}_B}{dt} \qquad (3.2)$$

The product of mass and acceleration in the above equation is the "change of motion" of Newton's second law and, according to that law, is proportional to the *force*. In other words, we can regard the second law as a quantitative definition of force; that is,

$$\mathbf{F} = km \frac{d\mathbf{v}}{dt} \qquad (3.3)$$

*In practice, mass ratios are found by weighing on a balance. This rests upon the experimental fact that gravitational force (weight) is proportional to mass.

where **F** is the force and k is a constant of proportionality. We shall take $k = 1$ and write

$$\mathbf{F} = m\,\frac{d\mathbf{v}}{dt} \tag{3.4}$$

The above equation is equivalent to

$$\mathbf{F} = \frac{d(m\mathbf{v})}{dt} = \frac{d\mathbf{p}}{dt} \tag{3.5}$$

if the mass is constant. (This is valid if the speed of the body is small compared to the speed of light.) The product $m\mathbf{v} = \mathbf{p}$ is called the *momentum*.

In the mks system the unit of force, defined by Eq. (3.4), is called the *newton*. Thus a force of 1 newton imparts acceleration of 1 m per sec^2 to an object of 1 kg mass. The cgs unit of force (1 g $\times$ 1 cm per sec^2) is called the *dyne*. In engineering, the most common unit of force is the *pound force* which imports an acceleration of 1 ft per sec^2 to an object of 1 *slug* mass. (1 slug = 32 pounds mass.)

According to our definition of force, we can now interpret Eq. (3.2) as a statement of the fact that two interacting bodies exert *equal* and *opposite* forces on one another. This is embodied in the statement of the third law. Forces are mutual influences and always occur in equal amounts on any two bodies that are causing each other's motion to change. One great advantage of the concept of force is that it enables us to concentrate our attention upon a single body.

3.4.   Motion of a Particle

The fundamental equation of motion of a particle is given by the analytical statement of Newton's second law, Eq. (3.4). When a particle is under the influence of more than one force, it may be regarded as an experimental fact that these forces add vectorially, namely,

$$\mathbf{F} = \Sigma\,\mathbf{F}_i = m\,\frac{d^2\mathbf{r}}{dt^2} = m\mathbf{a} \tag{3.6}$$

Expressed in rectangular coordinates, the above equation is equivalent to the three scalar equations

$$F_x = \Sigma F_{ix} = m\ddot{x} \quad F_y = \Sigma F_{iy} = m\ddot{y} \quad F_z = \Sigma F_{iz} = m\ddot{z} \tag{3.6(a)}$$

(Coordinate systems other than rectangular are often used and will be treated later.)

If the acceleration of a particle is known, then the equation of motion [Eq. (3.6)] gives the force that acts on the particle. The usual problems of particle dynamics, however, are those in which the forces are certain known functions of the coordinates (some types of forces also involve the time explicitly: time-varying forces), and the task is to find the position of the particle as a function of time. This involves the solution of a set of differential equations. In some problems it turns out to be impossible to obtain solutions of the differential equations of motion in terms of known analytic functions, in which case one must use some method of approximation. In many practical applications, such as ballistics, satellite motion, etc., the differential equations are so complicated that it is necessary to resort to numerical integration (often done on high-speed electronic computers) to determine the motion.

3.5. Rectilinear Motion

If a particle remains on a single straight line the motion is said to be *rectilinear*. In this case only one of the component equations {Eq. [3.6(a)]} is necessary, say the x equation, since we can regard the x axis as the line of motion. Dropping the subscript, we have

$$F(x,\dot{x},t) = m\ddot{x}$$

as the general equation for rectilinear motion. Let us consider some special forms of the force function for which the equation of motion can be integrated.

CASE A. THE FORCE AS CONSTANT: $F = $ constant.
In this case we have constant acceleration

$$dv/dt = \dot{v} = \ddot{x} = F/m = \text{constant} = a \tag{3.7}$$

and the solution is readily obtained by direct integration:

$$\int_{v_o}^{v} dv = \int_{o}^{t} a\, dt \qquad v - v_o = at$$

$$v = at + v_o = dx/dt \tag{3.7(a)}$$

$$\int_{x_o}^{x} dx = \int_{o}^{t} (at + v_o)\, dt \qquad x - x_o = \frac{1}{2} at^2 + v_o t$$

$$x = \frac{1}{2} at^2 + v_o t + x_o \tag{3.7(b)}$$

where v_o is the initial velocity, and x_o is the initial position. By eliminating the time t between Eqs. [3.7(a)] and [3.7(b)], we obtain

$$2a(x - x_o) = v^2 - v_o^2 \tag{3.7(c)}$$

The student will recall the above familiar equations of uniformly accelerated motion. There are a number of fundamental applications. For example, in the case of a body falling freely near the surface of the earth, neglecting air resistance, the acceleration is very nearly constant. We denote the acceleration of a freely falling body by **g**. (By measurement, $g = 9.8$ m per sec^2 = 32 ft per sec^2.) The downward force of gravity (the *weight*) is, accordingly, expressed as $m\mathbf{g}$. The gravitational force $m\mathbf{g}$ is always present, regardless of the motion of the body, and is independent of any other forces that may be acting.

Consider a particle that is sliding down a smooth plane inclined at an angle θ to the horizontal, as shown in Fig. 3.1(a). We choose the positive direction of the x axis to be down the plane, as indicated. The component of the gravitational force $m\mathbf{g}$ in the x direction is $mg \sin \theta$. This is a constant force, hence the motion is given by Eqs. [3.7(a), (b), (c)] where

$$a = \frac{F}{m} = g \sin \theta$$

Suppose that, instead of being smooth, the plane is rough; that is, it exerts a frictional force **f** on the particle. Then the net force in the x direction, as shown in Fig. 3.1(b), is $mg \sin \theta - f$. Now for sliding contact it is

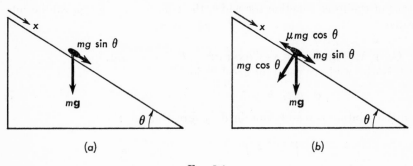

(a)   (b)

Fig. 3.1

found that the magnitude of the frictional force is proportional to the magnitude of the normal force N, that is,

$$f = \mu N$$

where the constant of proportionality μ is known as the *coefficient of sliding friction*. In the example under discussion the normal force N, as shown in the figure, is equal to $mg \cos \theta$, hence

$$f = \mu mg \cos \theta$$

Consequently, the net force in the x direction becomes

$$mg \sin \theta - \mu mg \cos \theta$$

Again the force is constant, and Eqs. [3.7(a), (b), (c)] apply, where

$$a = \frac{F}{m} = g(\sin \theta - \mu \cos \theta) \tag{3.8}$$

The speed of the particle will increase if the expression in parentheses is positive, that is, if $\theta > \tan^{-1} \mu$. The angle $\tan^{-1} \mu$, usually denoted by ϵ, is called the *angle of friction*. If $\theta = \epsilon$, then $a = 0$, and the particle slides down the plane with constant speed. If $\theta < \epsilon$, a is negative, and so the particle will eventually come to rest. It should be noted that for motion *up* the plane the direction of the frictional force is reversed; that is, it is in the positive x direction. The acceleration (actually deceleration) is then $a = g (\sin \theta + \mu \cos \theta)$.

CASE B. THE FORCE AS A FUNCTION OF POSITION ONLY: $F = F(x)$. In a great many instances the force that a particle experiences depends only on the particle's position with respect to other bodies. This is the case, for example, with electrostatic and gravitational forces. It also applies to forces of elastic tension or compression. The differential equation for rectilinear motion is, in this case, of the type

$$F(x) = m\ddot{x} \tag{3.9}$$

It is usually possible to solve this type of differential equation by one of several methods. One useful and significant method of solution is to write the acceleration in the following way:

$$\ddot{x} = \frac{d\dot{x}}{dt} = \frac{dx}{dt}\frac{d\dot{x}}{dx} = v\frac{dv}{dx} \tag{3.10}$$

so the differential equation of motion may be written

$$F(x) = mv\frac{dv}{dx} = \frac{m}{2}\frac{d(v^2)}{dx} = \frac{dT}{dx} \tag{3.11}$$

where the quantity $T = 1/2\ mv^2$ is called the *kinetic energy* of the particle. We can now express Eq. (3.11) in integral form

$$\int F(x)\ dx + \text{constant} = T \tag{3.12}$$

Now the integral $\int F(x)\ dx$ is the *work* done on the particle by the impressed force $F(x)$. Let us *define* a function $V(x)$ such that

$$-\frac{dV}{dx} = F(x) \tag{3.13}$$

The function $V(x)$ is called the *potential energy;* it is defined only to within an additive (arbitrary) constant. In terms of $V(x)$, the work integral is

$$\int F(x)\, dx = -\int \frac{dV}{dx}\, dx = -V(x) + \text{constant}$$

From Eq. (3.12) we may write

$$T + V = \frac{1}{2}mv^2 + V(x) = \text{constant} = E \qquad (3.14)$$

In words: If the impressed force is a function of position only, then the sum of the kinetic and potential energies remains constant throughout the motion. The force in this case is said to be *conservative.* Nonconservative forces, that is, those for which no potential function exists, are usually of a dissipational nature, such as friction.

The motion of the particle can be obtained by solving the energy equation [Eq. (3.14)] for v

$$v = \frac{dx}{dt} = \pm\sqrt{\frac{2}{m}[E - V(x)]} \qquad (3.15)$$

which can be written in integral form

$$\int \frac{\pm dx}{\sqrt{\frac{2}{m}[E - V(x)]}} = t \qquad [3.15(a)]$$

thus giving t as a function of x.

The motion of a freely falling body, mentioned under Case A above, is, of course, a special case of conservative motion. The force is $-mg$ if we choose the x direction to be positive upward. The potential energy is therefore given by $V = mgx + C$. We are free to choose any value for the constant C. We shall take $C = 0$ for convenience. The total energy E is then

$$E = \frac{1}{2}m\dot{x}^2 + mgx$$

Suppose, for example, a ball is thrown upward with initial speed v_o. Choosing $x = 0$ at the initial point of projection, we have

$$E = \frac{1}{2}mv_o^2 = \frac{1}{2}m\dot{x}^2 + mgx$$

or

$$\dot{x} = \pm\sqrt{v_o^2 - 2gx}$$

The positive sign refers to the upward motion of the ball, and the minus sign refers to the downward motion. We infer from the above equation that no values of x are physically permissible for which the quantity under the radical sign is negative. The limiting value of x — that is, the maximum height h — is that value for which $\dot{x} = 0$; that is,

$$v_o^2 - 2gh = 0 \qquad h = \frac{v_o^2}{2g}$$

The above considerations apply to the general case, Eq. (3.15). The allowable values of the quantity x, therefore, are those for which the expression $E - V(x)$ is positive. The limits of the motion are given by the roots of the equation $E - V(x) = 0$. These facts are illustrated in Fig. 3.2.

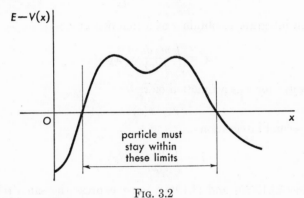

FIG. 3.2

For the falling body the integral of Eq. [3.15(a)] is

$$\int_0^x \frac{dx}{\sqrt{v_o^2 - 2gx}} = \frac{v_o}{g} - \sqrt{\frac{v_o^2}{g^2} - \frac{2x}{g}} = t$$

The student should verify that this reduces to the same relationship between x and t as that given by Eq. [3.7(b)] for $a = -g$.

CASE C. THE FORCE AS A FUNCTION OF VELOCITY ONLY: $F = F(v)$. It often happens that the force on a particle depends only on the velocity of the particle. This is, for example, true of viscous resistance exerted on a particle moving through a fluid (gas or liquid)*. The differential equation of motion then reads

$$F(v) = m \frac{dv}{dt} \tag{3.16}$$

*Neglecting, of course, any external forces.

A single integration yields t as a function of v

$$t = \int \frac{m \, dv}{F(v)} = t(v) \qquad [3.16(a)]$$

Assuming that we can solve the above equation for v, namely,

$$v = v(t) \qquad (3.17)$$

then a second integration gives

$$x = \int v(t) \, dt = x(t) \qquad [3.17(a)]$$

An alternate approach is to substitute $v \, dv/dx$ for dv/dt in Eq. (3.16), giving

$$F(v) = mv \frac{dv}{dx} \qquad (3.18)$$

We can then integrate to obtain x as a function of v

$$x = \int \frac{mv \, dv}{F(v)} = x(v) \qquad [3.18(a)]$$

If we now solve for v as a function of x

$$v = v(x) \qquad (3.19)$$

then, by a second integration

$$t = \int \frac{dx}{v(x)} = t(x) \qquad [3.19(a)]$$

Actually Eqs. [3.17(a)] and [3.19(a)] must express the same relationship between x and t.

In the case of fluid resistance, it is found that, for low velocities, the resistance is approximately proportional to the velocity, whereas, for higher velocities, the resistance is more nearly proportional to the square of v.

EXAMPLE

Suppose a block is projected with initial velocity v_o on a smooth horizontal plane, but that there is air resistance proportional to v; that is, $F(v) = -cv$, where c is a constant of proportionality. (The x axis is along the direction of motion.) The differential equation of motion is

$$-cv = m \frac{dv}{dt}$$

which gives, upon integrating,

$$t = \int_{v_0}^{v} -\frac{m \, dv}{cv} = -\frac{m}{c} \ln \left(\frac{v}{v_o} \right)$$

We can easily solve for v as a function of t by multiplying by $-c/m$ and taking the exponent of both sides. The result is

$$v = v_o \, e^{-ct/m}$$

Thus the velocity decreases exponentially with time. A second integration gives

$$x = \int_o^t v_o \, e^{-ct/m} \, dt$$

$$= \frac{mv_o}{c}(1 - e^{-ct/m})$$

We see, from the above equation, that the block never goes beyond the limiting distance mv_o/c.

The differential equation of motion can also be written

$$-cv = mv \, \frac{dv}{dx}$$

as in Eq. (3.18). Canceling the common factor v, and integrating,

$$-c \int_0^x dx = m \int_{v_0}^v dv$$

$$\frac{-c}{m}x = v - v_o$$

or

$$v_o - \frac{c}{m}x = v = \frac{dx}{dt}$$

Thus the speed of the block varies linearly with the distance. Integrating again,

$$t = \int_0^x \frac{dx}{v_o - (c/m)x} = \frac{-m}{c} \ln\left(\frac{v_o - (c/m)x}{v_o}\right)$$

Upon solving for x (by multiplying by $-c/m$ and taking the exponent), we find the same relation between x and t as that found above.

CASE D. THE FORCE AS A FUNCTION OF TIME ONLY: $F = F(t)$. In the event that the force depends explicitly on the time, the equation of motion

$$F(t) = m \, \frac{dv}{dt} \tag{3.20}$$

can be integrated directly

$$v = \frac{1}{m} \int F(t)\, dt = v(t) \qquad\qquad [3.20(a)]$$

giving v as a function of t. A second integration

$$x = \int v(t)\, dt = x(t) \qquad\qquad [3.20(b)]$$

yields x as a function of t.

EXAMPLE

A block is initially at rest on a smooth horizontal surface. At time $t = 0$ a constantly increasing horizontal force is applied: $F = ct$. Find the velocity and the displacement as functions of time.

We have, for the differential equation of motion,

$$ct = m \frac{dv}{dt}$$

Then

$$v = \frac{1}{m} \int_0^t ct\, dt = \frac{ct^2}{2m}$$

and

$$x = \int_0^t \frac{ct^2}{2m} = \frac{ct^3}{6m}$$

where the initial position of the block is at the origin $(x = 0)$.

3.6.   Vertical Motion in a Resisting Medium.   Terminal Velocity

An object falling vertically through the air or through any fluid is subject to viscous resistance, as mentioned in Sec. 3.5 (Case C). If the resistance is proportional to the first power of v (the linear case), we can express this force as $-cv$ regardless of the sign of v, because the resistance is always opposite to the direction of motion. The constant of proportionality c depends on the size and shape of the object and the viscosity of the fluid. Let us take the x axis to be positive upward. The force of gravity is then $-mg$, and the differential equation of motion is

$$-mg - cv = m \frac{dv}{dt} \qquad\qquad (3.21)$$

The force is a function of v, so we have, as in Sec. 3.5 (Case C),

$$t = \int \frac{m\,dv}{F(v)} = \int_{v_0}^{v} \frac{m\,dv}{-mg - cv}$$

$$= -\frac{m}{c} \ln \frac{mg + cv}{mg + cv_o} \qquad [3.21(a)]$$

We can readily solve for v

$$v = -\frac{mg}{c} + \left(\frac{mg}{c} + v_o\right)e^{-ct/m} \qquad [3.21(b)]$$

The exponential term drops to a negligible value after a sufficient time $(t \gg m/c)$, and the velocity approaches the limiting value $-mg/c$. The limiting velocity of a falling body is called the terminal *velocity;* it is that velocity at which the force of resistance is just equal and opposite to the weight of the body so that the total force is zero. The magnitude of the terminal velocity is called the *terminal speed.* The terminal speed of a falling raindrop, for instance, is roughly 10 to 20 ft per sec, depending on the size. A ping-pong ball has a terminal speed of about 30 ft per sec.

Equation [3.21(b)] expresses v as a function of t, so a second integration will give x as a function of t:

$$x - x_o = \int_0^t v(t)\,dt = -\frac{mg}{c}t + \left(\frac{m^2g}{c^2} + \frac{mv_o}{c}\right)(1 - e^{-ct/m}) \quad [3.21(c)]$$

Let us designate the terminal speed mg/c by v_t, and let us write τ (which we may call the *characteristic time*) for m/c. Equation [3.21(b)] may then be written in the more significant form

$$v = -v_t + (v_t + v_o)e^{-t/\tau} \qquad [3.21(d)]$$

and Eq. [3.21(c)] becomes

$$x = x_o - v_t t + x_1(1 - e^{-t/\tau}) \qquad [3.21(e)]$$

where

$$x_1 = m^2g/c^2 + mv_o/c = g\tau^2 + v_o$$

Thus, from Eq. [3.21(d)], an object dropped from rest ($v_o = 0$) will reach a speed of $1 - e^{-1}$ times the terminal speed in a time τ, $(1 - e^{-2})v_t$ in a time 2τ, etc. After an interval of 10τ the speed is practically equal to the terminal value, namely $0.99995\,v_t$.

If the viscous resistance is proportional to v^2 (the quadratic case), the differential equation of motion is, remembering that we are taking the positive direction upward,

$$-mg \pm cv^2 = m\frac{dv}{dt} \qquad (3.22)$$

The minus sign for the resistance term refers to upward motion (v positive), and the plus sign refers to downward motion (v negative). The double sign is necessary for any resistive force that involves an even power of v. As in the previous case, the differential equation of motion can be integrated to give t as a function of v:

$$t = \int \frac{m \, dv}{-mg - cv^2} = -\tau \tan^{-1} \frac{v}{v_t} + C \qquad \text{(rising)}$$

$$t = \int \frac{m \, dv}{-mg + cv^2} = -\tau \tanh^{-1} \frac{v}{v_t} + C' \qquad \text{(falling)}$$

where $\sqrt{m/cg} = \tau$ (the characteristic time),

and $\sqrt{mg/c} = v_t$ (the terminal speed). Solving for v,

$$v = v_t \tan \frac{C - t}{\tau} \qquad \text{(rising)} \qquad\qquad [3.22(a)]$$

$$v = -v_t \tanh \frac{t - C'}{\tau} \qquad \text{(falling)} \qquad\qquad [3.22(b)]$$

If the body is released from rest at time $t = 0$, then $C' = 0$. We have then, from the definition of the hyperbolic tangent,

$$v = -v_t \tanh \frac{t}{\tau} = -v_t \left(\frac{e^{t/\tau} - e^{-t/\tau}}{e^{t/\tau} + e^{-t/\tau}} \right) \qquad\qquad [3.22(c)]$$

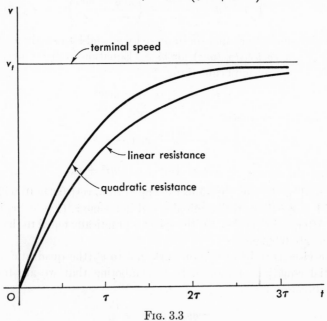

FIG. 3.3

Again we see that the terminal speed is practically attained after the lapse of a few characterist times, for example, for $t = 5\tau$, the speed is $0.99991\,v_t$. Graphs of speed versus time of fall for the linear and quadratic laws of resistance are shown in Fig. 3.3. It is interesting to note that, in both the linear and the quadratic cases, the characteristic time τ is equal to v_t/g. For instance, if the terminal speed of a parachute is 4 ft per sec, the characteristic time is 4 ft per sec/32 ft per sec^2 = 1/8 sec.

Equations [3.22(a)] and [3.22(b)] can be integrated to give explicit expressions for x as a function of t.

3.7. Variation of Gravity with Height

The gravitational attraction of the earth on a body above the surface, instead of being constant, actually falls off as the inverse square of the distance (Newton's law of gravity).* Thus

$$F = -\frac{GMm}{r^2} \tag{3.23}$$

where G is the gravitational constant, M the mass of the earth, and r the distance from the center of the earth to the body. If we neglect air resistance, the differential equation of motion is

$$m\ddot{r} = -\frac{GMm}{r^2}$$

Writing $\ddot{r} = \dot{r}\,d\dot{r}/dr$, we can integrate as follows:

$$m\int \dot{r}\,d\dot{r} = -GMm\int \frac{dr}{r^2}$$

$$\frac{1}{2}m\dot{r}^2 - \frac{GMm}{r} = \text{constant} \tag{3.24}$$

This is just the energy equation: the sum of the kinetic energy (the first term) and the potential energy $(-GMm/r)$ remains constant throughout the motion of a falling body. Let the body be dropped from rest $(\dot{r} = 0)$ a distance b from the center of the earth. The constant of integration in Eq. (3.24) is then equal to $-GMm/b$, and, upon canceling the common factor m and rearranging terms, we get

$$\dot{r}^2 = 2GM\left(\frac{1}{r} - \frac{1}{b}\right) \tag{3.24(a)}$$

*We shall study Newton's law of gravity in more detail in Chap. 6.

Now the force of gravity at the surface of the earth is $-GMm/R^2 = -mg$, hence g, the acceleration of gravity, is

$$g = \frac{GM}{R^2}$$

where R is the radius of the earth. We can express r in terms of the variable x measured relative to the surface, namely, $r = x + R$ and $\dot{r} = \dot{x} = v$. Equation [3.24(a)] then becomes

$$v^2 = 2gR^2\left(\frac{1}{x+R} - \frac{1}{h+R}\right) \qquad [3.24(\text{b})]$$

where $h = b - R$ is the height from which the body is dropped. The speed the body attains upon reaching the ground ($x = 0$) is therefore given by

$$v_o^2 = 2gR\left(1 - \frac{R}{h+R}\right) = 2gh\left(1 + \frac{h}{R}\right)^{-1} \qquad (3.25)$$

The above equation reduces to the usual formula

$$v_o^2 = 2gh \qquad [3.25(\text{a})]$$

if the last term h/R (the ratio of the distance of fall to the earth's radius) can be ignored. This is, of course, the case with most problems involving falling bodies. The above equations also apply to the motion of a body projected upward with initial speed v_o, in which case h is the maximum height attained. From Eq. (3.25) we see that the value of v_o corresponding to an infinite value of h (the *escape velocity*) is given by

$$v_e^2 = 2gR$$

or

$$v_e = (2gR)^{1/2} \simeq 7 \text{ miles per sec} \simeq 11 \text{ km per sec}$$

At the surface of the earth, the average speed of air molecules (O_2 and N_2) is about 0.5 km per sec* which is considerably less than the escape speed, so the earth retains its atmosphere. The moon, on the other hand, has no atmosphere, because the escape speed at the moon's surface, owing to the moon's small mass, is considerably smaller than that at the earth's surface; any oxygen or nitrogen would eventually disappear. The earth's atmosphere, however, contains no significant amount of hydrogen, even though hydrogen is the most abundant element in the universe as a whole. A hydrogen atmosphere would have escaped from the earth long ago, be-

---

*According to kinetic theory, the average speed of a gas molecule is equal to $(3kT/m)^{1/2}$ where $k = $ Boltzmann's constant $= 1.38 \times 10^{-16}$ erg per degree, T is the absolute temperature, and m is the mass of the molecule.

cause the molecular speed of hydrogen is large enough (owing to the small mass of the hydrogen molecule) so that a significant number of hydrogen molecules would have speeds exceeding the escape speed at any instant.

3.8. Linear Restoring Force. Harmonic Motion

One of the most important cases of rectilinear motion, from a practical as well as from a theoretical standpoint, is that produced by a *linear restoring force*. This is a force whose magnitude is proportional to the displacement of a particle from some equilibrium position and whose direction is always opposite to that of the displacement. Such a force is exerted by an elastic cord or by a spring obeying Hooke's law

$$F = -k(X - a) = -kx \tag{3.26}$$

where X is the total length, and a is the unstretched (zero load) length of the spring. The variable $x = X - a$ is the displacement of the spring from its equilibrium length. The proportionality constant k is called the *stiffness*. Let a particle of mass m be attached to the spring, as shown in Fig. 3.4(a);

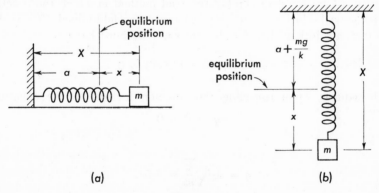

(a)   (b)

Fig. 3.4

the force acting on the particle is that given by Eq. (3.26). Let the same spring be held vertically, supporting the same particle, as shown in Fig. 3.4(b). The total force now acting on the particle is

$$F = -k(X - a) + mg \tag{3.27}$$

where the positive direction is downward. Now, in the latter case, let us measure x relative to the new equilibrium position; that is, let $x = X -$

$a - mg/k$. This gives again $F = -kx$, and so the differential equation of motion in either case is

$$-kx = m\ddot{x}$$

or

$$m\ddot{x} + kx = 0 \tag{3.28}$$

The above differential equation of motion is met in a wide variety of physical problems. In the particular example that we are using here, the constants m and k refer to the mass of a body and to the stiffness of a spring, respectively, and the displacement x is a distance. The same equation is encountered, as we shall see later, in the case of a pendulum, where the displacement is an angle, and where the constants involve the acceleration of gravity and the length of the pendulum. Again, in certain types of electrical circuits, this equation is found to apply, where the constants represent the circuit parameters, and the quantity x represents electric current or voltage.

Equation (3.28) can be solved in a number of ways. It is one example of an important class of differential equations known as *linear differential equations with constant coefficients.** Many, if not most, of the differential equations of physics are second-order linear differential equations. To solve Eq. (3.28) we shall employ the trial method in which the function Ae^{qt} is the trial solution where q is a constant to be determined. If $x = Ae^{qt}$ is, in fact, a solution, then for all values of t we must have

$$m\frac{d^2}{dt^2}(Ae^{qt}) + k(Ae^{qt}) = 0$$

which reduces, upon canceling the common factors, to the equation†

$$mq^2 + k = 0$$

that is

$$q = \pm i\sqrt{\frac{k}{m}} = \pm i\omega_o$$

where $i = \sqrt{-1}$, and $\omega_o = \sqrt{k/m}$. Now, for linear differential equations, solutions are additive. (That is, if f_1 and f_2 are solutions, then the sum

---

*The general nth-order equation of this type is

$$c_n \frac{d^n x}{dt^n} + \ldots + c_2 \frac{d^2 x}{dt^2} + c_1 \frac{dx}{dt} + c_o = b(t)$$

The equation is called *homogeneous* if $b = 0$.

†This equation is called the *indical equation*.

$f_1 + f_2$ is also a solution.) The general solution of Eq. (3.28) is then

$$x = A_+ e^{i\omega_o t} + A_- e^{-i\omega_o t} \qquad [3.28(a)]$$

Since $e^{iu} = \cos u + i \sin u$, alternate forms of the solution are

$$x = a \sin \omega_o t + b \cos \omega_o t \qquad [3.28(b)]$$

or

$$x = A \cos (\omega_o t + \theta_o) \qquad [3.28(c)]$$

The constants of integration in the above solutions are determined from the initial conditions. That all three expressions are solutions of Eq. (3.28) may be verified by direct substitution. The motion is a sinusoidal oscillation of the displacement x. For this reason Eq. (3.28) is often referred to as the differential equation of the *harmonic oscillator* or the *linear oscillator*.

The coefficient ω_o is called the *angular frequency*. The maximum value of x is called the *amplitude* of the oscillation; it is the constant A in Eq. [3.28(c)], or $(a^2 + b^2)^{1/2}$ in Eq. [3.28(b)]. The period T_o of the oscillation

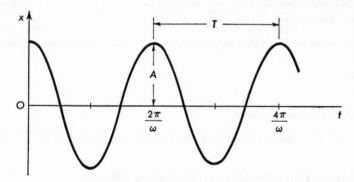

FIG. 3.5

is the time required for one complete cycle, as shown in Fig. 3.5; that is, the period is the time for which the product ωt increases by just 2π, thus

$$T_o = \frac{2\pi}{\omega_o} = 2\pi \sqrt{\frac{m}{k}} \qquad (3.29)$$

The *frequency* of oscillation f_o is defined as the number of cycles in unit time, therefore

$$f_o = \frac{1}{T_o} = \frac{1}{2\pi} \sqrt{\frac{k}{m}} \qquad (3.30)$$

EXAMPLE

A light spring is found to stretch by 20 cm when it supports a block of mass 250 g. If the block is pulled down a distance 5 cm below the equilibrium position and then released, find the period of oscillation and the maximum speed attained by the block.

Solution. For the static condition we have

$$k \, \Delta l = k \times 20 \text{ cm} = mg = 250 \text{ g} \times 980 \text{ cm per sec}^2$$

so

$$\frac{m}{k} = \frac{\Delta l}{g} = \frac{20 \text{ cm}}{980 \text{ cm per sec}^2} = \frac{1}{49} \text{ sec}^2$$

The angular frequency $\omega_o = \sqrt{k/m} = 7 \text{ sec}^{-1}$.
The period is then

$$T_o = 2\pi \sqrt{\frac{m}{k}} = \frac{2\pi}{7} \text{ sec}$$

Now, from the conditions of the problem, we have $x = 5$ cm and $\dot{x} = 0$ initially. Thus, using Eq. [3.28(b)], for $t = 0$:

$$5 \text{ cm} = a \sin 0 + b \cos 0 = b, \text{ and } \dot{x}_o = 0 = a\omega_o \cos 0 - b\omega_o \sin 0 = a\omega_o$$

Therefore

$$a = 0 \text{ and } b = 5 \text{ cm}$$

The maximum speed is then

$$b\omega_o = 5 \text{ cm} \times 7 \text{ sec}^{-1} = 35 \text{ cm per sec}$$

3.9.   Energy Considerations in Harmonic Motion

Let us calculate the work W done by an external force F_a in moving the particle from the equilibrium position ($x = 0$) to some position x. We have $F_a = -F = kx$, and so

$$W = \int F_a \, dx = \int_0^x (kx) \, dx = \frac{k}{2} x^2$$

The work W is stored in the spring as potential energy

$$V(x) = W = \frac{k}{2} x^2 \tag{3.31}$$

and $F = -dV/dx = -kx$ as required by the definition of V, Eq. (3.13).

The total energy E is then given by

$$\frac{1}{2}m\dot{x}^2 + \frac{1}{2}kx^2 = E \qquad (3.32)$$

Now solve the above equation for $\dot{x}$

$$\dot{x} = \pm \left[\frac{2E}{m} - \frac{kx^2}{m}\right]^{1/2} \qquad [3.32(a)]$$

This can be integrated [compare Eq. (3.15)] to give

$$t = \pm \int \frac{dx}{\sqrt{(2E/m) - (k/m)x^2}}$$

$$= \sqrt{\frac{m}{k}}\left[\begin{array}{l}\sin^{-1}(x/A) + \text{constant} \\ \cos^{-1}(x/A) + \text{constant}\end{array}\right] \qquad [3.32(b)]$$

where

$$A = \sqrt{\frac{2E}{k}} \qquad (3.33)$$

By solving Eq. [3.32(b)] for x, we find the very same relation between x and t as that found in the previous section, Eq. [3.28(b), (c)]. The above analysis, however, gives us an explicit value for the amplitude, namely, $\sqrt{2E/k}$. In fact, an examination of Eq. [3.32(a)] shows that x *must* lie between the values $\sqrt{2E/k}$ and $-\sqrt{2E/k}$ in order for $\dot{x}$ to be real. This is illustrated in Fig. 3.6. Here are shown curves of the potential-energy

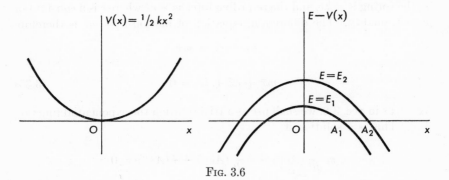

FIG. 3.6

function $V(x) = 1/2\ kx^2$ and curves of $E - V(x)$ versus x for different values of E.

From Eq. (3.32) we see that the maximum value of $\dot{x}$, which we shall call v_{max}, occurs when $x = 0$, and so we have

$$E = \frac{1}{2}mv_{\text{max}}^2 = \frac{1}{2}kA^2$$

or

$$v_{\text{max}} = \sqrt{\frac{k}{m}}A = \omega_o A \tag{3.34}$$

3.10. Damped Harmonic Motion

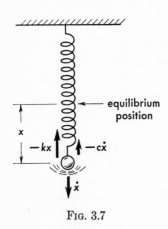

FIG. 3.7

The above analysis of the harmonic oscillator is somewhat idealized in that we have failed to take into account frictional forces. These are always present in a mechanical system, to some extent, at least. Analogously, there is always a certain amount of resistance in an electrical circuit. Let us consider, for example, the motion of an object that is supported by a spring of stiffness k. We shall assume that there is a viscous retarding force varying *linearly* with the speed (as in Sec. 3.6), that is, such as is produced by air resistance. The forces are indicated in Fig. 3.7.

If x is the displacement from the equilibrium position, then the restoring force exerted by the spring is $-kx$, and the retarding force is $-c\dot{x}$ where c is a constant of proportionality. The differential equation of motion $F = m\ddot{x}$ is therefore

$$-kx - c\dot{x} = m\ddot{x}$$

or

$$m\ddot{x} + c\dot{x} + kx = 0 \tag{3.35}$$

Again, as in Sec. 3.8, we shall use as a trial solution the exponential function Ae^{qt}. This is a solution if

$$m\frac{d^2}{dt^2}(Ae^{qt}) + c\frac{d}{dt}(Ae^{qt}) + k(Ae^{qt}) = 0$$

for all t. This will be the case if q satisfies the indical equation

$$mq^2 + cq + k = 0$$

The roots are given by the well-known quadratic formula

$$q = \frac{-c \pm (c^2 - 4mk)^{1/2}}{2m} \tag{3.36}$$

In the cases $c^2 > 4mk$ (*overdamping*) and $c^2 = 4mk$ (*critical damping*), q is real and *negative*, so the motion is nonoscillatory, the displacement x decaying to zero exponentially with time, as shown in Fig. 3.8. In the over-

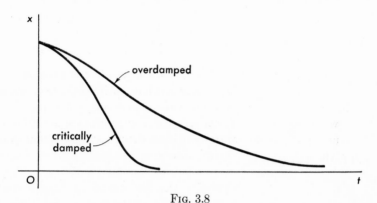

FIG. 3.8

damped case, let us call $-\gamma_1$ and $-\gamma_2$ the two values of q given by Eq. (3.36). The general solution may then be written

$$x = A_1 e^{-\gamma_1 t} + A_2 e^{-\gamma_2 t} \tag{3.37}$$

In the critically damped case the roots of the indical equation are equal, and the general solution is of the form

$$x = e^{-\gamma t}(A_1 + A_2 t) \tag{[3.37(a)]}$$

where $\gamma = c/2m$. (That the above is a solution may be verified by direct substitution).

If the resistance constant c is small enough so that $c^2 < 4mk$, we have the third case (*underdamping*). In this case q is complex. The two roots of the indical equation are conjugate complex numbers, and the motion is given by the general solution

$$x = A_+ e^{(-\gamma + i\omega_1)t} + A_- e^{(-\gamma - i\omega_1)t} \tag{[3.37(b)]}$$

where

$$\omega_1 = \sqrt{\frac{k}{m} - \frac{c^2}{4m^2}} = \sqrt{\omega_o^2 - \gamma^2} \tag{3.38}$$

Upon using the formula $e^{iu} = \cos u + i \sin u$, we see that the solution can be written

$$x = e^{-\gamma t}(A_+ e^{i\omega_1 t} + A_- e^{-i\omega_1 t})$$

$$= e^{-\gamma t}[(iA_+ - iA_-) \sin \omega_1 t + (A_+ + A_-) \cos \omega_1 t]$$

or

$$x = e^{-\gamma t}(a \sin \omega_1 t + b \cos \omega_1 t) \tag{3.39}$$

where $a = i(A_+ - A_-)$ and $b = A_+ + A_-$. We can further write the solution as

$$x = A e^{-\gamma t} \cos (\omega_1 t + \theta_o) \tag{3.39(a)}$$

where $A = (a^2 + b^2)^{1/2}$ and $\theta_o = -\tan^{-1}(b/a)$.

The form of the solution shows that the motion is oscillatory, and that the amplitude of the oscillation decays exponentially with time. From Eq. (3.38) we see that the angular frequency of oscillation ω_1 is less than that of the undamped oscillator ω_o. If γ is very small compared to ω_o we can write approximately

$$\omega_1 \simeq \omega_o - \frac{\gamma^2}{2\omega_o} \tag{3.40}$$

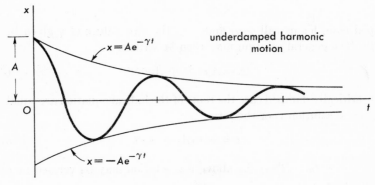

FIG. 3.9

by expanding the right side of Eq. (3.38) by the binomial theorem and retaining only the first two terms.

A plot of the motion is shown in Fig. 3.9. From Eq. [3.39(a)] it follows that the two curves $x = A e^{-\gamma t}$ and $x = -A e^{-\gamma t}$ form an envelope of the curve of motion, since the cosine factor takes values between $+1$ and -1, including $+1$ and -1, at which points the curve of motion touches the envelope. The points of contact are thus separated by a time interval of one half period, or π/ω_1, but these points are not quite the maxima and minima of the displacement x. It is left to the student to find the values of t at which the displacement does assume its extreme values.

Energy considerations. The total energy of the damped harmonic oscillator is, at any instant, equal to the sum of the kinetic energy $1/2\, m\dot{x}^2$ and the potential energy $1/2\, kx^2$:

$$E = \frac{1}{2}m\dot{x}^2 + \frac{1}{2}kx^2$$

which, we found, was constant for the undamped oscillator. Let us differentiate the above equation with respect to t to find the time rate of change of E. We have

$$\frac{dE}{dt} = m\ddot{x}\dot{x} + k\dot{x}x = (m\ddot{x} + kx)\,\dot{x}$$

But, from the differential equation of motion, Eq. (3.35),

$$m\ddot{x} + kx = -c\dot{x}$$

Consequently,

$$\frac{dE}{dt} = -c\dot{x}^2 \tag{3.41}$$

This is always negative and represents the rate at which the energy is being dissipated into heat by friction.

3.11. Forced Harmonic Motion. Resonance

In this section we shall study the motion of a damped harmonic oscillator that is driven by an external *harmonic force*, that is, a force that varies sinusoidally with time. Suppose this applied force F_{ext} has an angular frequency ω and a certain amplitude F, so that we could write

$$F_{ext} = F\cos(\omega t + \theta)$$

We shall find it convenient, however, to use the exponential form

$$F_{ext} = F e^{i(\omega t + \theta)}$$

rather than the trigonometric, although either can be used.* The total

---

*The exponential form is equivalent to writing $F_{ext} = F\cos(\omega t + \theta) + iF\sin(\omega t + \theta)$. The resulting differential equation is satisfied if the real and the imaginary parts on both sides of the equation are equal.

force, then, will be the sum of three forces: the elastic restoring force $-kx$, the viscous damping force $-c\dot{x}$, and the external force F_{ext}. The differential equation of motion is therefore

$$-kx - c\dot{x} + F_{ext} = m\ddot{x}$$

or

$$m\ddot{x} + c\dot{x} + kx = F_{ext} = Fe^{i(\omega t+\theta)} \tag{3.42}$$

The solution of the above linear differential equation is given by the sum of two parts, the first being the solution of the homogeneous equation $m\ddot{x} + c\dot{x} + kx = 0$, which we have already solved in the previous section; the second being any particular solution. As we have seen, the solution of the homogeneous equation represents an oscillation which eventually decays to zero — it is called the *transient term*. We are interested in a solution that depends on the nature of the applied force. Since this force is constant in amplitude and varies sinusoidally with time, we can reasonably expect to find a solution for which the displacement x also has a sinusoidal time dependence. Therefore, for the steady-state condition, we shall try a solution of the form

$$x = Ae^{i(\omega t+\theta')}$$

If this "guess" is correct, we must have

$$m\frac{d^2}{dt^2}[Ae^{i(\omega t+\theta')}] + c\frac{d}{dt}[Ae^{i(\omega t+\theta')}] + kAe^{i(\omega t+\theta')} = Fe^{i(\omega t+\theta)}$$

hold for all values of t. This reduces, upon performing the indicated operations and canceling the common factors, to

$$-m\omega^2 A + icA + kA = Fe^{i(\theta-\theta')} = F[\cos(\theta - \theta') + i\sin(\theta - \theta')]$$

Equating the real and the imaginary parts, we have

$$A(k - m\omega^2) = F\cos\varphi \tag{3.43}$$

$$c\omega A = F\sin\varphi \tag{3.44}$$

where the *phase difference* or phase *angle* $\theta - \theta'$ is denoted by φ. Upon dividing the second equation by the first and using the identity $\sin\varphi/\cos\varphi = \tan\varphi$, we obtain

$$\tan\varphi = \frac{c\omega}{k - m\omega^2} \tag{3.45}$$

By squaring both sides of Eqs. (3.43) and (3.44) and adding and employing the identity $\sin^2 \varphi + \cos^2 \varphi = 1$, we find

$$A^2(k - m\omega^2)^2 + c^2\omega^2 A^2 = F^2$$

Solving for A, the amplitude of the steady-state oscillation, yields

$$A = \frac{F}{\sqrt{(k - m\omega^2)^2 + c^2\omega^2}} \tag{3.46}$$

In terms of the abbreviations $\omega_o = \sqrt{k/m}$ and $\gamma = c/2m$, we can write

$$\tan \varphi = \frac{2\gamma\omega}{\omega_o^2 - \omega^2} \tag{3.47}$$

and

$$A = \frac{F/m}{\sqrt{(\omega_o^2 - \omega^2)^2 + 4\gamma^2\omega^2}} \tag{3.48}$$

The above equation relating the amplitude A to the impressed driving frequency ω is of fundamental importance. A graph, Fig. 3.10, shows that A assumes a maximum value at a certain frequency ω_r, called the *resonant frequency*.

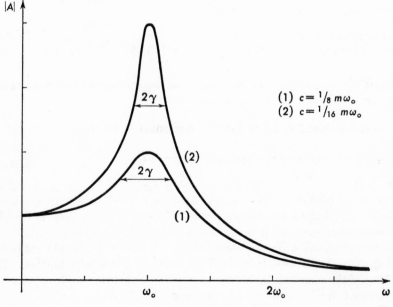

(1) $c = {}^1\!/_8 \, m\omega_o$
(2) $c = {}^1\!/_{16} \, m\omega_o$

FIG. 3.10

To find the resonant frequency, we calculate $dA/d\omega$ from Eq. (3.48) and set the result equal to zero. Upon solving the resulting equation for ω, we find that the resonant frequency is given by

$$\omega = \omega_r = (\omega_o^2 - 2\gamma^2)^{1/2} \tag{3.49}$$

In the case of weak damping, that is, when the damping constant c is very small, $c \ll 2/mk$, or, equivalently, if $\gamma \ll \omega_o$, then we see that the resonant frequency ω_r is very nearly equal to the natural frequency or the frequency of the freely running oscillator with no damping ω_o. If we expand the right side of Eq. (3.49) by the binomial theorem and retain only the first two terms, we get

$$\omega_r \simeq \omega_o - \frac{\gamma^2}{\omega_o} \tag{3.50}$$

Equations (3.49) and (3.50) should be compared to Eqs. (3.38) and (3.40), which give the frequency of oscillation ω_1 of the freely running oscillator *with* damping. Let ϵ denote the quantity γ^2/ω_o. Then we may write

$$\omega_1 \simeq \omega_o - \frac{1}{2}\epsilon$$

and

$$\omega_r \simeq \omega_o - \epsilon$$

The steady-state amplitude at the resonant frequency, which we shall call $A_{\max}$, is obtained from Eqs. (3.48) and (3.49). The result is

$$A_{\max} = \frac{F/m}{2\gamma\sqrt{\omega_o^2 - \gamma^2}} = \frac{F}{c\sqrt{\omega_o^2 - \gamma^2}} \tag{3.51}$$

In the case of weak damping, we can neglect γ^2 and write

$$A_{\max} \simeq \frac{F}{2\gamma m\omega_o} = \frac{F}{c\omega_o} \tag{3.51(a)}$$

Thus the amplitude of the induced oscillation at the resonant condition becomes very large if the damping constant c is very small, and conversely. In mechanical systems it may, or may not, be desirable to have large resonant amplitudes. In the case of electric motors, for example, rubber or spring mounts are used to minimize the transmission of vibration. The stiffness of these mounts is chosen so as to ensure that the resulting resonant frequency is far from the running frequency of the motor.

The sharpness of the resonance peak is frequently of interest. Let us consider the case of weak damping, so that $\omega_r \simeq \omega_o$. Now let $\Delta\omega = \omega - \omega_o$; then in Eq. (3.48) we can make the following substitutions:

$$\omega_o^2 - \omega^2 = (\omega_o - \omega)(\omega_o + \omega) \simeq -2\omega_o\,\Delta\omega, \quad \gamma^2\omega^2 \simeq \gamma^2\omega_o^2$$

which, together with [3.51(a)], allow us to write Eq. (3.48) in the form

$$A = \frac{A_{\max}\gamma}{\sqrt{(\Delta\omega)^2 + \gamma^2}} \tag{3.52}$$

From the above equation we see that $A^2 = 1/2\ A_{\max}^2$ when $\Delta\omega = \gamma$. This means that γ is the "half width" of the resonance peak at the points for which the amplitude is down by $\sqrt{1/2}$ or 0.707 from the maximum (the half-power points), as indicated in Fig. 3.10. The ratio $\omega_r/2\gamma$ is known as the quality factor or Q of a resonant system.

The phase difference φ between the applied driving force and the response, as given by Eq. (3.47), is plotted in Fig. 3.11 as a function of

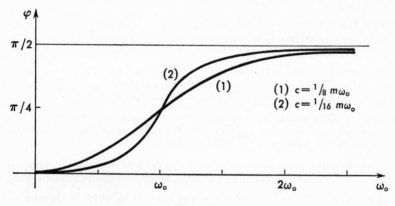

FIG. 3.11

driving frequency. The phase lag is zero at $\omega = 0$, increases to $\pi/4$ at resonance, and approaches $\pi/2$ for large values of ω. It is interesting to note that at high frequencies the oscillation of the particle is just 180 degrees out of phase with the applied force.

PROBLEMS

1. A particle of mass m is initially at rest. A constant force F_o acts on the particle for a time t_o. The force then increases linearly with the time such

that after an additional interval t_o the force is equal to $2F_o$. Find the total distance traveled by the particle in the total time $2t_o$.

2. A block is projected up an inclined plane with initial speed v_o. If the inclination of the plane is 30°, and the coefficient of sliding friction between the plane and the block is 0.1, find the time required for the block to return to the initial point of projection.

3. A block slides on a horizontal surface which has been lubricated with heavy oil such that the block suffers a viscous resistance that varies as the square root of the speed. Find the velocity and the position as functions of the time if the initial speed is v_o. Is there a limiting position of the block?

4. Given that the force acting on a particle is the product of a function of the velocity by a function of the distance, namely, $F(x,\dot{x}) = f(x)g(\dot{x})$. Show that the differential equation of motion can be solved by integration. If the force is a product of a function of distance by a function of time, can the equation of motion be solved by simple integration? Can it be solved if the force is a product of the time by a function of velocity?

5. A particle of mass m is released from rest a distance b from a fixed origin of force that attracts the particle according to the inverse square law $F(x) = -cx^{-2}$. Show that the time required for the particle to reach the origin is $\pi(mb^3/8c)^{1/2}$.

6. Find the distance as a function of the velocity for a falling body released from rest and subject to air resistance that is (a) proportional to the velocity, and (b) proportional to the second power of the velocity.

7. A projectile is fired vertically upward with initial speed v_o. Assuming that the air resistance is proportional to the square of the speed, find the speed the projectile has when it hits the ground on its return.

8. Two identical springs, each of stiffness k, are used in a vertical position to support a single object of mass m. Find the period of oscillation if the springs are (a) tied in series, and (b) tied in parallel.

9. Show that the time average (over one period) of the kinetic energy of a harmonic oscillator is equal to the time average of the potential energy.

10. A spring of stiffness k supports a box of mass M in which is placed a block of mass m. If the system is pulled downward a distance d from the equilibrium position and then released, find the force of reaction between the block and the box as a function of time. For what value of d will the block just begin to leave the bottom of the box at the top of the vertical oscillations? Neglect air resistance.

11. The terminal speed of a freely falling basketball is 40 ft per sec. When the ball is supported statically by a light elastic cord, the cord is found to stretch 6 in. If the ball is made to undergo vertical oscillations, find the period. Find also the number of oscillations such that the amplitude drops to one half the initial value. Assume a linear air resistance.

12. Show that the total energy of a lightly damped harmonic oscillator diminishes approximately exponentially with time.

13. Show that the ratio of two successive maxima in the displacement of a damped harmonic oscillator is constant. (NOTE: The maxima do not occur at the points of contact of the displacement curve with the curve $Ae^{-\gamma t}$.)

14. Given that the amplitude of a damped harmonic oscillator drops to $1/e$ of its initial value after n complete cycles. Show that the ratio of the period of oscillation to the period of the same oscillator with no damping is given by

$$\frac{T}{T_o} = \left[1 + \frac{1}{4\pi^2 n^2}\right]^{1/2} \simeq 1 + \frac{1}{8\pi^2 n^2}$$

15. Show that the driving frequency ω' for which the amplitude of oscillation of a driven harmonic oscillator is one half the amplitude at the resonant frequency is approximately $\omega_o \pm \gamma\sqrt{3}$.

16. Find the driving frequency for which the velocity of the forced harmonic oscillator is maximum.

4

Dynamics of a Particle.
General Motion

PART I. MOTION IN A PLANE

If a particle moves entirely in a plane, we can express its position in plane rectangular coordinates x, y. The differential equation of motion $\mathbf{F} = m\mathbf{a}$ is then equivalent to the two equations

$$F_x(x,\dot{x},y,\dot{y},t) = m\ddot{x}$$
$$F_y(x,\dot{x},y,\dot{y},t) = m\ddot{y}$$

In some cases it may happen that the force components are of the *separated* type: $F_x = F_x(x,\dot{x},t)$, $F_y = F_y(y,\dot{y},t)$. The equations of motion are then directly separated, that is,

$$F_x(x,\dot{x},t) = m\ddot{x}$$
$$F_y(y,\dot{y},t) = m\ddot{y}$$

and therefore can be solved individually by the methods discussed under rectilinear motion in the previous chapter.

4.1. Projectiles

An example of two-dimensional motion in which the components of the force acting on a particle are in separated form is that of a projectile.

CASE A. NO AIR RESISTANCE. If air resistance is neglected, then the only force acting on a moving projectile is the downward force of gravity $m\mathbf{g}^*$. The equation of motion is then $m\mathbf{a} = m\mathbf{g}$, which, if we choose the x axis horizontal and the y axis vertical, resolves into the component equations

$$m\ddot{x} = 0 \qquad m\ddot{y} = -mg$$

or

$$\ddot{x} = 0 \qquad \ddot{y} = -g \tag{4.1}$$

These can be integrated with respect to the time to obtain the components of the velocity

$$\dot{x} = \text{constant} = \dot{x}_o \qquad \dot{y} = -gt + \dot{y}_o \tag{[4.1(a)]}$$

where the constants of integration $\dot{x}_o$ and $\dot{y}_o$ are the initial components. A second integration gives

$$x = \dot{x}_o t \qquad y = -\frac{1}{2}gt^2 + \dot{y}_o t \tag{[4.1(b)]}$$

where we have taken $x_o = y_o = 0$; that is, the projectile is initially at the origin. Elimination of the time t between the two equations, Eq. [4.1(b)], yields the rectangular equation of the path (*trajectory*) of the projectile:

$$y = -\frac{g}{2\dot{x}_o^2}x^2 + \frac{\dot{y}_o}{\dot{x}_o}x \tag{4.2}$$

The trajectory is thus parabolic, as shown in Fig. 4.1. Setting $y = 0$, we find that the two roots are $x = 0$ and $x = 2\dot{x}_o\dot{y}_o/g$. The latter root is the horizontal *range*. Suppose the projectile is fired with an initial speed v_o

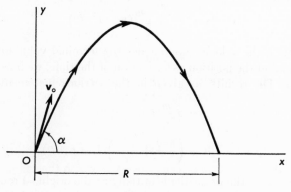

Fig. 4.1

*Effects arising from the earth's rotation are not considered here. These will be treated in a later chapter.

(the *muzzle velocity*) at an angle α from the horizontal (the *elevation*). Then $\dot{x}_o = v_o \cos \alpha$ and $\dot{y}_o = v_o \sin \alpha$. The horizontal range R is then given by

$$R = \frac{2v_o^2 \sin \alpha \cos \alpha}{g} = \frac{v_o^2 \sin 2\alpha}{g} \tag{4.3}$$

The range is clearly a maximum, for a given v_o, when $\sin 2\alpha = 1$; that is, when $\alpha = 45°$.

CASE B. AIR RESISTANCE VARYING LINEARLY WITH THE VELOCITY. The resistance of the air acting on a moving projectile acts so as to oppose the motion. The resistive force, then, is in the direction of $-\mathbf{v}$. In the linear case* the equation of motion can therefore be written

$$m\mathbf{g} - c\mathbf{v} = m\mathbf{a} \tag{4.4}$$

where c, as in the problem of the falling body (Sec. 3.6), is the constant of proportionality for the resistance. In our coordinates $\mathbf{g} = -\mathbf{j}g$ and $\mathbf{v} = \mathbf{i}\dot{x} + \mathbf{j}\dot{y}$. Equation (4.4) then resolves into the two component equations

$$-c\dot{x} = m\ddot{x} \qquad -mg - c\dot{y} = m\ddot{y} \tag{4.4(a)}$$

These equations are in separated form. We have already encountered them in the previous chapter, namely, Sec. 3.5 (example) and Sec. 3.6. Thus, the components of $\mathbf{v}$ are given by

$$\dot{x} = \dot{x}_o e^{-ct/m} \qquad \dot{y} = \frac{-mg}{c} + \left(\frac{mg}{c} + \dot{y}_o\right)e^{-ct/m} \tag{4.4(b)}$$

The above equations may be combined to express the velocity vectorially by the equation

$$\mathbf{v} = \mathbf{v}_o e^{-ct/m} + \mathbf{g}\frac{m}{c}(1 - e^{-ct/m}) \tag{4.4(c)}$$

Thus, for large t, the velocity approaches the terminal value $\mathbf{g}m/c$.

In order to find the position as a function of the time, we must integrate Eqs. [4.4(b)]. The results, as given in the sections just mentioned, are

$$x = \dot{x}_o \frac{m}{c}(1 - e^{-ct/m}) \tag{4.5}$$

$$y = -\frac{mg}{c}t + \left(\frac{m^2g}{c^2} + \frac{m\dot{y}_o}{c}\right)(1 - e^{-ct/m}) \tag{4.6}$$

where, as in Case A, the projectile is initially at the origin. From Eq. (4.5) we see that the limiting value of x for large values of t is $\dot{x}_o m/c$. The

---

*The linear law, of course, is not accurate physically. The actual resistance is a rather complicated function of velocity.

complete trajectory thus has as a vertical asymptote the line $x = \dot{x}_o m/c$, as shown in Fig. 4.2.

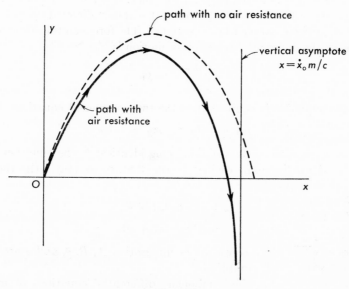

path with no air resistance

vertical asymptote
$x = \dot{x}_o m/c$

path with
air resistance

O

y

x

Fig. 4.2

It is instructive to compare the above expressions of the position coordinates with those obtained in Case A, Eq. [4.1(b)]. To do this, let us use the exponential series

$$e^u = 1 + u + u^2/2! + u^3/3! + \cdots$$

for the terms $e^{-ct/m}$ in Eqs. (4.5) and (4.6). The results are

$$x = \dot{x}_o \frac{m}{c}\left(\frac{ct}{m} - \frac{c^2 t^2}{m^2 2!} + \cdots\right) = \dot{x}_o t - \frac{c\dot{x}_o}{2m}t^2 + \cdots \tag{4.7}$$

$$y = \frac{-mg}{c}t + \left(\frac{m^2 g}{c^2} + \frac{m\dot{y}_o}{c}\right)\left(\frac{ct}{m} - \frac{c^2 t^2}{m^2 2!} + \frac{c^3 t^3}{m^3 3!} - \cdots\right)$$

$$= \dot{y}_o t - \frac{1}{2}gt^2 - \frac{c}{m}\left(\frac{\dot{y}_o t^2}{2} - \frac{gt^3}{6}\right) + \cdots \tag{4.8}$$

We observe that the first terms on the right are just those for no air resistance (Case A). The remaining terms can be regarded as corrections to be applied to the parabolic path in order to obtain the true path. These corrections are very small if the quantity ct/m is very small compared to unity.

4.2.   The Two-Dimensional Harmonic Oscillator

In this section we shall study the motion of a particle moving in a plane and subject to a *linear* restoring force that is always directed toward a fixed point (the origin of our coordinate system). The force can thus be expressed as $-k\mathbf{r}$, so the differential equation of motion is

$$m\frac{d^2\mathbf{r}}{dt^2} = -k\mathbf{r} \tag{4.9}$$

The above equation is equivalent to the two component equations

$$m\ddot{x} = -kx \qquad m\ddot{y} = -ky \tag{[4.9(a)]}$$

These are separated, each equation being identical to the equation of the one-dimensional harmonic oscillator (Sec. 3.8), so we may write the solutions in the form

$$\begin{aligned} x &= A \cos (\omega t + \theta) \\ y &= B \cos (\omega t + \varphi) \end{aligned} \tag{4.10}$$

where $\omega = \sqrt{k/m}$. The constants of integration A, B, θ, and φ are determined from the initial conditions.

From the form of the component differential equations of motion, Eq. [4.9(a)], we see that the motion can be approximately represented by the oscillation of a particle of mass m attached to four identical springs, as shown in Fig. 4.3.

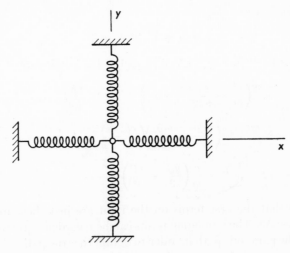

FIG. 4.3

In order to find the rectangular equation of the path, we must eliminate t between Eqs. (4.10). To do this, let us write the second equation in the form

$$\frac{y}{B} = \cos\left[\omega t + \theta + (\varphi - \theta)\right]$$

Since $\cos(\alpha + \beta) = \cos\alpha\cos\beta - \sin\alpha\sin\beta$, we have

$$\frac{y}{B} = \cos(\omega t + \theta)\cos(\varphi - \theta) - \sin(\omega t + \theta)\sin(\varphi - \theta)$$

or, from the first cf Eqs. (4.10),

$$\frac{y}{B} = \frac{x}{A}\cos(\varphi - \theta) - \sqrt{1 - \frac{x^2}{A^2}}\sin(\varphi - \theta)$$

Upon transposing, squaring, and collecting terms, we obtain

$$\frac{x^2}{A^2} - xy\frac{2\cos(\varphi - \theta)}{AB} + \frac{y^2}{B^2} = \sin^2(\varphi - \theta) \qquad (4.11)$$

Now the general quadratic

$$ax^2 + bxy + cy^2 + dx + ey = f$$

is the equation of an ellipse, a parabola, or a hyperbola, depending on whether the discriminant $b^2 - 4ac$ is negative, zero, or positive, respectively In Eq. (4.11) the discriminant is equal to $-[2\sin(\varphi - \theta)/AB]^2$, so the path is an ellipse (Fig. 4.4).

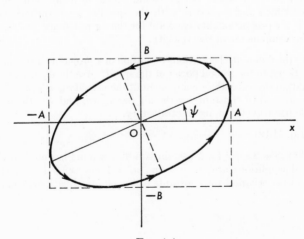

FIG. 4.4

In particular, if the phase difference $\varphi - \theta$ is equal to $\pi/2$, the equation of the path reduces to the well-known equation

$$\frac{x^2}{A^2} + \frac{y^2}{B^2} = 1$$

which is the equation of an ellipse whose axes coincide with the coordinate axes, and are of length $2A$ and $2B$, respectively. On the other hand, if the phase difference is zero, or π, the equation of the path reduces to that of a straight line, namely,

$$y = \pm \frac{B}{A} x$$

The positive sign is taken if $\varphi - \theta = 0$, and the negative sign holds for $\varphi - \theta = \pi$. In the general case, it is possible to show that the axis of the elliptical path is inclined to the x axis by the angle ψ (Fig. 4.4), where

$$\tan 2\psi = \frac{2AB \cos (\varphi - \theta)}{A^2 - B^2} \qquad (4.12)$$

The derivation is left as an exercise.

PROBLEMS

1. Show that the maximum distance a gun can land a projectile up the slope of a mountain of constant inclination θ is $(v_o^2/g)(1 + \sin \theta)^{-1}$, where v_o is the muzzle velocity.

2. Show that the decrease in the horizontal range of a projectile owing to air resistance which varies linearly with the speed is approximately $8c\dot{x}_o\dot{y}_o^2/3g^2$, where c is the proportionality constant for the air resistance, and $\dot{x}_o$ and $\dot{y}_o$ are the initial components of the velocity.

3. What are the differential equations of motion of a projectile if the air resistance is proportional to the second power of the speed? Are the equations separated? Show that, in this case, the x component of the velocity is $\dot{x} = \dot{x}_o e^{-cs}$, where c is the proportionality constant for the air resistance, and s is the distance the projectile has traveled along the trajectory.

4. Derive Eq. (4.12).

5. Given that $\omega = 2$ sec^{-1} for a certain two-dimensional harmonic oscillator. If the initial conditions are: $x_o = 2$ cm, $y_o = 1$ cm, $\dot{x}_o = 1$ cm per sec, and $\dot{y}_o = 5$ cm per sec, find the constants of the elliptical path and make a rough plot.

PART II. THREE-DIMENSIONAL MOTION

The component differential equations of motion for the general case of three dimensions are, in rectangular coordinates,

$$F_x(x,\dot{x},y,\dot{y},z,\dot{z},t) = m\ddot{x}$$

$$F_y(x,\dot{x},y,\dot{y},z,\dot{z},t) = m\ddot{y}$$

$$F_z(x,\dot{x},y,\dot{y},z,\dot{z},t) = m\ddot{z}$$

These can be integrated by elementary procedures in certain special cases. As in the two-dimensional case, the equations may be solved separately by the methods discussed under rectilinear motion if the force components are of the separated type: $F_x = F_x(x,\dot{x},t)$, $F_y = F_y(y,\dot{y},t)$, $F_z = F_z(z,\dot{z},t)$.

4.3. Motion of a Projectile in Three Dimensions

If we take the z axis in the vertical direction, the differential equation of motion of a projectile with no air resistance, $m\mathbf{a} = m\mathbf{g}$, takes the component form

$$m\ddot{x} = 0$$

$$m\ddot{y} = 0 \qquad\qquad (4.13)$$

$$m\ddot{z} = -mg$$

Clearly, the solutions are

$$x = \dot{x}_o t$$

$$y = \dot{y}_o t \qquad\qquad [4.13(a)]$$

$$z = \dot{z}_o t - \frac{1}{2}gt^2$$

where, as in the plane case (Sec. 4.1), the origin is taken as the initial position, and the initial velocity is

$$\mathbf{v}_o = \mathbf{i}\dot{x}_o + \mathbf{j}\dot{y}_o + \mathbf{k}\dot{z}_o$$

Elimination of t between the first two of Eqs. [4.13(a)] yields

$$y = bx$$

where $b = \dot{y}_o/\dot{x}_o$. This means that the path of motion lies entirely in the plane given by the above equation. The trajectory, of course, is a parabola in that plane (Fig. 4.5).

Let us now consider the case of a projectile subject to a linear air re-

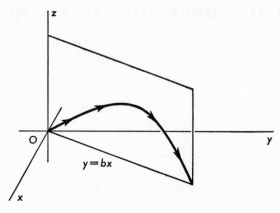

Fig. 4.5

sistance (as in Sec. 4.1 Case B). Let us suppose also that there is a constant drift force $\mathbf{F}_o$ which might be produced, for example, by a cross wind. The total force on the projectile is now the vector sum of three forces: the force of gravity $m\mathbf{g}$, the air resistance $-c\mathbf{v}$, and the drift force $\mathbf{F}_o$. The differential equation of motion now reads

$$m\mathbf{g} - c\mathbf{v} + \mathbf{F}_o = m \frac{d^2\mathbf{r}}{dt^2} \qquad (4.14)$$

We shall choose the z axis vertical, as before, and, for simplicity, let us take the initial velocity to be in the xz plane and the drift force in the y direction. With this choice the above differential equation takes the component form

$$-c\dot{x} = m\ddot{x}$$

$$-c\dot{y} + F_o = m\ddot{y} \qquad [4.14\text{(a)}]$$

$$-c\dot{z} - mg = m\ddot{z}$$

Again the equations are separated, and the solutions are readily obtained. The component equations are, in fact, of the same type as those found in Sec. 4.1, Case B, Eqs. [4.4(a)].

4.4.   The Three-Dimensional Harmonic Oscillator

If a particle that is free to move in three dimensions has acting upon it a restoring force that is directly proportional to the displacement of the particle from a fixed point and is always directed toward that point (as in the two-dimensional case, Sec. 4.2), then the differential equation of motion $m\mathbf{a} = -k\mathbf{r}$ is equivalent to the three equations

$$m\ddot{x} = -kx \qquad m\ddot{y} = -ky \qquad m\ddot{z} = -kz \qquad (4.15)$$

which are separated. Hence the solutions may be written

$$
\begin{aligned}
x &= A \cos (\omega t + \theta_1) \\
y &= B \cos (\omega t + \theta_2) \\
z &= C \cos (\omega t + \theta_2)
\end{aligned}
\qquad [4.15(a)]
$$

or, alternately, we may write

$$
\begin{aligned}
x &= a_1 \sin \omega t + b_1 \cos \omega t \\
y &= a_2 \sin \omega t + b_2 \cos \omega t \\
z &= a_3 \sin \omega t + b_3 \cos \omega t
\end{aligned}
\qquad [4.15(b)]
$$

where $\omega = \sqrt{k/m}$. The six constants of integration in either set of equations are determined from the initial position and velocity of the particle. Now consider the first two of Eqs. [4.15(b)]. From these equations we can solve for $\sin \omega t$ and for $\cos \omega t$ in terms of x,y, and the constants a_1, b_1, a_2, and b_2. The results, when substituted into the third equation, yield an equation of the form

$$z = \alpha x + \beta y \qquad (4.16)$$

where α and β are constants determined from the a's and the b's. The path of motion therefore lies in a plane which passes through the origin. The path is an ellipse (as in the two-dimensional case). This can be seen from the following argument. If we transform to a new set of coordinate axes x',y',z' having the same origin as the old axes but oriented so that the $x'y'$ plane coincides with the plane of motion, Eq. (4.16), then the differential equation of motion referred to the new coordinates will be unchanged in form, namely,

$$m\ddot{x}' = -kx' \qquad m\ddot{y}' = -ky'$$

with

$$z' = 0$$

Hence, the path is the same as that for the two-dimensional case, namely, an ellipse in the $x'y'$ plane. The orientation of the plane of motion is, of course, dependent on the initial position and velocity of the particle.

Equations (4.15) and the resulting solutions represent the motion of the so-called three-dimensional *isotropic oscillator*, wherein the restoring force is the same in all directions. If the restoring force depends on the direction of the displacement, we have the case of the *nonisotropic oscillator*. For a suitable choice of axes, the differential equations for the nonisotropic case can be written

$$m\ddot{x} = -k_1 x \qquad m\ddot{y} = -k_2 y \qquad m\ddot{z} = -k_3 z \qquad (4.17)$$

Here we have a case of *three* different frequencies of oscillation: $\omega_1 = \sqrt{k_1/m}$, $\omega_2 = \sqrt{k_2/m}$, $\omega_3 = \sqrt{k_3/m}$, and the motion is given by the solutions

$$x = A \cos (\omega_1 t + \theta_1)$$
$$y = B \cos (\omega_2 t + \theta_2) \qquad [4.17(a)]$$
$$z = C \cos (\omega_3 t + \theta_3)$$

Again, the six constants of integration in the above equations are determined from the initial conditions. The resulting oscillation of the particle lies entirely within a rectangular box (whose sides are $2A$, $2B$, and $2C$) centered on the origin. In the event that ω_1, ω_2, and ω_3 are commensurate, that is, if

$$\frac{\omega_1}{n_1} = \frac{\omega_2}{n_2} = \frac{\omega_3}{n_3} \qquad (4.18)$$

where n_1, n_2, and n_3 are integers, the path will be closed, because after a time $2\pi n_1/\omega_1 = 2\pi n_2/\omega_2 = 2\pi n_3/\omega_3$ the particle will return to its initial position and the motion will be repeated. [In Eq. (4.18) it is assumed that any common integral factor is canceled out.] On the other hand, if the ω's are *not* commensurate, the path is not closed. In this case the path may be said to fill completely the rectangular box mentioned above, at least in the sense that if we wait long enough, the particle will come arbitrarily close to any given point.

The net restoring force exerted on a given atom in a solid crystalline substance is approximately linear in the displacement in many cases. The resulting frequencies of oscillation $\omega/2\pi$ usually lie in the infrared region of the spectrum: 10^{12} to 10^{14} cycles per sec.

4.5.   Potential Energy and Conservative Forces

Consider the general equation of motion of a particle

$$\mathbf{F} = m \frac{d\mathbf{v}}{dt}$$

Let us take the dot product of both sides with the velocity $\mathbf{v}$:

$$\mathbf{F} \cdot \mathbf{v} = m \frac{d\mathbf{v}}{dt} \cdot \mathbf{v}$$

But, from the rule for differentiation of the dot product [Sec. 2.6, Eq. (2.9)], we may write

$$\mathbf{F} \cdot \mathbf{v} = \frac{m}{2} \frac{d}{dt} (\mathbf{v} \cdot \mathbf{v}) = \frac{dT}{dt} \tag{4.19}$$

where $T = m/2 \, (\mathbf{v} \cdot \mathbf{v}) = 1/2 \, mv^2$ is the kinetic energy of the particle. Integrating with respect to t, we have

$$\int (\mathbf{F} \cdot \mathbf{v}) \, dt = T + \text{constant}$$

$$\int (F_x \dot{x} + F_y \dot{y} + F_z \dot{z}) \, dt = T + \text{constant}$$

$$\int (F_x \, dx + F_y \, dy + F_z \, dz) = T + \text{constant} \tag{4.20}$$

The integral in the above equation is just the work W done on the particle by the impressed force $\mathbf{F}$. (We can write the integral as $\int \mathbf{F} \cdot d\mathbf{r} = W$.) Now suppose that the force components are derivable from a certain scalar function of the coordinates $V(x,y,z)$ such that

$$F_x = -\frac{\partial V}{\partial x} \quad F_y = -\frac{\partial V}{\partial y} \quad F_z = -\frac{\partial V}{\partial z} \tag{4.21}$$

The function V so defined is called the *potential energy*, as in the one-dimensional case where $F(x) = -dV/dx$. If a potential energy function exists, then we can write Eq. (4.20) as follows:

$$\int \mathbf{F} \cdot d\mathbf{r} = \int \left(-\frac{\partial V}{\partial x} \, dx - \frac{\partial V}{\partial y} \, dy - \frac{\partial V}{\partial z} \, dz \right) = T + \text{constant}$$

$$\int (-dV) = T + \text{constant}$$

$$T + V = E = \text{constant} \tag{4.22}$$

where E is the total energy. Thus, if the force is derivable from a potential function V as defined in Eqs. (4.21), then the sum of the kinetic and the potential energies remains constant throughout the motion; the motion is conservative.

EXAMPLES

1. In a uniform gravitational field (say at the surface of the earth) the force components are $(0,0, -mg)$ where the z axis is vertical. Thus

$$F_x = -\frac{\partial V}{\partial x} = 0 \quad F_y = -\frac{\partial V}{\partial y} = 0 \quad F_z = -\frac{\partial V}{\partial z} = -mg$$

These equations are clearly satisfied by the function

$$V(x,y,z) = mgz + \text{constant}$$

Therefore the motion is such that

$$\frac{1}{2}m(\dot{x}^2 + \dot{y}^2 + \dot{z}^2) + mgz = E = \text{constant}$$

2. In the case of the three-dimensional harmonic oscillator, we have

$$F_x = -\frac{\partial V}{\partial x} = -kx \quad F_y = -\frac{\partial V}{\partial y} = -ky \quad F_z = -\frac{\partial V}{\partial z} = -kz$$

It is easy to verify that the above equations are satisfied by the potential function

$$V(x,y,z) = \frac{k}{2}(x^2 + y^2 + z^2) = \frac{1}{2}kr^2$$

so that

$$\frac{1}{2}mv^2 + \frac{1}{2}kr^2 = E = \text{constant}$$

3. Consider the following potential function:

$$V(x,y,z) = -\frac{k}{(x^2 + y^2 + z^2)^{1/2}} = -\frac{k}{r}$$

The force components are

$$F_x = -\frac{\partial V}{\partial x} = -\frac{kx}{(x^2 + y^2 + z^2)^{3/2}} = -\frac{kx}{r^3}$$

$$F_y = -\frac{\partial V}{\partial y} = -\frac{ky}{r^3}$$

$$F_z = -\frac{\partial V}{\partial z} = -\frac{kz}{r^3}$$

The force may then be expressed vectorially as follows:

$$\mathbf{F} = \mathbf{i}F_x + \mathbf{j}F_y + \mathbf{k}F_z$$

$$= \mathbf{i}\left(-\frac{kx}{r^3}\right) + \mathbf{j}\left(-\frac{ky}{r^3}\right) + \mathbf{k}\left(-\frac{kz}{r^3}\right)$$

$$= -\frac{k}{r^3}(\mathbf{i}x + \mathbf{j}y + \mathbf{k}z)$$

$$= -\frac{k}{r^2}\left(\frac{\mathbf{r}}{r}\right) = -\frac{k}{r^2}\lambda_r$$

where λ_r is a unit vector in the direction of **r**. Thus we see that the force is the familiar inverse-square law. (The force is attractive if k is positive, and conversely.) In an inverse-square field of force, then,

$$\frac{1}{2}mv^2 + \frac{k}{r} = E = \text{constant}$$

4.6. Conditions for the Existence of a Potential Function. The Del Operator

In Sec. 3.5, Case B, we found that one-dimensional motion of a particle is always conservative if the force is a function of position only. The question naturally arises as to whether or not the corresponding statement is true for the general case of two- and three-dimensional motion. That is, if the force acting on a particle is a function of the position coordinates only, is there always a function V which satisfies Eqs. (4.21) and (4.22) above? The answer to this question is *no;* only if the force components

$$F_x = F_x (x,y,z)$$
$$F_y = F_y (x,y,z)$$
$$F_z = F_z (x,y,z)$$

satisfy certain criteria does a potential function exist.

Let us assume that a potential function *does* exist, that is, that Eqs. (4.21) hold. Then, if we take the partial derivative of F_x with respect to y, and the partial derivative of F_y with respect to x, we have

$$\frac{\partial F_x}{\partial y} = -\frac{\partial^2 V}{\partial y\,\partial x} \qquad \frac{\partial F_y}{\partial x} = -\frac{\partial^2 V}{\partial x\,\partial y}$$

But $\partial^2 V/\partial y\,\partial x = \partial^2 V/\partial x\,\partial y$, because the order of differentiation is immaterial. (It is assumed that V is a continuous function with continuous first and second derivatives.) A similar argument can be made with the pairs (F_x,F_z) and (F_y,F_z). Thus we can write

$$\frac{\partial F_x}{\partial y} = \frac{\partial F_y}{\partial x} \qquad \frac{\partial F_x}{\partial z} = \frac{\partial F_z}{\partial x} \qquad \frac{\partial F_y}{\partial z} = \frac{\partial F_z}{\partial y} \qquad [4.22(\text{a})]$$

These are the *necessary* conditions, then, on F_x, F_y, and F_z if a potential function exists; they express the condition that $\mathbf{F}\cdot d\mathbf{r} = F_x\,dx + F_y\,dy + F_z\,dz$ is an exact differential. It is also possible to show that they are sufficient conditions,* that is, if Eqs. [4.22(a)] hold, then the force com-

*See any advanced calculus textbook, for example, A. E. Taylor, *Advanced Calculus*, Ginn, Boston, 1955.

ponents are derivable from a potential function $V(x,y,z)$, and the motion is conservative — the sum $1/2\ mv^2 + V$ is constant throughout the motion. (In the case of two-dimensional motion in a plane, only the first of Eqs. [4.22(a)] is required to express the condition for conservative motion.)

EXAMPLE

Given that $F_x = ax + by^2$, $F_y = cxy$, where a, b, and c are constants. Then

$$\frac{\partial F_x}{\partial y} = 2by \qquad \frac{\partial F_y}{\partial x} = cy$$

Hence the motion is conservative only if $c = 2b$.

If it happens that the forces are of the separated type and involve only the coordinates, namely,

$$F_x = F_x(x) \qquad F_y = F_y(y) \qquad F_z = F_z(z)$$

then the partial derivatives in Eqs. [4.22(a)] are all equal to zero. In this case the equations are identically satisfied, and the force is conservative. This is the case, for example, with the three-dimensional harmonic oscillator (Sec. 4.4).

If the force $\mathbf{F}$ is conservative, we have

$$\mathbf{F} = -\mathbf{i}\frac{\partial V}{\partial x} - \mathbf{j}\frac{\partial V}{\partial y} - \mathbf{k}\frac{\partial V}{\partial z} \tag{4.23}$$

We can write the above equation in the following abbreviated form:

$$\mathbf{F} = -\nabla V \tag{[4.23(a)]}$$

where the vector differentiation operator ∇ (called "del")* is defined by

$$\nabla = \mathbf{i}\frac{\partial}{\partial x} + \mathbf{j}\frac{\partial}{\partial y} + \mathbf{k}\frac{\partial}{\partial z} \tag{4.24}$$

From the properties of partial derivatives it is easy to show that ∇ is a linear operator, that is,

$$\nabla(U + V) = \nabla U + \nabla V$$

$$\nabla(nV) = n\,\nabla V$$

where U and V are scalar functions of x, y, and z, and n is a constant. Consistent with the definition of the dot product, the operation $\nabla \cdot \mathbf{F}$ is

---

*∇V is also sometimes written *grad* V (called the "gradient" of V).

defined by the equation

$$\nabla \cdot \mathbf{F} = \frac{\partial F_x}{\partial x} + \frac{\partial F_y}{\partial y} + \frac{\partial F_z}{\partial z} \tag{4.25}$$

where $\mathbf{F}$ is any vector function of the coordinates.*

Also, consistent with the definition of the cross product, the operation $\nabla \times \mathbf{F}$ is defined by the equation

$$\nabla \times \mathbf{F} = \mathbf{i}\left(\frac{\partial F_z}{\partial y} - \frac{\partial F_y}{\partial z}\right) + \mathbf{j}\left(\frac{\partial F_x}{\partial z} - \frac{\partial F_z}{\partial x}\right) + \mathbf{k}\left(\frac{\partial F_y}{\partial x} - \frac{\partial F_x}{\partial y}\right) \tag{4.26}$$

where $\mathbf{F}$ is any vector function of the coordinates.†

Referring to Eqs. [4.22(a)], we see that the coefficients of $\mathbf{i}$, $\mathbf{j}$, and $\mathbf{k}$ all vanish in Eq. (4.26) if $\mathbf{F}$ is a conservative force, that is, the equation

$$\nabla \times \mathbf{F} = \mathbf{0} \tag{4.26(a)}$$

expresses the criterion for conservative motion.

4.7. Motion of Charged Particles in Electric and Magnetic Fields

When an electrically charged particle is in the vicinity of other electric charges, it experiences a force. This force $\mathbf{F}$ is said to be due to the electric field $\mathbf{E}$ which arises from these other charges. We write

$$\mathbf{F} = q\mathbf{E} \tag{4.27}$$

where q is the electric charge carried by the particle in question.‡ The equation of motion of the particle is then

$$m\frac{d^2\mathbf{r}}{dt^2} = q\mathbf{E} \tag{4.27(a)}$$

or, in component form,

$$m\ddot{x} = qE_x \qquad m\ddot{y} = qE_y \qquad m\ddot{z} = qE_z \tag{4.27(b)}$$

The field components are, in general, functions of the position coordinates x, y, and z. In the case of time-varying fields (that is, if the charges producing $\mathbf{E}$ are moving) the components, of course, also involve t.

Let us consider a simple case, namely that of a uniform constant electric field. We can choose one of the axes, say the z axis, to be in the direction of

---

*$\nabla \cdot \mathbf{F}$ is also sometimes written **div F** (called the "divergence" of **F**).

†$\nabla \times \mathbf{F}$ is called the "curl" of **F**, and is sometimes written **curl F**.

‡In mks units F is in newtons, q in coulombs, and E in volts per meter. In cgs units F is in dynes, q in electrostatic units, and E in statvolts per centimeter.

the field.   Then $E_x = E_y = 0$, and $E = E_z$.   The equations of motion Eqs. [4.27(b)], of a particle of charge q moving in this field are then

$$\ddot{x} = 0 \qquad \ddot{y} = 0 \qquad \ddot{z} = \frac{qE}{m} = \text{constant}$$

These are of exactly the same form as those for a projectile in a uniform gravitational field [Eqs. (4.13)].   The path is therefore a parabola.

It is shown in textbooks dealing with electromagnetic theory* that

$$\nabla \times \mathbf{E} = \mathbf{0}$$

if $\mathbf{E}$ is due to static charges.   This means that motion in such a field is conservative, and that there exists a potential function φ such that $\mathbf{E} = -\nabla\varphi$.   The potential energy of a particle of charge q in such a field is then $q\varphi$, and the total energy is constant and is equal to $1/2\ mv^2 + q\varphi$.

In the presence of a static magnetic field $\mathbf{B}$ (called the magnetic induction) the force acting on a moving particle is conveniently expressed by means of the cross product, namely,

$$\mathbf{F} = q(\mathbf{v} \times \mathbf{B}) \tag{4.28}$$

where $\mathbf{v}$ is the velocity, and q is the charge.†   The differential equation of motion of a particle moving in a purely magnetic field is then

$$m \frac{d^2\mathbf{r}}{dt^2} = q(\mathbf{v} \times \mathbf{B}) \tag{4.28(a)}$$

The above equation states that the acceleration of the particle is always at right angles to the direction of motion.   This means that the tangential component of the acceleration $(\dot{v})$ is zero, and so the particle moves with constant speed.   [See Sec. 2.7, Eq. (2.14)]   This is true even if $\mathbf{B}$ is a varying function of the position $\mathbf{r}$ as long as it does not involve the time t.

Let us examine the motion of a charged particle in a uniform constant magnetic field.   Suppose we choose the z axis to be in the direction of the field; that is, we shall write

$$\mathbf{B} = \mathbf{k}B \tag{4.29}$$

*For example, J. C. Slater and N. H. Frank, *Electromagnetism*, McGraw-Hill, New York, 1947.

†Equation (4.28) is valid for mks units: F is in newtons, q in coulombs, v in meters per second, and B in webers per square meter.   In cgs units we must write $F = (q/c)$ ($\mathbf{v} \times \mathbf{B}$), where F is in dynes, q in electrostatic units, c is the speed of light -3×10^{10} cm per sec—and B is in gauss.   (See Slater and Frank, *op. cit.*)

The differential equation of motion Eq. [4.28(a)], now reads

$$m\frac{d^2\mathbf{r}}{dt^2} = q(\mathbf{v} \times \mathbf{k}B) = qB\begin{vmatrix} \mathbf{i} & \mathbf{j} & \mathbf{k} \\ \dot{x} & \dot{y} & \dot{z} \\ 0 & 0 & 1 \end{vmatrix}$$

$$m(\mathbf{i}\ddot{x} + \mathbf{j}\ddot{y} + \mathbf{k}\ddot{z}) = qB(\mathbf{i}\dot{y} - \mathbf{j}\dot{x}) \qquad (4.30)$$

Equating components,

$$m\ddot{x} = qB\dot{y} \qquad m\ddot{y} = -qB\dot{x} \qquad \ddot{z} = 0 \qquad [4.30(a)]$$

Here, for the first time, we meet a set of differential equations of motion which are *not* of the separated type. The solution is relatively simple, however, for we can integrate at once with respect to t to obtain

$$m\dot{x} = qBy + c_1 \qquad m\dot{y} = -qBx + c_2 \qquad \dot{z} = \text{constant} = \dot{z}_o$$

or

$$\dot{x} = \omega y + C_1 \qquad \dot{y} = -\omega x + C_2 \qquad \dot{z} = \dot{z}_o \qquad [4.30(b)]$$

where we have used the abbreviation $\omega = qB/m$. The c's are constants of integration, and $C_1 = c_1/m$ $C_2 = c_2/m$. Upon inserting the expression for $\dot{y}$ from the second part of Eq. [4.30(b)] into the first part of Eq. [4.30(a)], we obtain the following separated equation for x:

$$\ddot{x} + \omega^2 x = \omega^2 a \qquad (4.31)$$

where $a = C_2/\omega$. The solution of Eq. (4.31) is clearly

$$x = a + A\cos(\omega t + \theta_o) \qquad [4.31(a)]$$

where A and θ_o are constants of integration. Now, if we differentiate Eq. [4.31(a)] with respect to t, we have

$$\dot{x} = -A\omega\sin(\omega t + \theta_o) \qquad [4.31(b)]$$

The above expression for $\dot{x}$ may be substituted for the left side of the first of Eqs. [4.30(b)] and the resulting equation solved for y. The result is

$$y = b - A\sin(\omega t + \theta_o) \qquad [4.31(c)]$$

where $b = -C_1/\omega$. To find the form of the path of motion, we eliminate t between Eq. [4.31(a)] and Eq. [4.31(c)] to get

$$(x - a)^2 + (y - b)^2 = A^2 \qquad (4.32)$$

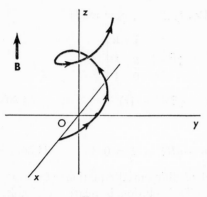

Fig. 4.6

Thus the projection of the path of motion on the xy plane is a circle of radius A centered at the point (a, b). Since, from the third of Eqs. [4.30(b)], the speed in the z direction is constant, we conclude that the path is a *spiral*. The axis of the spiral path is in the direction of the magnetic field, as shown in Fig. 4.6. From Eq. [4.31(c)] we have

$$\dot{y} = -A\omega \cos (\omega t + \theta_o) \qquad (4.33)$$

Upon eliminating t between Eq. [4.31(b)] and Eq. (4.33), we find

$$\dot{x}^2 + \dot{y}^2 = A^2\omega^2 = A^2(qB/m)^2 \qquad (4.34)$$

Letting $v_1 = (\dot{x}^2 + \dot{y}^2)^{1/2}$, we see that the radius A of the spiral is given by

$$A = v_1/\omega = v_1 \frac{m}{qB} \qquad (4.35)$$

If there is no component of the velocity in the z direction, the path is a circle of radius A. It is evident that A is directly proportional to the speed v_1, and that the angular frequency ω of motion in the circular path is *independent* of the speed. ω is known as the cyclotron frequency. (The fact that it is independent of the speed of the charged particle was utilized by Ernest Lawrence in the construction of the cyclotron.)

PROBLEMS

1. A projectile is fired from the origin at an angle of elevation of 45° in the xz plane. The muzzle velocity is v_o, and there is a constant drift force in the y direction. If the air resistance varies linearly with the speed, find where the projectile lands, assuming that the ground is level.

2. Prove that the trajectory of the projectile in Prob. 1 lies entirely in a plane.

3. Given the following potential-energy functions:

   (a) $V = cxy/z$

   (b) $V = ax + by^2 + cz^3$

   (c) $V = ae^{c(x+y+z)}$

   (d) $V = c(x^2 + y^2 + z^2)^{n/2}$

   Find the force $\mathbf{F}$ in each case.

4. Test the following forces to see whether or not they are conservative:

(a) $\mathbf{F} = \mathbf{i}e^{c(x+y)} + \mathbf{j}e^{c(x+y)}$

(b) $\mathbf{F} = \mathbf{i}e^{c(x^2+y^2)} + \mathbf{j}e^{c(x^2+y^2)}$

(c) $\mathbf{F} = \mathbf{i}cyz + \mathbf{j}cxz + \mathbf{k}cxy$

(d) $\mathbf{F} = \mathbf{i}cxy + \mathbf{j}cyz + \mathbf{k}cxz$

(e) $\mathbf{F} = \mathbf{i}\dfrac{cy}{z} + \mathbf{j}\dfrac{cx}{z} - \mathbf{k}\dfrac{cxy}{z^2}$

5. An atom is situated in a simple cubic crystal lattice. If the potential energy of interaction between two atoms is of the form cr^{-m} where r is the distance between them, show that the total potential energy of interaction of a given atom with its six nearest neighbors is reducible to that of the three-dimensional harmonic oscillator $V \cong k/2(x^2 + y^2 + z^2)$. [NOTE: Assume that the six neighboring atoms are fixed and are located at the points $(\pm d,0,0)$, $(0, \pm d,0)$, $(0,0, \pm d)$, and that the displacement of the given atom from the origin is small compared to d.]

6. A charged particle moves in a uniform electric field $\mathbf{E}$ and a uniform magnetic field $\mathbf{B}$ which is at right angles to $\mathbf{E}$. Show that, if the initial velocity of the particle is perpendicular to $\mathbf{B}$, the particle will remain in a plane and that the path is a cycloid (*ordinary; curtate,* wavy; or *prolate,* with cusps) depending on the magnitude and direction of the initial velocity. Cycloidal motion of electrons is utilized in the *magnetron*—an electronic tube used to produce high-frequency radio waves.

PART III. CONSTRAINED MOTION

When a moving particle is restricted geometrically in the sense that it must stay on a certain definite surface or curve, the motion is said to be *constrained*. A piece of ice sliding around in a bowl, or a bead sliding on a wire, are examples of constrained motion. The constraint may be complete, as with the bead, or it may be one sided, as in the former example. Constraints may be fixed, or they may be moving. In this part we shall study only fixed constraints.

4.8. The Energy Equation for Smooth Constraints

The total force acting on a particle moving under constraint can be expressed as the vector sum of the external force $\mathbf{F}$ and the force of constraint $\mathbf{R}$. The latter force is the reaction of the constraining agent upon the particle. The equation of motion may therefore be written

$$m \frac{d\mathbf{v}}{dt} = \mathbf{F} + \mathbf{R} \tag{4.36}$$

If we take the dot product with the velocity $\mathbf{v}$ we have

$$m \frac{d\mathbf{v}}{dt} \cdot \mathbf{v} = \mathbf{F} \cdot \mathbf{v} + \mathbf{R} \cdot \mathbf{v} \tag{4.37}$$

Now in the case of a *smooth* constraint — for example, a frictionless surface — the reaction $\mathbf{R}$ is normal to the surface or curve while the velocity $\mathbf{v}$ is tangent to the surface. Hence $\mathbf{R}$ is perpendicular to $\mathbf{v}$ and the dot product $\mathbf{R} \cdot \mathbf{v}$ vanishes. Equation (4.37) then reduces to

$$\frac{d}{dt} \left(\frac{1}{2} m \mathbf{v} \cdot \mathbf{v} \right) = \mathbf{F} \cdot \mathbf{v} \tag{4.38}$$

Consequently, if $\mathbf{F}$ is conservative, we can integrate as in Sec. 4.5, and we find the same energy equation, namely,

$$\frac{1}{2} m v^2 + V(x,y,z) = \text{constant} = E \tag{4.39}$$

Thus the particle, although remaining on the surface or curve, moves in such a way that the total energy is constant. We might, of course, have expected this to be the case for frictionless constraints.

EXAMPLE

A particle is placed on top of a smooth sphere of radius a. If the particle is slightly disturbed, at what point will it leave the sphere?

The forces acting on the particle are the downward force of gravity $m\mathbf{g}$ and the reaction $\mathbf{R}$ of the spherical surface. The equation of motion is

$$m \frac{d\mathbf{v}}{dt} = m\mathbf{g} + \mathbf{R}$$

Let us choose coordinate axes as shown in Fig. 4.7. The potential energy is then mgz, and the energy equation reads

$$\frac{1}{2} m v^2 + mgz = E$$

From the initial conditions ($v = 0$ for $z = a$) we have $E = mga$, so

$$v^2 = 2g(a - z)$$

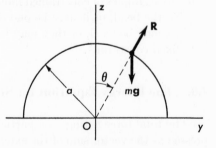

FIG. 4.7

Now, if we take radial components of the equation of motion, we can write

$$-\frac{mv^2}{a} = -mg \cos \theta + R = -mg\frac{z}{a} + R$$

Hence

$$R = mg\frac{z}{a} - \frac{mv^2}{a} = mg\frac{z}{a} - \frac{m}{a}2g(a-z)$$

$$= \frac{mg}{a}(3z - 2a)$$

Thus R vanishes when $z = \frac{2}{3}a$, at which point the particle will leave the sphere.

4.9.   Motion on a Curve

For the case in which a particle is constrained to move on a certain curve, the energy equation Eq. (4.39), together with the equations of the curve in parametric form

$$x = x(s) \qquad y = y(s) \qquad z = z(s) \qquad (4.40)$$

suffice to determine the motion. (The parameter s is the distance measured along the curve from some arbitrary reference point.) That this is so may be seen by consideration of the fact that the potential energy can be expressed as a function of s alone, while the kinetic energy is just $\frac{1}{2}m\dot{s}^2$. Thus the energy equation may be written

$$\frac{1}{2}m\dot{s}^2 + V(s) = E \qquad (4.41)$$

from which s (hence x, y, and z) can be obtained by integration. Alternately, by differentiating the above equation with respect to t and canceling the common factor $\dot{s}$, we obtain the following differential equation of motion:

$$m\ddot{s} + \frac{dV}{ds} = 0 \qquad (4.42)$$

This equation is equivalent to the equation

$$m\ddot{s} - F_s = 0 \qquad (4.43)$$

where F_s is the component of the external force $\mathbf{F}$ in the direction of s. This means that $F_s = -dV/ds$.

4.10.   The Simple Pendulum

The above considerations are well illustrated by the simple pendulum — a heavy particle attached to the end of a light inextensible rod or cord, the motion being in a vertical plane. The simple pendulum is also dynamically equivalent to a bead sliding on a smooth wire in the form of a vertical circular loop. As shown in Fig. 4.8, let θ be the angle between the vertical and the line CP where C is the center of the circular path and P is the instantaneous position of the particle. The distance s is measured from the equilibrium position O. From the figure, we see that the component F_s of the force of gravity $m\mathbf{g}$ in the direction of s is equal to $-mg \sin \theta$. If L is the length of the pendulum, then $\theta = s/L$. The differential equation of motion Eq. (4.43), then reads

$$m\ddot{s} + mg \sin (s/L) = 0 \qquad (4.44)$$

or, in terms of θ, we may write

$$\ddot{\theta} + \frac{g}{L} \sin \theta = 0 \qquad (4.45)$$

It should be noted that the potential energy V can be expressed as mgz where z is the vertical distance of the particle from O, namely,

$$V = mgz = mgL(1 - \cos \theta)$$

$$= mgL - mgL \cos (s/L) \qquad (4.46)$$

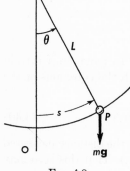

FIG. 4.8

Hence $-dV/ds = -mg \sin (s/L) = -mg \sin \theta = F_s$, as stated above.

In order to find an approximate solution of the differential equation of motion Eq. (4.45), let us assume that θ remains small. In this case

$$\sin \theta \simeq \theta$$

so we have

$$\ddot{\theta} + \frac{g}{L}\theta = 0 \qquad (4.47)$$

The solution, as we have seen in Sec. 3.8, is

$$\theta = \theta_o \cos (\omega_o t + \varphi_o) \qquad [4.47(a)]$$

where $\omega_o = \sqrt{g/L}$. θ_o is the amplitude of oscillation, and φ_o is a phase factor. Thus, to the extent that θ is a valid approximation for $\sin \theta$, the motion is simple harmonic, and the period of oscillation T_o is given by

$$T_o = \frac{2\pi}{\omega_o} = 2\pi\sqrt{\frac{L}{g}} \qquad (4.48)$$

the well-known elementary formula.

★4.11. More Accurate Solution of the Simple Pendulum Problem and the Nonlinear Oscillator

The differential equation of motion of the simple pendulum

$$\ddot{\theta} + \frac{g}{L}\sin\theta = 0$$

is a special case of the general differential equation for motion under a nonlinear restoring force, that is, a force which varies in some manner other than in direct proportion to the displacement. The equation of the general one-dimensional problem (with no damping) may be written

$$m\ddot{\xi} + \frac{dV}{d\xi} = 0 \qquad (4.49)$$

or

$$m\ddot{\xi} - F(\xi) = 0 \qquad (4.50)$$

where ξ is the variable denoting the displacement from the equilibrium position, so that,

$$F(0) = -\left(\frac{dV}{d\xi}\right)_{\xi=0} = 0 \qquad (4.51)$$

Nonlinear differential equations usually require some method of approximation for their solution. Suppose that the potential-energy function is expanded as a power series in ξ, namely,

$$V = V_o + \frac{b}{2}\xi^2 + \frac{c}{6}\xi^3 + \ldots \qquad (4.52)$$

where $b = (d^2V/d\xi^2)_{\xi=0}$, $c = (d^3V/d\xi^3)_{\xi=0}$, etc. [The linear term is zero from Eq. (4.51).] The force F will then be of the form

$$F = -\frac{dV}{d\xi} = -b\xi - \frac{c}{2}\xi^2 - \ldots \qquad (4.53)$$

and the differential equation of motion may be written

$$m\ddot{\xi} + b\xi + \frac{c}{2}\xi^2 + \ldots = 0 \qquad (4.54)$$

The term $b\xi$ in the above equation is the *linear* term. If this term is predominant, that is, if b is much larger than the other coefficients $c, \ldots$, then the motion will be approximately simple harmonic with angular frequency $(b/m)^{1/2}$. A more accurate solution must take into account the remaining nonlinear terms.

To illustrate, let us return to the problem of the simple pendulum. If we use the series expansion

$$\sin \theta = \theta - \frac{\theta^3}{3!} + \frac{\theta^5}{5!} - \cdots$$

and retain only the first two terms, we obtain

$$\ddot{\theta} + \frac{g}{L}\theta - \frac{g}{6L}\theta^3 = 0 \tag{4.55}$$

as a second approximation to the differential equation of motion. We know that the motion is periodic. Suppose we *try* a solution in the form a simple sinusoidal function

$$\theta = A \cos \omega t$$

Inserting this into the differential equation, Eq. (4.55), we obtain

$$-A\omega^2 \cos \omega t + \frac{g}{L}A \cos \omega t - \frac{g}{6L}A^3 \cos^3 \omega t = 0$$

or, upon using the trigonometric identity

$$\cos^3 u = \frac{3}{4} \cos u + \frac{1}{4} \cos 3u$$

we have, after collecting terms,

$$\left(-A\omega^2 + \frac{g}{L}A - \frac{gA^3}{8L}\right) \cos \omega t - \frac{gA^3}{24L} \cos 3\omega t = 0 \tag{4.56}$$

Excluding the trivial case $A = 0$, we see that the above equation cannot hold for all values of t. Hence our trial function $A \cos \omega t$ cannot be a solution. From the fact that the term in $\cos 3\omega t$ appears in the above equation, however, we might suspect that a trial solution of the form

$$\theta = A \cos \omega t + B \cos 3\omega t \tag{4.57}$$

will represent a better approximation than $A \cos \omega t$. This turns out to be the case. If we insert the above solution into Eq. (4.55), we find, after a procedure similar to that above, the following equation:

$$\left(-A\omega^2 + \frac{g}{L}A - \frac{gA^3}{8L}\right) \cos \omega t + \left(-9B\omega^2 + \frac{g}{L}B - \frac{gA^3}{24L}\right) \cos 3\omega t$$

$$+ \text{(terms in higher powers of } B \text{ and higher multiples of } \omega t)$$

$$= 0 \tag{4.58}$$

Again the equation will not hold for all values of t, but our approximate solution, Eq. (4.57), will be reasonably accurate if the coefficients of the first two cosine terms can be made to vanish separately:

$$-A\omega^2 + \frac{g}{L}A - \frac{gA^3}{8L} = 0 \qquad -9B\omega^2 + \frac{g}{L}B - \frac{gA^3}{24L} = 0 \qquad (4.59)$$

From the first equation

$$\omega^2 = \frac{g}{L}\left(1 - \frac{A^2}{8}\right) \qquad\qquad [4.59(a)]$$

With this value of ω^2, we find from the second part of Eq. (4.59)

$$B = -A^3\frac{1}{3(64 + 27A^2)} \simeq -\frac{A^3}{192} \qquad\qquad [4.59(b)]$$

(We are assuming that A^2 is small compared to 64/27.)

Now, from our trial solution [Eq. (4.57)], we see that the amplitude θ_o of the oscillation of the pendulum is given by

$$\theta_o = A + B$$

$$= A - \frac{A^3}{192}$$

or, if A is small,

$$\theta_o \simeq A$$

The meaning of Eq. [4.59(a)] is now clear. The frequency of oscillation depends on the amplitude θ_o. In fact, we can write

$$\omega \simeq \sqrt{\frac{g}{L}}\left(1 - \frac{1}{8}\theta_o^2\right)^{1/2}$$

or, for the period, we have

$$T = \frac{2\pi}{\omega} \simeq 2\pi\sqrt{\frac{L}{g}}\left(1 - \frac{1}{8}\theta_o^2\right)^{-1/2}$$

$$\simeq 2\pi\sqrt{\frac{L}{g}}\left(1 + \frac{1}{16}\theta_o^2 + \dots\right)$$

$$\simeq T_o\left(1 + \frac{1}{16}\theta_o^2 + \dots\right) \qquad\qquad (4.60)$$

where T_o is the period for zero amplitude as obtained in Sec. 4.10.

The above analysis, although it is admittedly very crude, brings out two essential features of motion under a nonlinear restoring force; namely, that the period of oscillation is a function of the amplitude of vibration, and that the oscillation is not strictly sinusoidal but can be considered as the superposition of a mixture of harmonics. It can be shown that the vibration of a nonlinear system driven by a purely sinusoidal driving force will also be distorted; that is, it will contain harmonics. The loudspeaker of a radio receiver or a "hi-fi" system, for example, may introduce distortion (harmonics) over and above that introduced by the electronic amplifying system.

EXAMPLE

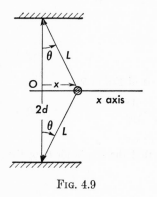

FIG. 4.9

Consider the motion of a particle of mass m attached to the center of a light elastic cord or spring. Let the ends of the cord be fixed a distance $2d$ apart, as shown in Fig. 4.9. Suppose that the particle is constrained to move only in the transverse or x direction. Now the tension S in each part of the cord, assuming that Hooke's law holds, is

$$S = k(L - a)$$

where L is the stretched length (as shown), k is the stiffness, and a is the length of each part under no tension. Hence the net force in the x direction is given by

$$F_x = -2S \cos \theta = -2k(L - a)\frac{x}{L} = -2kx + 2ka\frac{x}{\sqrt{d^2 + x^2}} = m\ddot{x}$$

Expanding the term under the radical by the binomial theorem, we obtain, after transposing and collecting terms,

$$m\ddot{x} + \frac{2k(d - a)}{d}x + \frac{ka}{d^3}x^3 + \ldots = 0$$

This differential equation is nonlinear; consequently, the oscillation is not strictly simple harmonic and the period of oscillation will depend on the amplitude.

4.12.   Exact Solution of the Motion of the Simple Pendulum by Means of Elliptic Integrals

From the expression for the potential energy of the simple pendulum, Eq. (4.46), we can write the energy equation as follows:

$$\frac{1}{2}m(L\dot{\theta})^2 + mgL(1 - \cos \theta) = E \tag{4.61}$$

If the pendulum is pulled aside at an angle θ_o (the amplitude) and released ($\dot{\theta}_o = 0$), then $E = mgL(1 - \cos \theta_o)$. The above equation then reduces to

$$\dot{\theta}^2 = \frac{2g}{L}(\cos \theta - \cos \theta_o) \tag{4.62}$$

after transposing terms and dividing by mL^2. By use of the identity $\cos \theta = 1 - 2 \sin^2 (\theta/2)$, we can further write

$$\dot{\theta}^2 = \frac{4g}{L}\left(\sin^2 \frac{\theta_o}{2} - \sin^2 \frac{\theta}{2} \right) \qquad [4.62(\text{a})]$$

It is expedient to express the motion in terms of the variable φ defined by the equation

$$\sin \varphi = \frac{\sin (\theta/2)}{\sin (\theta_o/2)} = \frac{1}{k} \sin \frac{\theta}{2} \qquad (4.63)$$

Upon differentiating with respect to t, we have

$$(\cos \varphi)\, \dot{\varphi} = \frac{1}{k} \cos \left(\frac{\theta}{2} \right)\frac{\dot{\theta}}{2} \qquad [4.63(\text{a})]$$

From Eqs. (4.63) and [4.63(a)] we can readily transform Eq. [4.62(a)] into the corresponding equation in φ, namely,

$$\dot{\varphi}^2 = \frac{g}{L} (1 - k^2 \sin^2 \varphi) \qquad (4.64)$$

The relationship between φ and t is then found by separating variables and integrating:

$$t = \sqrt{\frac{L}{g}} \int_0^{\varphi} \frac{d\varphi}{\sqrt{1 - k^2 \sin^2 \varphi}} = \sqrt{\frac{L}{g}}\, F(k,\varphi) \qquad (4.65)$$

The function $F(k,\varphi) = \int_0^{\varphi} (1 - k^2 \sin^2 \varphi)^{-1/2}\, d\varphi$ is known as the *incomplete elliptic integral of the first kind*. The period of the pendulum is obtained by noting that θ increases from 0 to θ_o in one quarter of a cycle, and, from Eq. (4.64), we see that φ goes from 0 to $\pi/2$ in the same time interval. Therefore, we may write for the period T

$$T = 4\sqrt{\frac{L}{g}} \int_0^{\pi/2} \frac{d\varphi}{\sqrt{1 - k^2 \sin^2 \varphi}} = 4\sqrt{\frac{L}{g}}\, K(k) \qquad (4.66)$$

The function $K(k) = \int_0^{\pi/2} (1 - k^2 \sin^2 \varphi)^{-1/2}\, d\varphi = F(k,\pi/2)$ is called the *complete elliptic integral of the first kind*. Values of the elliptic integrals are tabulated.* An approximate expression may be obtained, however, by expanding the integrand in Eq. (4.66) by the binomial theorem and in-

---

*See, for example, L. M. Milne-Thomson, *Jacobian Elliptic Function Tables*, Dover, New York, 1950; or B. O. Peirce, *A Short Table of Integrals*, Ginn, Boston, 1929.

tegrating term by term. The result is

$$T = 4\sqrt{\frac{L}{g}} \int_0^{\pi/2} (1 + \frac{k^2}{2} \sin^2 \varphi + \dots)d\varphi = 2\pi \sqrt{\frac{L}{g}} (1 + \frac{k^2}{4} + \dots)$$

$$(4.67)$$

Now, for small values of the amplitude θ_o, we have

$$k^2 = \sin^2 \frac{\theta_o}{2} \simeq \frac{\theta_o^2}{4}$$

Thus we may write approximately

$$T \simeq 2\pi \sqrt{\frac{L}{g}} \left(1 + \frac{\theta_o^2}{16} + \dots \right)$$

$$[4.67(a)]$$

which agrees with the value of T found in the previous section [Sec. 4.11, Eq. (4.60)].

EXAMPLE

Find the period of a simple pendulum swinging with an amplitude of 20°. Use tables of elliptic functions, and also compare with the values calculated by the above approximations.

For an amplitude of 20°, $k = \sin 10° = 0.17365$, and $\theta_o/2 = 0.17453$ radians. The results are as follows:

From tables [Eq. (4.66)] $T = 4\sqrt{L/g}\, K(10°) = \sqrt{L/g}\, (6.3312)$

From Eq. (4.67) $T = 2\pi \sqrt{L/g}\, (1 + 1/4 \sin^2 10°) = \sqrt{L/g}\, (6.3301)$

From Eq. [4.67(a)] $T = 2\pi \sqrt{L/g}\, (1 + 1/16\, \theta_o^2) = \sqrt{L/g}\, (6.3300)$

Elementary formula $T_o = 2\pi \sqrt{L/g} = \sqrt{L/g}\, (6.2831)$

★4.13.   The Isochronous Problem

It is interesting to investigate the question of whether or not there is a curve of constraint for which a particle will oscillate under gravity *isochronously*, that is, with a period that is independent of the amplitude.

Let θ be the angle between the horizontal and the tangent to the constraining curve (Fig. 4.10). Then the component of the force of gravity mg in the direction of motion is $-mg \sin \theta$. The differential equation of motion along the path of constraint (assumed smooth) is then

$$m\ddot{s} = -mg \sin \theta$$

$$(4.68)$$

But if the above equation represents simple harmonic motion along the curve, we must have

$$m\ddot{s} = -ks \qquad (4.69)$$

Therefore, a constraining curve which satisfies the equation

$$s = c \sin \theta \qquad (4.70)$$

will produce simple harmonic motion.

Now we can find x and y in terms of θ from the above equation, as follows:

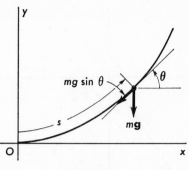

FIG. 4.10

$$\frac{dx}{d\theta} = \frac{dx}{ds}\frac{ds}{d\theta} = (\cos \theta)(c \cos \theta) \qquad (4.71)$$

Hence

$$x = \int c \cos^2 \theta \, d\theta = \frac{c}{4}(2\theta + \sin 2\theta) \qquad (4.72)$$

Similarly,

$$\frac{dy}{d\theta} = \frac{dy}{ds}\frac{ds}{d\theta} = (\sin \theta)(c \cos \theta) \qquad (4.73)$$

So

$$y = \int c \sin \theta \cos \theta \, d\theta = -\frac{c}{2} \cos 2\theta \qquad (4.74)$$

Equations (4.72) and (4.74) are the parametric equations of a *cycloid*. Thus a constraining curve in the form of a cycloid will produce motion such that s varies harmonically with time, and the period of oscillation will be independent of the amplitude. As a corollary, we see that a particle starting from rest on a smooth cycloidal curve takes the same time to reach the bottom regardless of the point at which it begins.

4.14. The Spherical Pendulum

An interesting problem in constrained motion is that of a particle which is required to move on a smooth spherical surface, for example, a particle sliding inside a smooth spherical bowl. The case is also illustrated by a heavy bob attached to a light inextensible rod or cord which is free to swing in any direction (the so-called *spherical pendulum*).

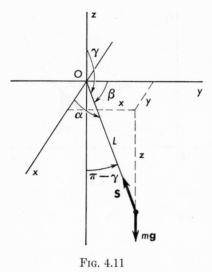

Fig. 4.11

1. *Approximate solution in rectangular coordinates.* We shall first use rectangular coordinates x, y, and z, the directions of the axes being defined as shown in Fig. 4.11. There are two forces acting on the particle — the downward force of gravity $m\mathbf{g}$, and the tension $\mathbf{S}$ in the constraining rod or cord (or the reaction of the surface in the case of the bowl). The differential equation of motion $m\ddot{\mathbf{r}} = m\mathbf{g} + \mathbf{S}$ then resolves into components

$$m\ddot{x} = S_x = -S \cos \alpha$$
$$m\ddot{y} = S_y = -S \cos \beta \qquad (4.75)$$
$$m\ddot{z} = S_z - mg = -S \cos \gamma - mg$$

where $\cos \alpha$, $\cos \beta$, and $\cos \gamma$ are the direction cosines of the vector $-\mathbf{S}$, as shown. From the figure, we see that these direction cosines may be expressed as follows:

$$\cos \alpha = \frac{x}{L} \qquad \cos \beta = \frac{y}{L} \qquad \cos \gamma = -\frac{z}{L} \qquad (4.76)$$

where L is the length of the pendulum.

Let us consider, for the moment, only the case in which the displacement from the vertical (equilibrium) position is very small: $|x| \ll L$, $|y| \ll L$, $z \simeq -L$. The tension S is then very nearly constant

$$S \simeq mg \qquad (4.77)$$

and so the first two of Eqs. (4.75) may be written

$$m\ddot{x} = -mg\frac{x}{L}$$

$$m\ddot{y} = -mg\frac{y}{L}$$

or

$$\ddot{x} + \frac{g}{L}x = 0 \qquad \ddot{y} + \frac{g}{L}y = 0 \qquad (4.78)$$

These equations are similar to the equation of motion of the two-dimensional harmonic oscillator treated in Sec. 4.2. The solutions are

$$x = A \cos (\omega t + \theta) \qquad y = B \cos (\omega t + \varphi) \qquad [4.78(a)]$$

where $\omega = \sqrt{g/L}$. Therefore, to the extent that Eq. (4.77) is a valid approximation, the motion is such that the projection of the path on the xy plane is an ellipse, and the period of oscillation is the same as that of the simple pendulum $2\pi\sqrt{L/g}$.

★*2. Solution in spherical coordinates.* For a more accurate treatment of the spherical pendulum than that given in 1, we shall use spherical coordinates r, θ, and φ, as shown in Fig. 4.12. From a study of the figure, we see that the tension S has only a radial component, and that the weight $m\mathbf{g}$ has the components $mg \cos \theta$ and $-mg \sin \theta$ in the radial direction and in the transverse (θ direction), respectively. The equation of motion $m\mathbf{a} = m\mathbf{g} + \mathbf{S}$ may be written in components as follows:

$$ma_r = F_r = mg \cos \theta - S \tag{4.79}$$

$$ma_\theta = F_\theta = -mg \sin \theta \tag{4.80}$$

$$ma_\varphi = F_\varphi = 0 \tag{4.81}$$

The components of the acceleration a_r, a_θ, and a_φ, as given in Chap. 2, Sec. 2.9, are

$$a_r = \ddot{r} - r\dot{\theta}^2 - r\dot{\varphi}^2 \sin^2 \theta \tag{4.82}$$

$$a_\theta = r\ddot{\theta} + 2\dot{r}\dot{\theta} - r\dot{\varphi}^2 \sin \theta \cos \theta \tag{4.83}$$

$$a_\varphi = r\ddot{\varphi} \sin \theta + 2\dot{r}\dot{\varphi} \sin \theta + 2r\dot{\varphi}\dot{\theta} \cos \theta \tag{4.84}$$

Now the constraint is that $r = L =$ constant. Hence Eqs. (4.83) and (4.84) reduce to

$$a_\theta = L\ddot{\theta} - L\dot{\varphi}^2 \sin \theta \cos \theta \tag{4.85}$$

$$a_\varphi = L\ddot{\varphi} \sin \theta + 2L\dot{\varphi}\dot{\theta} \cos \theta \tag{4.86}$$

Equations (4.80) and (4.81) then become

$$\ddot{\theta} - \dot{\varphi}^2 \sin \theta \cos \theta + \frac{g}{L} \sin \theta = 0 \tag{4.87}$$

$$\ddot{\varphi} \sin \theta + 2\dot{\varphi}\dot{\theta} \cos \theta = 0 \tag{4.88}$$

after transposing terms and performing the obvious cancellations. The above two equations are the final differential equations of motion of the spherical pendulum.

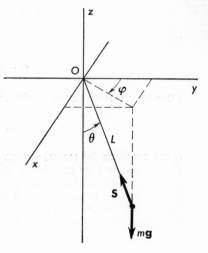

Fig. 4.12

It is easy to verify that Eq. (4.88) can be written

$$\frac{1}{\sin \theta} \frac{d}{dt} (\dot{\varphi} \sin^2 \theta) = 0$$

Therefore

$$\dot{\varphi} \sin^2 \theta = \text{constant} = h$$

so

$$\dot{\varphi} = \frac{h}{\sin^2 \theta} \tag{4.89}$$

Upon inserting the above value of $\dot{\varphi}$ into Eq. (4.87), we obtain the following *separated* equation in θ:

$$\ddot{\theta} + \frac{g}{L} \sin \theta - h^2 \frac{\cos \theta}{\sin^3 \theta} = 0 \tag{4.90}$$

It is instructive to consider some special cases at this point. First, if the angle φ is constant, then $\dot{\varphi} = 0$ and so $h = 0$. Consequently, Eq. (4.90) reduces to

$$\ddot{\theta} + \frac{g}{L} \sin \theta = 0$$

which, of course, is just the differential equation of the simple pendulum. The motion takes place in the plane $\varphi = \varphi_o = $ constant. The second special case is that of the *conical pendulum;* $\theta = \theta_o = $ constant. In this case $\dot{\theta} = 0$ and $\ddot{\theta} = 0$, so Eq. (4.90) reduces to

$$\frac{g}{L} \sin \theta_o - h^2 \frac{\cos \theta_o}{\sin^3 \theta_o} = 0$$

or

$$h^2 = \frac{g}{L} \sin^4 \theta_o \sec \theta_o \tag{4.91}$$

From the value of h given by the above equation, we find from Eq. (4.89) that

$$\dot{\varphi}_o^2 = \frac{g}{L} \sec \theta_o \tag{4.92}$$

as the condition for conical motion of the pendulum. The above equation can also be obtained by considering the forces acting on the particle undergoing circular motion, as shown in Fig. 4.13. The acceleration is constant in magnitude, namely, v^2/ρ, and is directed toward the center of the circular path. The vertical forces are in equilibrium. Hence, taking horizontal and vertical components, we have

$$\frac{mv^2}{\rho} = S \sin \theta_o \qquad mg = S \cos \theta_o \tag{4.93}$$

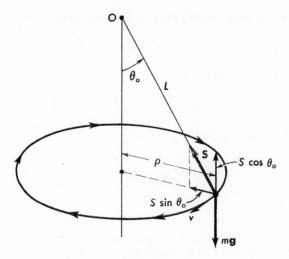

Fig. 4.13

Upon eliminating S, we get

$$\frac{v^2}{\rho} = g \tan \theta_o \tag{4.94}$$

But $\rho = L \sin \theta_o$, and $v = \rho\dot\varphi_o = (L \sin \theta_o)\dot\varphi_o$. Therefore

$$\frac{(L \sin \theta_o)^2\dot\varphi_o^2}{L \sin \theta_o} = g \tan \theta_o$$

which easily reduces to Eq. (4.92).

Let us now consider the case in which the motion is *almost* conical; that is, the value of θ remains close to the value θ_o. If we insert the expression for h^2 given in Eq. (4.91) into the separated differential equation for θ [Equation (4.90)], the result is

$$\ddot\theta + \frac{g}{L}\left(\sin\theta - \frac{\sin^4\theta_o}{\cos\theta_o}\frac{\cos\theta}{\sin^3\theta}\right) = 0 \quad \text{or} \quad \ddot\theta + \frac{g}{L}[f(\theta)] = 0 \tag{4.95}$$

It is convenient at this point to introduce the new variable ξ defined as

$$\xi = \theta - \theta_o \tag{4.96}$$

The expression in parentheses in Eq. (4.95) may be expanded as a power series in ξ according to the standard formula

$$f(\xi) = f(0) + f'(0)\xi + f''(0)\frac{\xi^2}{2!} + \cdots$$

We find, after performing the indicated operations, that $f(0) = 0$ and $f'(0) = 3\cos\theta_o + \sec\theta_o$. Since we are concerned with the case of small values of ξ, we shall neglect higher powers of ξ than the first, and so we can write Eq. (4.95) as

$$\ddot{\xi} + \frac{g}{L}b\xi = 0 \qquad (4.97)$$

where $b = 3 \cos \theta_o + \sec \theta_o$. The motion in ξ or θ is therefore given by

$$\xi = \theta - \theta_o = \xi_o \cos \left(\sqrt{\frac{gb}{L}}\, t + \epsilon \right) \qquad [4.97(\text{a})]$$

Thus θ oscillates harmonically about the value θ_o with a period

$$T_1 = 2\pi \sqrt{\frac{L}{gb}}$$

$$= 2\pi \sqrt{\frac{L}{g(3 \cos \theta_o + \sec \theta_o)}} \qquad (4.98)$$

Now the value of $\dot{\varphi}$, from Eq. (4.89), does not vary greatly from the value given by the purely conical motion $\dot{\varphi}_o$, so φ increases steadily during the oscillation of θ about θ_o. The path of the particle is shown in Fig. 4.14. During one complete oscillation of θ, the value of the azimuth angle φ increases by the amount

$$\Delta\varphi = \dot{\varphi}_o T_1$$

$$= \sqrt{\frac{g}{L}} \sec \theta_o \;\; 2\pi \sqrt{\frac{L}{g(3 \cos \theta_o + \sec \theta_o)}}$$

$$= \frac{2\pi}{\sqrt{3 \cos^2 \theta_o + 1}} \qquad (4.99)$$

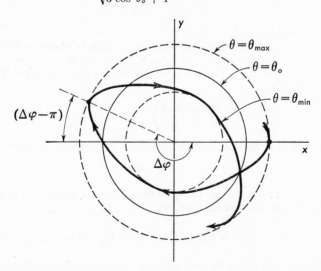

Fɪɢ. 4.14

Let the radius of the circle $\theta = \theta_o$ be denoted by ρ, as in Fig. 4.13. Then $\cos^2 \theta_o = 1 - \rho^2/L^2$, and so Eq. (4.99) may be written

$$\Delta\varphi = \frac{2\pi}{\sqrt{4 - 3\frac{\rho^2}{L^2}}} \simeq \pi + \frac{3\pi}{8}\frac{\rho^2}{L^2} + \ldots \tag{4.100}$$

In Part A of this section we showed that the projection of the path on the xy plane is an ellipse if θ is small. We can now interpret the above equation to mean that the axis of the ellipse is not steady, but *precesses* in the direction of increasing φ; the angle of precession is just the excess of $\Delta\varphi$ over π, or approximately $3\pi\rho^2/8L^2$ radians for every oscillation in θ. This is shown in Fig. 4.14.

PROBLEMS

1. A bead slides on a smooth wire bent into the form of a coil or helix of radius a with n turns per unit length, the axis of the helix being vertical. Analyze the motion and find the acceleration of the bead.

2. A bead slides on a smooth wire bent into the form of a vertical circular loop of radius a. If the bead starts from rest at a point which is level with the center of the loop, find how long it will take the bead to reach the bottom.

3. In Prob. 2, find the speed of the bead at the bottom of the circle, and find the reaction of the loop on the bead at that point.

4. In a laboratory experiment a simple pendulum is used to determine the value of g. If the amplitude of the pendulum is 30°, find the error incurred in the use of the elementary formula [Eq. (4.48)].

5. Find the differential equations of motion for a particle which is constrained to move on the inner surface of a smooth right-circular cone. The axis of the cone is vertical, and the vertex is the lowest point.

6. In Prob. 5, find the period for small oscillations about a circular path of radius ρ.

7. A spherical pendulum of length 1m is undergoing small oscillations about a conical angle θ_o. Find the period of this oscillation and the angle of precession $\Delta\varphi$ for (a) $\theta_o = 10°$ and (b) $\theta_o = 45°$. Make a sketch of the projection of the path in the xy plane for the two cases.

5

Moving Reference Systems

It is frequently very convenient, in describing the motion of a particle, to use a coordinate system which, itself, is moving. A coordinate system fixed to the earth, for example, is the most convenient one to use in expressing the motion of a projectile, although the earth is moving and rotating.

5.1. Translation of the Coordinate System

The simplest type of motion of the coordinate system is that of pure translation. In Fig. 5.1 $QXYZ$ are the primary coordinate axes (assumed

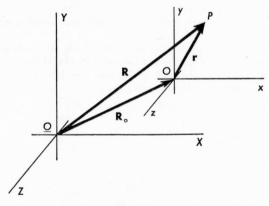

FIG. 5.1

fixed), and $Oxyz$ are the moving axes. In the case of pure translation, the respective axes QX and Ox, etc., remain parallel. The position vector of a particle P is denoted by $\mathbf{R}$ in the primary system, and by $\mathbf{r}$ in the moving system. The displacement $\overrightarrow{QO}$ of the moving origin is called $\mathbf{R}_o$. Thus

$$\mathbf{R} - \mathbf{R}_o = \mathbf{r} \tag{5.1}$$

Taking the first and second derivatives with respect to the time t, we have

$$\dot{\mathbf{R}} - \mathbf{V}_o = \dot{\mathbf{r}} \tag{5.2}$$

$$\ddot{\mathbf{R}} - \mathbf{A}_o = \ddot{\mathbf{r}} \tag{5.3}$$

where $\mathbf{V}_o$ is velocity and $\mathbf{A}_o$ is the acceleration of the moving origin. If, in particular, the velocity of the moving origin is constant, then $\mathbf{A}_o = \mathbf{O}$ and so $\ddot{\mathbf{R}} = \ddot{\mathbf{r}}$. That is, the acceleration is the same in either system.

Example

Consider a particle fixed to the rim of a rolling wheel. Let us take the moving origin O to be the center of the wheel, as shown in Fig. 5.2. The

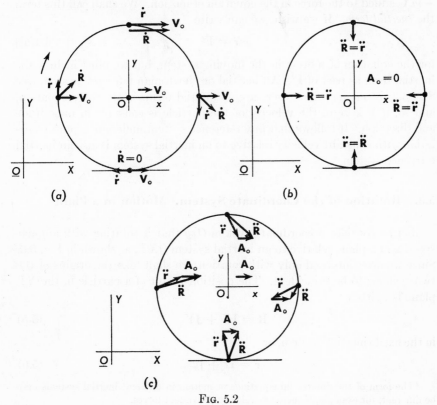

Fig. 5.2

velocity vectors for various positions of the particle are shown in Fig. 5.2(a). In Fig. 5.2(b) are shown the acceleration vectors for the case of constant velocity of $O(\mathbf{A}_o = \mathbf{O})$, and in Fig. 5.2(c) the acceleration vectors are shown for the case of a forward acceleration of the wheel.

5.2. Inertial Reference Systems

If the fundamental equation of motion (Newton's second law)

$$m\ddot{\mathbf{R}} = \mathbf{F}$$

is valid in the primary system ($QXYZ$), then, from Eq. (5.3), the equation of motion in the moving system ($Oxyz$) is

$$m\ddot{\mathbf{r}} = \mathbf{F} - m\mathbf{A}_o \tag{5.4}$$

Thus an acceleration $\mathbf{A}_o$ of the reference system requires an additional term $-m\mathbf{A}_o$ added to the force in the equation of motion. We shall call this term the *inertial term*. If we wish, we can write

$$m\ddot{\mathbf{r}} = \mathbf{F}' \tag{5.4(a)}$$

for the equation of motion in the moving system, but we must include the inertial term as part of $\mathbf{F}'$. An inertial or Newtonian reference system (see Sec. 3.2) is one for which there are no inertial terms in the force equation, and so, if $\mathbf{F}$ is zero, the velocity of the particle is constant in magnitude and direction. It follows that any reference system undergoing pure translation with constant velocity relative to an inertial system is also an inertial reference system.*

5.3. Rotation of the Coordinate System. Motion in a Plane

Let us consider a coordinate system Oxy that is rotating with angular speed ω in a plane relative to an inertial system QXY, as shown in Fig. 5.3. Since we are concerned only with rotation, we shall take the origins of the two systems to be coincident. The position vector of a particle in the XY plane is written

$$\mathbf{R} = \mathbf{I}X + \mathbf{J}Y \tag{5.5}$$

in the fixed (inertial) system, or

$$\mathbf{r} = \mathbf{i}x + \mathbf{j}y \tag{5.6}$$

*The form of the differential equations of motion in different inertial systems may be different, for example, if there are velocity-dependent forces.

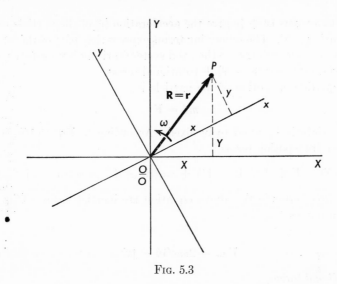

FIG. 5.3

in the rotating system. Now, if we take the derivative of $\mathbf{r}$ with respect to t, we must take into account the fact that the unit vectors $\mathbf{i}$ and $\mathbf{j}$ are not constant, namely,

$$\frac{d\mathbf{r}}{dt} = \mathbf{i}\dot{x} + \mathbf{j}\dot{y} + x\frac{d\mathbf{i}}{dt} + y\frac{d\mathbf{j}}{dt} \qquad (5.7)$$

But, from the argument presented in Sec. 2.8 leading to Eqs. (2.17) and (2.18), we have

$$\frac{d\mathbf{i}}{dt} = \mathbf{j}\frac{d\theta}{dt} = \mathbf{j}\omega \qquad \frac{d\mathbf{j}}{dt} = -\mathbf{i}\omega \qquad (5.8)$$

Consequently,

$$\dot{\mathbf{r}} = \frac{d\mathbf{r}}{dt} = \mathbf{i}\dot{x} + \mathbf{j}\dot{y} + \mathbf{i}(-\omega y) + \mathbf{j}(\omega x) \qquad (5.9)$$

Now the sum $\mathbf{i}\dot{x} + \mathbf{j}\dot{y}$ represents the velocity of the particle relative to the rotating system; let us call it $[\dot{\mathbf{r}}]$. The last two terms in Eq. (5.9) represent the velocity of rotation relative to the fixed system. We can write Eq. (5.9) as

$$\dot{\mathbf{r}} = [\dot{\mathbf{r}}] + \mathbf{v}_{\text{rot}} \qquad [5.9(a)]$$

where $\mathbf{v}_{\text{rot}} = \omega(-\mathbf{i}y + \mathbf{j}x)$. A second differentiation yields, after use of Eqs. (5.8), the following equation for the acceleration:

$$\ddot{\mathbf{r}} = \frac{d^2\mathbf{r}}{dt^2} = \mathbf{i}\ddot{x} + \mathbf{j}\ddot{y} + \mathbf{i}(-2\omega\dot{y}) + \mathbf{j}(2\omega\dot{x}) + \mathbf{i}(-\omega^2 x) + \mathbf{j}(-\omega^2 y)$$
$$+\mathbf{i}(-\dot{\omega}y) + \mathbf{j}(\dot{\omega}x) \qquad (5.10)$$

The first two terms $i\ddot{x} + j\ddot{y}$ give the acceleration $[\ddot{r}]$ of the particle relative to the rotating axes. The remaining terms express that part of the acceleration of the particle (relative to the fixed system) arising from rotation of the xy coordinate system: $\ddot{r} = [\ddot{r}] +$ rotational terms.

The equation of motion of the particle is

$$m\ddot{r} = F$$

since the origin is assumed to be fixed. According to Eq. (5.10), we can write, after transposing terms,

$$m[\ddot{r}] = F + 2m\omega(i\dot{y} - j\dot{x}) + m\omega^2(ix + jy) + m\dot{\omega}(iy - jx) \quad (5.11)$$

The last three terms in the above equation are inertial terms. They have been given names as follows:

The *Coriolis* force

$$F_{\text{Cor}} = 2m\omega(i\dot{y} - j\dot{x}) \tag{5.12}$$

The *centrifugal* force

$$F_{\text{cent}} = m\omega^2(ix + jy) = m\omega^2 r \tag{5.13}$$

The *transverse* force

$$F_{\text{trans}} = m\dot{\omega}(iy - jx) \tag{5.14}$$

Equation (5.11) is accordingly written

$$m[\ddot{r}] = F + F_{\text{Cor}} + F_{\text{cent}} + F_{\text{trans}} \tag{5.15}$$

The above "forces" are sometimes called *fictitious* forces, because, like the inertial term $-mA_o$ in Eq. (5.4), they are not due to interaction of the particle with other bodies, but, rather, they stem from the particular type of coordinate system used to describe the motion of the particle.

The Coriolis force has a direction which is at right angles to the velocity vector $[\dot{r}]$ of the particle *in* the rotating coordinate system, because $[\dot{r}] \cdot F_{\text{cor}} = 0$. The centrifugal force is always directed outward away from the axis of rotation; in this case it is in the direction of r. The transverse force is present only if there is an angular acceleration. This force is perpendicular to the position vector r, since $r \cdot F_{\text{trans}} = 0$. All three forces are basically due to the inertial character of matter.

The Coriolis force is particularly interesting. It is present only if a particle is *moving* in a rotating coordinate system. Being at right angles to the direction of motion, the Coriolis force tends to deflect the moving particle either to the right or to the left, depending on the direction of rotation of the coordinate system.

EXAMPLE

A bug crawls outward with constant speed v_o along the spoke of a wheel which is rotating with constant angular speed ω. Let us calculate the directions and magnitudes of the forces involved. If we let the x axis be along the spoke, then

$$[\dot{\mathbf{r}}] = \mathbf{i}\dot{x} + \mathbf{j}\dot{y} = \mathbf{i}v_o$$

and, since the acceleration [a] in the rotating system is zero, we have

$$m[\mathbf{a}] = \mathbf{0} = \mathbf{F} + 2m\omega(-\mathbf{j}v_o) + m\omega^2(\mathbf{i}x)$$

Here $\mathbf{F}$ is the force exerted *on* the bug by the wheel. The second term on the right is the Coriolis force, which is thus in the direction of $-\mathbf{j}$. The last term is the centrifugal force. There is no transverse force, since ω is constant. The forces are shown in Fig. 5.4.

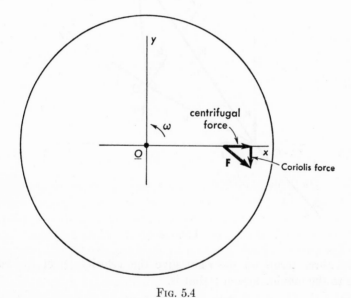

Fig. 5.4

5.4. General Motion of the Coordinate System

Using the same notation as in the previous sections, we now consider a coordinate system $Oxyz$ that is both moving and rotating relative to an inertial system $QXYZ$. In the inertial system the position vector of the particle is given by

$$\mathbf{R} = \mathbf{I}X + \mathbf{J}Y + \mathbf{K}Z \tag{5.16}$$

and in the moving system the position vector is written

$$\mathbf{r} = \mathbf{i}x + \mathbf{j}y + \mathbf{k}z \qquad (5.17)$$

Again, as in Sec. 5.1, we have

$$\mathbf{R} - \mathbf{R}_o = \mathbf{r} = \mathbf{i}x + \mathbf{j}y + \mathbf{k}z \qquad (5.18)$$

where $\mathbf{R}_o$ is the position vector of the moving origin (Fig. 5.5). Differentiating with respect to t, we obtain

$$\dot{\mathbf{R}} - \mathbf{V}_o = \dot{\mathbf{r}} = \mathbf{i}\dot{x} + \mathbf{j}\dot{y} + \mathbf{k}\dot{z} + x\frac{d\mathbf{i}}{dt} + y\frac{d\mathbf{j}}{dt} + z\frac{d\mathbf{k}}{dt} \qquad (5.19)$$

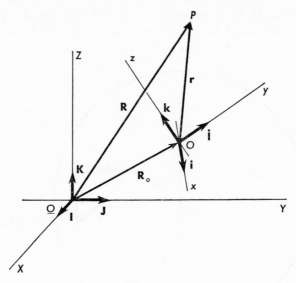

FIG. 5.5

The first three terms on the right give the velocity $[\dot{\mathbf{r}}]$ of the particle relative to the moving system; that is,

$$[\dot{\mathbf{r}}] = \mathbf{i}\dot{x} + \mathbf{j}\dot{y} + \mathbf{k}\dot{z} \qquad (5.20)$$

The last three terms in Eq. (5.19) represent the velocity of the particle resulting from rotation of the $Oxyz$ coordinate system. Let the direction of the axis of rotation of the $Oxyz$ system be designated by the unit vector $\boldsymbol{\lambda}$ (Fig. 5.6), and let the angular speed of rotation about this axis be ω. We shall call the product $\omega\boldsymbol{\lambda}$ the *angular velocity* of the rotating coordinate system, and we can write

$$\boldsymbol{\omega} = \omega\boldsymbol{\lambda} \qquad (5.21)$$

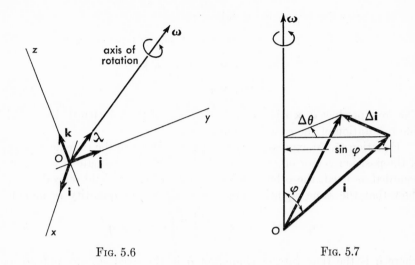

Fig. 5.6   Fig. 5.7

The sense of the angular velocity vector $\boldsymbol{\omega}$ is given by the right-hand rule, as shown in the figure.

In order to find $d\mathbf{i}/dt$, $d\mathbf{j}/dt$, and $d\mathbf{k}/dt$ in terms of $\boldsymbol{\omega}$, consider Fig. 5.7. Here the change $\Delta\mathbf{i}$ in the unit vector $\mathbf{i}$ is shown. (The vectors $\mathbf{j}$ and $\mathbf{k}$ are omitted for clarity.) From the figure we see that the magnitude of $\Delta\mathbf{i}$ is given by

$$|\Delta\mathbf{i}| \simeq (\sin \varphi)\Delta\theta \tag{5.22}$$

where $\Delta\theta$ is the amount of rotation of the $Oxyz$ system that occurs in a certain time interval Δt, and φ is the angle between $\mathbf{i}$ and $\boldsymbol{\omega}$. Therefore

$$\left|\frac{d\mathbf{i}}{dt}\right| = \lim_{\Delta t \to 0}\left|\frac{\Delta\mathbf{i}}{\Delta t}\right| = (\sin \varphi)\frac{d\theta}{dt} = \omega \sin \varphi \tag{5.23}$$

But $\Delta\mathbf{i}$ is perpendicular to both $\boldsymbol{\omega}$ and $\mathbf{i}$; consequently, we can express $d\mathbf{i}/dt$ as the cross product of $\boldsymbol{\omega}$ and $\mathbf{i}$, namely,

$$\frac{d\mathbf{i}}{dt} = \boldsymbol{\omega} \times \mathbf{i} \tag{5.24}$$

Similarly,

$$\frac{d\mathbf{j}}{dt} = \boldsymbol{\omega} \times \mathbf{j} \tag{5.24(a)}$$

$$\frac{d\mathbf{k}}{dt} = \boldsymbol{\omega} \times \mathbf{k} \tag{5.24(b)}$$

We can now write Eq. (5.19) as follows:

$$\dot{\mathbf{R}} - \mathbf{V}_o = \dot{\mathbf{r}} = [\dot{\mathbf{r}}] + x(\boldsymbol{\omega} \times \mathbf{i}) + y(\boldsymbol{\omega} \times \mathbf{j}) + z(\boldsymbol{\omega} \times \mathbf{k})$$

$$= [\dot{\mathbf{r}}] + \boldsymbol{\omega} \times (\mathbf{i}x + \mathbf{j}y + \mathbf{k}z)$$

$$= [\dot{\mathbf{r}}] + \boldsymbol{\omega} \times \mathbf{r} \qquad (5.25)$$

The cross product $\boldsymbol{\omega} \times \mathbf{r}$ is therefore that part of the velocity of the particle due to rotation of the coordinate axes.

Equation (5.25) expresses the relationship between the time derivatives of the position vector of a particle relative to two coordinate systems, one regarded as fixed, the other moving and rotating. A little reflection will show that the same equation applies to any vector quantity $\mathbf{q}$, namely,

$$\dot{\mathbf{q}} = [\dot{\mathbf{q}}] + \boldsymbol{\omega} \times \mathbf{q} = \left[\frac{d}{dt}\right]\mathbf{q} + \boldsymbol{\omega} \times \mathbf{q} \qquad (5.26)$$

where $\dot{\mathbf{q}}$ is the time rate of change of $\mathbf{q}$ in the fixed system, and $[\dot{\mathbf{q}}]$ or $\left[\dfrac{d}{dt}\right]\mathbf{q}$ is the corresponding rate in the moving system. Thus, regarding $\mathbf{q}$ as $\dot{\mathbf{r}}$, the acceleration vector $\ddot{\mathbf{r}}$ is given by

$$\ddot{\mathbf{R}} - \mathbf{A}_o = \ddot{\mathbf{r}} = \frac{d\dot{\mathbf{r}}}{dt} = \frac{d}{dt}\left([\dot{\mathbf{r}}] + \boldsymbol{\omega} \times \mathbf{r}\right)$$

$$= \left(\left[\frac{d}{dt}\right] + \boldsymbol{\omega} \times\right)([\dot{\mathbf{r}}] + \boldsymbol{\omega} \times \mathbf{r}) \qquad (5.27)$$

$$= [\ddot{\mathbf{r}}] + 2\boldsymbol{\omega} \times [\dot{\mathbf{r}}] + [\dot{\boldsymbol{\omega}}] \times \mathbf{r} + \boldsymbol{\omega} \times (\boldsymbol{\omega} \times \mathbf{r})$$

(It should be noted that $[\dot{\boldsymbol{\omega}}] = \dot{\boldsymbol{\omega}}$, since $\boldsymbol{\omega} \times \boldsymbol{\omega}$ is null.) The term $[\ddot{\mathbf{r}}]$ is the acceleration of the particle in the moving system. The remaining three terms on the right in the last equation arise from rotation of the $Oxyz$ system. The direction of $\boldsymbol{\omega} \times (\boldsymbol{\omega} \times \mathbf{r})$ is always toward the axis of rotation (which is the direction of $\boldsymbol{\omega}$) and is perpendicular to it, as shown in Fig. 5.8. The magnitude of $\boldsymbol{\omega} \times (\boldsymbol{\omega} \times \mathbf{r})$ is $r\omega^2 \sin\theta$ or $\rho\omega^2$, where θ is the angle between $\boldsymbol{\omega}$ and $\mathbf{r}$, and ρ is the distance from the moving particle to the axis of rotation.

Since the $QXYZ$ system was assumed to be an inertial system, we have

$$m\ddot{\mathbf{R}} = \mathbf{F}$$

for the equation of motion of the particle. Upon multiplying through by m in Eq. (5.27), we find, after transposing terms,

$$m[\ddot{\mathbf{r}}] = \mathbf{F} - m\mathbf{A}_o - 2m\boldsymbol{\omega} \times [\dot{\mathbf{r}}] - m[\dot{\boldsymbol{\omega}}] \times \mathbf{r} - m\boldsymbol{\omega} \times (\boldsymbol{\omega} \times \mathbf{r}) \quad (5.28)$$

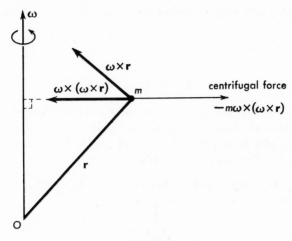

Fig. 5.8

This is the equation of motion in the moving system. The last four terms on the right side are inertial terms. The significance of the term $-m\mathbf{A}_o$ has been discussed in Sec. 5.2. As in the case of motion in a plane [Eqs. (5.11) to (5.15)], the term $-2m\boldsymbol{\omega}\times[\dot{\mathbf{r}}]$ is called the Coriolis force, $-m[\dot{\boldsymbol{\omega}}]\times\mathbf{r}$ is the transverse force, and $-m\boldsymbol{\omega}\times(\boldsymbol{\omega}\times\mathbf{r})$ is the centrifugal force.

5.5.   Effects of the Earth's Rotation

Let us apply the above results to a coordinate system which is moving with the earth. Since the angular speed of the earth's rotation is 2π radians per day $\simeq 7.3\times10^{-5}$ radian per sec, we might expect the effects of such rotation to be relatively small. Nevertheless, it is the spin of the earth that produces the equatorial bulge; the equatorial radius is some 13 miles greater than the polar radius. It is the Coriolis force on moving air that produces a general clockwise motion of the air in the Northern Hemisphere and a counterclockwise motion in the Southern Hemisphere. The Coriolis force is also an important factor in computing the trajectories of long-range projectiles.

1. Static effects. The plumb-line.   We consider first the case of a particle which is at rest on the surface of the earth. For definiteness, we shall take the particle to be the bob at the end of a plumb line. Let us choose the origin of our coordinate system to be at the position of the bob, so that $\mathbf{r} = \mathbf{O}$. Now the angular velocity vector $\boldsymbol{\omega}$ is in the direction of the earth's axis and is very nearly constant; that is, the angular acceleration $\dot{\omega}$ is zero. For the static case, then, all terms in the equation of motion Eq. (5.28), vanish except the applied force $\mathbf{F}$ and the inertial term $-m\mathbf{A}_o$. The result is

$$\mathbf{F} - m\mathbf{A}_o = \mathbf{O} \qquad (5.29)$$

The applied force $\mathbf{F}$ is given by the vector sum of two forces: the gravitational attraction of the earth (which we shall call $\mathbf{G}$) and the vertical tension of the plumb line (which we shall denote by $-m\mathbf{g}$). The forces are shown in Figs. 5.9 and 5.10. We have then

$$\mathbf{G} - m\mathbf{g} - m\mathbf{A}_o = \mathbf{O} \quad \text{or} \quad m\mathbf{g} = \mathbf{G} - m\mathbf{A}_o \qquad [5.29(a)]$$

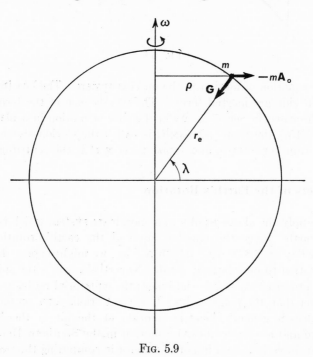

FIG. 5.9

Now the force $\mathbf{G}$ is in the direction of the center of the earth. The acceleration $\mathbf{A}_o$ is just the centripetal acceleration of our moving origin. Its magnitude is $\rho\omega^2$ or $(r_e \cos \lambda)\omega^2$, where r_e is the radius of the earth, and λ is the *geocentric latitude*. The force $-m\mathbf{A}_o$ (the centrifugal force) is of magnitude $(mr_e \cos \lambda)\omega^2$. It is directed away from and is perpendicular to the earth's axis, as indicated in Fig. 5.9. Thus the plumb line does not point to the earth's center, but deviates by a small angle ϵ. From Eq. [5.29(a)], the vector $m\mathbf{g}$ may be represented diagrammatically as the third side of a triangle, the other two sides of which are $\mathbf{G}$ and $-m\mathbf{A}_o$ (Fig. 5.10). Applying the law of sines, we have

$$\frac{\sin \epsilon}{mr_e\omega^2 \cos \lambda} = \frac{\sin \lambda}{mg}$$

or, since ϵ is small,

$$\sin \epsilon \simeq \epsilon = \frac{r_e\omega^2}{g} \sin \lambda \cos \lambda = \frac{r_e\omega^2}{2g} \sin 2\lambda \qquad (5.30)$$

Thus ϵ vanishes at the equator ($\lambda = 0$) and at the poles ($\lambda = \pm\,90°$), as we would expect. The maximum deviation of the plumb line from the "true" vertical is at $\lambda = 45°$ where

$$\epsilon_{max} = \frac{r_e\omega^2}{2g} \simeq 1.7 \times 10^{-3}\,\text{radian} \simeq \frac{1}{10}\,\text{degree}$$

The shape of the earth is such that the plumb line is normal to the surface of the earth at any point. The resulting cross section is approximately elliptical (Fig. 5.11). In the above analysis it is assumed that the gravita-

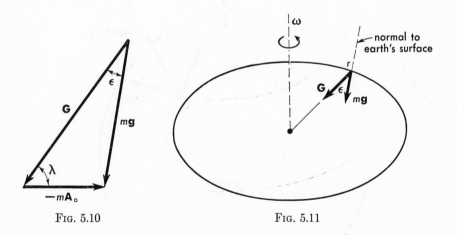

FIG. 5.10   FIG. 5.11

tional force $\mathbf{G}$ is constant and is directed toward the center of the earth. (This assumption is not strictly valid, because the earth is not a true sphere. Local variations in $\mathbf{G}$ owing to mountains, mineral deposits, etc., also affect the direction of the plumb line to a slight extent.)

2. Dynamic effects. Motion of a projectile. The equation of motion Eq. (5.28) can be written

$$m[\ddot{\mathbf{r}}] = \mathbf{F} + (\mathbf{G} - m\mathbf{A}_o) - 2m\boldsymbol{\omega} \times [\dot{\mathbf{r}}] - m\boldsymbol{\omega} \times (\boldsymbol{\omega} \times \mathbf{r})$$

where $\mathbf{F}$ represents any applied forces other than gravity. But, from Eq. [5.29(a)], the combination $\mathbf{G} - m\mathbf{A}_o$ is called $m\mathbf{g}$, hence

$$m[\ddot{\mathbf{r}}] = \mathbf{F} + m\mathbf{g} - 2m\boldsymbol{\omega} \times [\dot{\mathbf{r}}] - m\boldsymbol{\omega} \times (\boldsymbol{\omega} \times \mathbf{r}) \qquad (5.31)$$

Let us consider the motion of a projectile. If we neglect air resistance, then $\mathbf{F} = 0$. Furthermore, the term $-m\boldsymbol{\omega} \times (\boldsymbol{\omega} \times \mathbf{r})$ is very small compared to the other terms, so we shall neglect it. The equation of motion, Eq. (5.31), then reduces to

$$m[\ddot{\mathbf{r}}] = m\mathbf{g} - 2m\boldsymbol{\omega} \times [\dot{\mathbf{r}}] \qquad (5.32)$$

To solve the above equation we shall choose the directions of the coordinate axes $Oxyz$ such that the z axis is vertical (in the direction of the plumb line), the x axis is to the east, and the y axis points north (Fig. 5.12). With this choice of axes, we have

$$\mathbf{g} = -\mathbf{k}g \qquad (5.33)$$

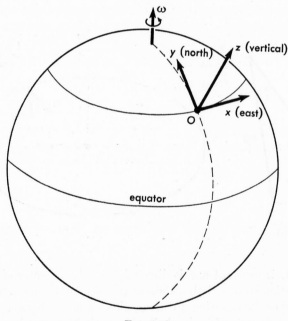

Fig. 5.12

and

$$\omega = \omega_x \mathbf{i} + \omega_y \mathbf{j} + \omega_z \mathbf{k}$$

$$= (\omega \cos \lambda)\mathbf{j} + (\omega \sin \lambda)\mathbf{k} \tag{5.34}$$

Therefore

$$\omega \times [\dot{\mathbf{r}}] = \begin{vmatrix} \mathbf{i} & \mathbf{j} & \mathbf{k} \\ \omega_x & \omega_y & \omega_z \\ \dot{x} & \dot{y} & \dot{z} \end{vmatrix}$$

$$= \mathbf{i}(\omega \dot{z} \cos \lambda - \omega \dot{y} \sin \lambda)$$

$$+ \mathbf{j}(\omega \dot{x} \sin \lambda)$$

$$+ \mathbf{k}(-\omega \dot{x} \cos \lambda) \tag{5.35}$$

Canceling the m's and equating components in Eq. (5.32), we have

$$\ddot{x} = -2\omega(\dot{z} \cos \lambda - \dot{y} \sin \lambda) \tag{5.36}$$

$$\ddot{y} = -2\omega(\dot{x} \sin \lambda) \tag{5.37}$$

$$\ddot{z} = -g + 2\omega \dot{x} \cos \lambda \tag{5.38}$$

for the component differential equations of motion. These equations are not of the separated type, but we can integrate once with respect to t to obtain

$$\dot{x} = -2\omega(z \cos \lambda - y \sin \lambda) + \dot{x}_o \tag{5.39}$$

$$\dot{y} = -2\omega x \sin \lambda + \dot{y}_o \tag{5.40}$$

$$\dot{z} = -gt + 2\omega x \cos \lambda + \dot{z}_o \tag{5.41}$$

The constants of integration $\dot{x}_o$, $\dot{y}_o$, and $\dot{z}_o$ are the initial components of the velocity. (The projectile is assumed to be at the origin at $t = 0$.) The values of $\dot{y}$ and $\dot{z}$ from the last two equations above may be substituted into Eq. (5.36). The result is

$$\ddot{x} = 2\omega gt \cos \lambda - 2\omega(\dot{z}_o \cos \lambda - \dot{y}_o \sin \lambda) \tag{5.42}$$

where terms involving ω^2 have been neglected. We now integrate again to get

$$\dot{x} = \omega gt^2 \cos \lambda - 2\omega t(\dot{z}_o \cos \lambda - \dot{y}_o \sin \lambda) + \dot{x}_o$$

and

$$x = \frac{1}{3}\omega gt^3 \cos \lambda - \omega t^2(\dot{z}_o \cos \lambda - \dot{y}_o \sin \lambda) + \dot{x}_o t \tag{5.43}$$

The above value of x may be inserted into Eqs. (5.40) and (5.41). The resulting equations, when integrated, yield

$$y = \dot{y}_o t - \omega \dot{x}_o t^2 \sin \lambda \qquad (5.44)$$

$$z = -\frac{1}{2}g t^2 + \dot{z}_o t + \omega \dot{x}_o t^2 \cos \lambda \qquad (5.45)$$

where, again, terms of order ω^2 have been ignored.

Let us consider some special cases. First, if a particle is dropped from rest $(\dot{x}_o = \dot{y}_o = \dot{z}_o = 0)$, we have

$$x = \frac{1}{3}\omega g t^3 \cos \lambda \quad y = 0 \quad z = -\frac{1}{2}g t^2 \qquad (5.46)$$

Thus the particle drifts to the east. If it falls through a vertical distance h, then $t^2 \simeq 2h/g$, and so the eastward drift is

$$\frac{1}{3}\omega \cos \lambda (8h^3/g)^{1/2}$$

As a second special case, consider a projectile fired with a very high velocity in a nearly horizontal direction, and let us take this direction to be east. Then $\dot{x}_o = v_o$, and $\dot{y}_o = \dot{z}_o = 0$. From Eq. (5.44) we have

$$y = -\omega v_o t^2 \sin \lambda$$

which means that the projectile drifts to the right. If H is the horizontal range, then $H \simeq v_o t_1$, where t_1 is the time of flight. The drift of the projectile to the right (in traversing the eastward distance H) is then approximately

$$\frac{\omega H^2}{v_o} \sin \lambda$$

It can be shown that this is the amount of drift, regardless of the direction at which the projectile is initially aimed, provided the trajectory is flat.

★5.6.   The Foucault Pendulum

In this section we shall study the effect of the earth's rotation on the motion of a spherical pendulum. As in the approximate treatment of the spherical pendulum given in Sec. 4.14(1), we shall use rectangular coordinates. As shown in Fig. 5.13, the force acting on the pendulum bob is the vector sum of the vertical force $m\mathbf{g}$ and the tension $\mathbf{S}$ in the cord. The differential equation of motion is then

$$m[\ddot{\mathbf{r}}] = m\mathbf{g} + \mathbf{S} - 2m\boldsymbol{\omega} \times [\dot{\mathbf{r}}] \qquad (5.47)$$

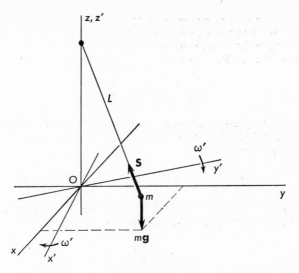

Fɪɢ. 5.13

where the term $-m\boldsymbol{\omega} \times (\boldsymbol{\omega} \times \mathbf{r})$ has been neglected. The components of $\boldsymbol{\omega} \times [\dot{\mathbf{r}}]$ are given by Eq. (5.35) above, and the x-y components of $\mathbf{S}$ are, as in Sec. 4.14(1),

$$S_x = \frac{-x}{L}S \qquad S_y = \frac{-y}{L}S$$

Equation (5.47) then resolves into

$$m\ddot{x} = \frac{-x}{L}S - 2m\omega(\dot{z}\cos\lambda - \dot{y}\sin\lambda) \qquad [5.47(\text{a})]$$

$$m\ddot{y} = \frac{-y}{L}S - 2m\omega\dot{x}\sin\lambda \qquad [5.47(\text{b})]$$

$$m\ddot{z} = S_z - mg + 2m\omega\dot{x}\cos\lambda \qquad [5.47(\text{c})]$$

We are interested in the case where the displacement from the vertical is small, so that the tension S is very nearly constant and equal to mg. Also, in this case, we can neglect $\dot{z}$ compared to $\dot{y}$ in Eq. [5.47(a)]. The x-y motion is then given by the following differential equations:

$$\ddot{x} = -\frac{g}{L}x + 2\omega'\dot{y} \qquad (5.48)$$

$$\ddot{y} = -\frac{g}{L}y - 2\omega'\dot{x} \qquad (5.49)$$

where $\omega' = \omega \sin \lambda$. The motion represented by the above differential equations is perhaps easiest to visualize by transforming to a new set of coordinate axes $Ox'y'$ rotating in the xy plane with constant angular speed $-\omega'$ relative to the Oxy system (Fig. 5.13). The equations of transformation are

$$x = x' \cos \omega't + y' \sin \omega't$$

$$y = y' \cos \omega't - x' \sin \omega't$$

Upon substituting the values of $\dot{x}$, y, and $\ddot{y}$ (obtained by differentiating the above equations) into Eq. (5.49), we find, after canceling and collecting terms and dropping terms in ω'^2,

$$\left(\ddot{x}' + \frac{g}{L}x'\right)\cos \omega't + \left(\ddot{y}' + \frac{g}{L}y'\right)\sin \omega't = 0 \qquad (5.50)$$

Since the above equation must hold for all values of t, the coefficients of the sine and the cosine must both vanish, namely,

$$\ddot{x}' + \frac{g}{L}x' = 0 \qquad (5.51)$$

$$\ddot{y}' + \frac{g}{L}y' = 0 \qquad (5.52)$$

As we have seen in Sec. 4.14(1), these differential equations represent motion in an elliptical path. The major axis of the ellipse has a fixed orientation in the $Ox'y'$ system, and therefore this axis undergoes a steady precession in a clockwise direction (in the Northern Hemisphere) with angular speed $\omega' = \omega \sin \lambda$ referred to the Oxy system. This precession is, of course, in addition to the precession discussed in Sec. 4.14(2). If, however, the initial motion of the pendulum is in a plane in the $Ox'y'z$ system, it will remain in this plane. (To start the pendulum in this way, it is merely necessary to draw it aside with a thread and let it begin from rest by cutting the thread.) The period of precession of the pendulum is $2\pi/\omega' = 24$ hr/$\sin \lambda$. At a latitude of 45° the period is thus about 34 hr. This result was first demonstrated by the French physicist Jean Foucault in 1851 in Paris.

PROBLEMS

1. Particles of mud are thrown from the rim of a rolling wheel. If the forward speed of the wheel is v_o, and the radius is a, find the maximum height above the ground which the mud can attain. At what point on the wheel does this mud leave?

2. An automobile is traveling with constant forward acceleration a_o. At a given instant the forward speed is v_o. Find which point on the tire has the greatest acceleration, relative to the ground, and give the direction and magnitude of this acceleration.

3. On a merry-go-round revolving with angular frequency ω, a boy holds a small toy tied to a string of length L. Find the period of oscillation of the toy about the equilibrium position when it moves as a simple pendulum of small am-

plitude. Let b denote the distance from the toy to the axis of the merry-go-round.

4. A bug crawls in a circular path on a phonograph turntable that revolves with constant angular speed ω. The path is concentric with the center of rotation. Show that in a coordinate system fixed to the turntable with origin at the center, the Coriolis force and the centrifugal force cancel the term $m[\ddot{\mathbf{r}}]$ if the speed of the bug is such that the bug is stationary relative to the outside.

5. Find the magnitude and direction of the Coriolis force on a 2000-lb automobile that is traveling north at 80 mph at a latitude of 40° N.

6. A particle is dropped from rest at a height of 500 ft. Where does it hit the ground?

7. A projectile is shot vertically with an initial speed v_o. Neglecting air resistance, find where it lands on the ground.

8. A spherical pendulum undergoes small oscillations about the conical angle θ_o. For what value of θ_o will the precession owing to the earth's rotation just cancel the natural precession [Sec. 4.14(1)]. Take $\lambda = 40°N$.

9. The differential equation of motion of a charged particle in an electric field $\mathbf{E}$ and a magnetic field $\mathbf{B}$ is

$$m\ddot{\mathbf{r}} = q\mathbf{E} + q\mathbf{v} \times \mathbf{B}$$

Show that if the motion is referred to a coordinate system rotating with angular velocity $-\dfrac{q}{2m}\,\mathbf{B}$, the equation of motion becomes

$$m[\ddot{\mathbf{r}}] = q\mathbf{E}$$

where it is assumed that B is small enough so that terms of order B^2 can be neglected. This result is known as *Larmor's theorem*.

6

Central Forces and Celestial Mechanics

A force whose line of action passes through a fixed point or center of force is called a *central force*. Central forces are of fundamental importance in physics, for they include such forces as gravity, electrostatic forces, and others.

6.1. The Law of Gravity

Newton announced his law of universal gravitation in 1666. It is no exaggeration to state that this marked the beginning of modern astronomy, for the law of gravity accounts for the motions of the planets of the solar system, their satellites, binary or double stars, and even stellar systems. The law may be stated:

Every particle in the universe attracts every other particle with a force that varies directly as the product of the masses of the two particles and inversely as the square of their distance apart. The direction of the force is along the straight line joining the two particles.

We can express the law vectorially by the equation

$$\mathbf{F}_{ij} = G\frac{m_i m_j}{r_{ij}^2}\left(\frac{\mathbf{r}_{ij}}{r_{ij}}\right) \tag{6.1}$$

where $\mathbf{F}_{ij}$ is the force on particle i, of mass m_i, exerted by particle j, of mass m_j. The vector $\mathbf{r}_{ij}$ is the directed line segment running from particle i to particle j, as shown in Fig. 6.1. The law of action and reaction requires that $\mathbf{F}_{ij} = -\mathbf{F}_{ji}$. The constant of proportionality G is known as the universal constant of gravitation. Its value is determined in the laboratory

by carefully measuring the force between
two spherical bodies of known mass. The
currently accepted value of G, as obtained at
the U.S. National Bureau of Standards, is

$$G = (6.673 \pm 0.003) \times 10^{-8} \frac{\text{dyne cm}^2}{\text{g}^2}$$

All of our present knowledge of the masses of
astronomical bodies, including the earth, is
based on the value of G.

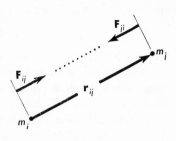

FIG. 6.1

6.2. Gravitational Force Between a Uniform Sphere and a Particle

In Sec. 3.7, where we discussed the motion of a falling body, it was
asserted that the gravitational force of the earth on a particle above the
earth's surface is inversely proportional to the square of the particle's
distance from the center of the earth; that is, the earth attracts as if all of its
mass were concentrated at a single point. We shall now prove that this is
true for any uniform spherical body, or any spherically symmetric distribution of matter.

Consider first a thin uniform shell of mass M and radius R. Let r be the
distance from the center O to a test particle P of mass m (Fig. 6.2). It is

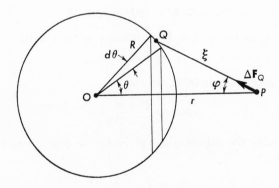

FIG. 6.2

assumed that $r > R$. We shall divide the shell into circular rings of width
$R \, \Delta\theta$ where, as shown in the figure, the angle POQ is denoted by θ, Q being
a point on the ring. The circumference of our representative ring element is

therefore $2\pi R \sin \theta$, and its mass ΔM is given by

$$\Delta M \simeq \rho 2\pi R^2 \sin \theta \, \Delta\theta$$

where ρ is the mass per unit area of the shell.

Now the gravitational force exerted on P by a small subelement Q of the ring (which we shall regard as a particle) is in the direction PQ. Let us resolve this force $\Delta\mathbf{F}_q$ into two components, one component along PO, of magnitude $\Delta F_q \cos \varphi$, the other perpendicular to PO, of magnitude $\Delta F_q \sin \varphi$. Here φ is the angle OPQ, as shown in the figure. From symmetry we can easily see that the vector sum of all of the perpendicular components exerted on P by the whole ring vanishes. The force $\Delta\mathbf{F}$ exerted by the entire ring is therefore in the direction PO, and its magnitude ΔF is obtained by summing the components $\Delta F_q \cos \varphi$. The result is clearly

$$\Delta F = G\frac{m \, \Delta M}{\xi^2} \cos \varphi = G\frac{m 2\pi\rho R^2 \sin \theta \cos \varphi}{\xi^2} \Delta\theta$$

where ξ is the distance PQ (the distance from the particle P to the ring) as shown. The magnitude of the force exerted on P by the whole shell is then obtained by taking the limit of $\Delta\theta$ and integrating:

$$F = Gm2\pi\rho R^2 \int_0^\pi \frac{\sin \theta \cos \varphi \, d\theta}{\xi^2}$$

The integral is most easily evaluated by expressing the integrand in terms of ξ. From the triangle OPQ we have, from the law of cosines,

$$r^2 + R^2 - 2rR \cos \theta = \xi^2$$

Differentiating, we have, since both R and r are constant,

$$rR \sin \theta \, d\theta = \xi \, d\xi$$

Also, in the same triangle OPQ, we can write

$$\cos \varphi = \frac{\xi^2 + r^2 - R_2}{2r\xi}$$

Upon performing the substitutions given by the above two equations, we obtain

$$F = Gm2\pi\rho R^2 \int_{\theta=0}^{\theta=\pi} \frac{\xi^2 + r^2 - R^2}{2Rr^2\xi^2} \, d\xi$$

$$= \frac{GmM}{4Rr^2} \int_{r-R}^{r+R} \left(1 + \frac{r^2 - R^2}{\xi^2}\right) d\xi$$

$$= \frac{GmM}{r^2}$$

where $M = 4\pi\rho R^2$ is the mass of the shell. We can then write vectorially

$$\mathbf{F} = -G\frac{Mm}{r^2}\boldsymbol{\lambda}_r \tag{6.2}$$

where $\boldsymbol{\lambda}_r$ is the unit radial vector from the origin O. The above result means that a uniform spherical shell of matter attracts an external particle as if the whole mass of the shell were concentrated at its center. This will be true for every concentric spherical portion of a solid uniform sphere. A uniform spherical body, therefore, attracts an external particle as if the entire mass of the sphere were located at the center. The same is true also for a nonuniform sphere as long as the distribution of mass is radially symmetric.

It can be shown that the gravitational force on a particle located *inside* a uniform spherical shell is zero. The proof is left as an exercise.

6.3. Potential Energy in a Gravitational Field. Gravitational Potential

Let us consider the work W required to move a test particle of mass m along some prescribed path in the gravitational field of another particle of mass M.

We shall place the particle of mass M at the origin of our coordinate system, as shown in Fig. 6.3a). Since the force $\mathbf{F}$ on the test particle is given by $\mathbf{F} = -(GMm/r^2)\boldsymbol{\lambda}_r$, then, to overcome this force, an external force $-\mathbf{F}$ must be applied. The work dW done in moving the test particle through a

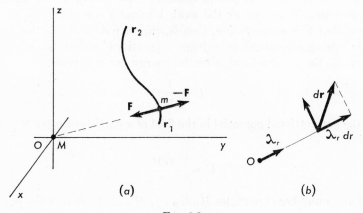

(a)   (b)

Fig. 6.3

distance $d\mathbf{r}$ is thus given by

$$dW = -\mathbf{F} \cdot d\mathbf{r} = \frac{GMm}{r^2}\boldsymbol{\lambda}_r \cdot d\mathbf{r} \tag{6.3}$$

Now we can resolve $d\mathbf{r}$ into two components: $\boldsymbol{\lambda}_r \, dr$ parallel to $\boldsymbol{\lambda}_r$ (the radial component) and the other at right angles to $\boldsymbol{\lambda}_r$ [Fig. 6.3(b)]. Clearly,

$$\boldsymbol{\lambda}_r \cdot d\mathbf{r} = dr$$

and so W is given by

$$W = GMm \int_{r_1}^{r_2} \frac{dr}{r^2} = -GMm\left(\frac{1}{r_2} - \frac{1}{r_1}\right) \tag{6.4}$$

where r_1 and r_2 are the radial distances of the particle at the beginning and end, respectively, of the path. Thus the work is independent of the particular path taken; it depends only on the end points. (It can be shown that this is equivalent to the criterion given in Sec. 4.6 for the existence of a potential function.) We can define the potential energy V of a particle of mass m at a given point in the gravitational field of another particle as the work done in moving the test particle from some (arbitrary) reference position to the point in question. It is convenient to take the reference position at infinity. Putting $r_1 = \infty$ and $r_2 = r$ in Eq. (6.4), we have

$$V(r) = GMm \int_{\infty}^{r} \frac{dr}{r^2} = -\frac{GMm}{r} \tag{6.5}$$

As a matter of fact, we showed earlier in Sec. 4.5 (Example 3) that the potential-energy function $V(r) = -k/r$ yields the inverse-square law of force $\mathbf{F} = -(k/r^2)\boldsymbol{\lambda}_r$. (It is important to note that it is not legitimate to *define* potential energy as the work integral $\mathbf{F} \cdot d\mathbf{r}$ unless we know in advance that $\mathbf{F}$ is conservative, that is, that a potential function exists.)

It is sometimes convenient to define a quantity U, called the *gravitational potential*, as the gravitational potential energy per unit mass:

$$U = \frac{V}{m}$$

Thus the gravitational potential in the field of a particle of mass M is given by

$$U = -\frac{GM}{r} \tag{6.6}$$

If we have a number of particles $M_1, M_2, \ldots M_i, \ldots$ located at the positions $\mathbf{r}_1, \mathbf{r}_2, \ldots \mathbf{r}_i, \ldots$, then the gravitational potential at the point (x,y,z) is the sum of the potentials of all the particles, namely,

$$U(x,y,z) = \Sigma \, U_i = -G \, \Sigma \, \frac{M_i}{\xi_i} \tag{6.7}$$

where ξ_i is the distance from the particle M_i to the field point $\mathbf{r}(x,y,z)$, that is,

$$\xi_i = |\mathbf{r} - \mathbf{r}_i|$$

The force on a test particle of unit mass is denoted by $\mathbf{f}$ and is called the *field intensity*. Thus

$$\mathbf{f} = \frac{\mathbf{F}}{m}$$

The relationship between $\mathbf{f}$ and U is identical with that between $\mathbf{F}$ and V, established in Sec. 4.6, namely,

$$\mathbf{f} = -\nabla U \tag{6.8}$$

The components of $\mathbf{f}$ are given by

$$f_x = -\frac{\partial U}{\partial x} \qquad f_y = -\frac{\partial U}{\partial y} \qquad f_z = -\frac{\partial U}{\partial z} \tag{6.9}$$

Thus the force on a particle (of unit mass) can be found by first calculating the potential [Eq. (6.7)] and then using Eq. (6.9). This method is usually simpler than that of finding the force directly (as was done in Sec. 6.2), because the potential is a scalar sum whereas the force is a vector sum.

EXAMPLES

1. The potential in the field of a uniform spherical shell, using the same notation as that given in Fig. 6.3, is

$$U = -G \int \frac{dM}{\xi} = -G \int \frac{\rho 2\pi R^2 \sin\theta \, d\theta}{\xi} = -G \frac{\rho 2\pi R^2}{rR} \int_{r-R}^{r+R} d\xi = -\frac{GM}{r} \tag{6.10}$$

This is the same as the potential of a single particle of mass M located at O, so we can conclude that the force is the same as that of a single particle of mass M located at the center.

   ★2. Find the field intensity in the plane of a thin circular ring of mass M and radius R. We have, for an exterior point P in the plane of the ring (Fig. 6.4),

$$U = -G \int \frac{dM}{\xi} = -G \int_0^{2\pi} \frac{\mu R \, d\theta}{\xi}$$

where μ is the linear density of the ring. In order to evaluate the above integral,

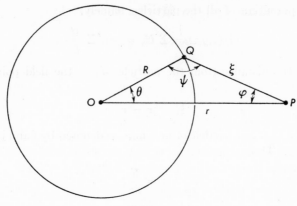

Fig. 6.4

we shall express the integrand in terms of the angle ψ shown. In the triangle OPQ we have

$$R \sin \psi = r \sin \varphi$$

Differentiating,

$$R \cos \psi \, d\psi = r \cos \varphi \, d\varphi = r \cos \varphi \, (-d\theta - d\psi)$$

The last step follows from the fact that $\theta + \varphi + \Psi = \pi$. Upon transposing terms and using the relation $\xi = R \cos \psi + r \cos \varphi$, we obtain

$$\xi \, d\psi = -r \cos \varphi \, d\theta = -(r^2 - R^2 \sin^2 \psi)^{1/2} \, d\theta$$

Hence the integral above becomes

$$U = -G\mu R4 \int_0^{\pi/2} (r^2 - R^2 \sin^2 \psi)^{-1/2} \, d\psi = -G\frac{4\mu R}{r} K\left(\frac{R}{r}\right) \qquad (6.11)$$

where K is the complete elliptic integral as defined in Sec. 4.12. By expanding the integrand and integrating term by term, we can also write

$$U = -G\frac{4\mu R}{r}\left(\frac{\pi}{2} + \frac{\pi R^2}{8r^2} + \dots\right) \qquad (6.12)$$

$$= -\frac{GM}{r}\left(1 + \frac{R^2}{4r^2} + \dots\right)$$

The force per unit mass on a particle at a distance r from the center of the ring is then in the radial direction (since U is not a function of θ), and is given by

$$\mathbf{f} = -\frac{\partial U}{\partial r}\boldsymbol{\lambda}_r = \left(-\frac{GM}{r^2} - \frac{3GMR^2}{4r^4} - \dots\right)\boldsymbol{\lambda}_r \qquad (6.13)$$

Thus the force is *not* given by an inverse-square law. If r is very large compared to R, however, the first term predominates, and the force is approximately of the inverse-square type.

6.4. Angular Momentum in Central-Force Fields

The gravitational field of force surrounding a spherically symmetric body is a special case of a central force. In this section we wish to discuss some of the general properties of motion under a central force. A general central force can be expressed vectorially as follows:

$$\mathbf{F} = f(r)\frac{\mathbf{r}}{r} = f(r)\lambda_r \tag{6.14}$$

where λ_r is the unit radial vector, the center of force being at the origin.

Consider now the general equation of motion of a particle

$$\mathbf{F} = m\mathbf{a}$$

where $\mathbf{a} = \dot{\mathbf{v}} = \ddot{\mathbf{r}}$. (Here $\mathbf{F}$ is not necessarily a central force.) Let us multiply both sides by $\mathbf{r} \times$

$$\mathbf{r} \times \mathbf{F} = \mathbf{r} \times m\mathbf{a} \tag{6.15}$$

The left side of the above equation is the moment of the force about the origin (Sec. 1.13). The right side is just the time derivative of the quantity $\mathbf{r} \times m\mathbf{v}$, namely,

$$\frac{d}{dt}(\mathbf{r} \times m\mathbf{v}) = \mathbf{v} \times m\mathbf{v} + \mathbf{r} \times m\mathbf{a} = \mathbf{r} \times m\mathbf{a} \tag{6.16}$$

The cross product $\mathbf{r} \times m\mathbf{v}$ is called the moment of momentum or the *angular momentum* of the particle about the point O (the origin). We shall denote the angular momentum by $\mathbf{J}$. Equation (6.15) can then be written

$$\mathbf{r} \times \mathbf{F} = \frac{d}{dt}(\mathbf{r} \times m\mathbf{v}) = \dot{\mathbf{J}} \tag{6.17}$$

In words: The moment of the force $\mathbf{F}$ acting on a particle is equal to the time rate of change of the angular momentum.

In particular, if the force $\mathbf{F}$ is *central*, then $\mathbf{r}$ and $\mathbf{F}$ are parallel, and the cross product $\mathbf{r} \times \mathbf{F}$ vanishes. In this case

$$\dot{\mathbf{J}} = \mathbf{O}$$

and

$$\mathbf{J} = \text{constant} \tag{6.18}$$

One important consequence of the above result is that a particle moving in a central field remains in a single plane, because the vector $\mathbf{J}$, being perpendicular to both $\mathbf{r}$ and to $\mathbf{v}$, is therefore normal to the plane of motion.

We can calculate the magnitude J of the angular momentum by resolving $\mathbf{v}$ into its radial and its transverse components:

$$\mathbf{v} = \lambda_r \dot{r} + \lambda_\theta\, r\theta$$

where (as in Sec. 2.8) λ_θ is the unit transverse vector. Since $|\lambda_r \times \lambda_r| = 0$ and $|\lambda_r \times \lambda_\theta| = 1$, we find

$$J = |\mathbf{r} \times m\mathbf{v}| = m|r\lambda_r \times (\lambda_r r + \lambda_\theta r\theta)| = mr^2\dot{\theta} \qquad (6.19)$$

6.5. The Areal Velocity. Kepler's Laws of Planetary Motion

The angular momentum of a particle is related to the rate at which the position vector sweeps out area. In Fig. 6.5 are shown the respective position vectors $\mathbf{r}$ and $\mathbf{r} + \Delta\mathbf{r}$ representing the motion of a particle in a time interval Δt. The area ΔA of the shaded triangular segment lying between the vectors $\mathbf{r}$ and $\mathbf{r} + \Delta\mathbf{r}$ is given by

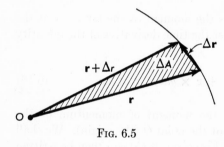

$$\Delta A = \frac{1}{2} r\, \Delta r \sin\varphi = \frac{1}{2} |\mathbf{r} \times \Delta\mathbf{r}| \qquad (6.20)$$

where φ is the angle between $\mathbf{r}$ and $\Delta\mathbf{r}$. Dividing by Δt and taking the limit, we have

$$\frac{dA}{dt} = \frac{1}{2} |\mathbf{r} \times \dot{\mathbf{r}}| = \frac{1}{2m} |\mathbf{J}| \qquad (6.21)$$

Fig. 6.5

Since the angular momentum $\mathbf{J}$ is constant in any central field, it follows that the areal velocity $\dot{A}$ is constant in such a force field.

The fact that the planets move about the sun in such a way that the areal velocities are constant was discovered empirically by Johannes Kepler in 1609. Kepler deduced this rule, and two others,* from a painstaking study of planetary positions recorded by Tycho Brahe. Kepler's three laws are:

(1) Each planet moves in an ellipse with the sun as a focus.
(2) The radius vector sweeps out equal areas in equal times.
(3) The square of the period of revolution about the sun is proportional to the cube of the major axis of the orbit.

Newton showed that Kepler's three laws are consequences of the law of gravity. From the argument leading to Eq. (6.21), we see that the second law comes about from the fact that the gravitational field of the sun is

---

*The third law was announced in 1619.

central. The other two laws, as we shall show later, are consequences of the fact that the force varies as the inverse square of the distance.

6.6.   Orbit of a Particle in a Central-Force Field

To study the motion of a particle in a central field, it is convenient to express the differential equation of motion

$$m\ddot{\mathbf{r}} = f(r)\boldsymbol{\lambda}_r$$

in polar coordinates. As shown in Sec. 2.8, the radial component of $\ddot{\mathbf{r}}$ is $\ddot{r} - r\dot{\theta}^2$, and the transverse component is $2\dot{r}\dot{\theta} + r\ddot{\theta}$. The component differential equations of motion are then

$$m(\ddot{r} - r\dot{\theta}^2) = f(r) \tag{6.22}$$

$$m(2\dot{r}\dot{\theta} + r\ddot{\theta}) = 0 \tag{6.23}$$

From the latter equation it follows that

$$\frac{d}{dt}(r^2\dot{\theta}) = 0$$

or

$$r^2\dot{\theta} = \text{constant} = h \tag{6.24}$$

From Eq. (6.19) we see that

$$h = \frac{J}{m} \tag{6.25}$$

(This is simply a restatement of a fact which we already know, namely, that the angular momentum of a particle is constant when it is moving under the action of a central force.)

Given a certain radial force function $f(r)$, we could, in theory, solve the pair of differential equations [Eqs. (6.22) and (6.24)] to obtain r and θ as functions of t. It is often the case that one is interested only in the path in space (the *orbit*) without regard to the time t. To find the equation of the orbit, we shall use the variable u defined by

$$r = \frac{1}{u} \tag{6.26}$$

Then

$$\dot{r} = -\frac{1}{u^2}\dot{u} = -\frac{1}{u^2}\dot{\theta}\frac{du}{d\theta} = -h\frac{du}{d\theta} \tag{6.27}$$

The last step follows from the fact that

$$\dot\theta = hu^2 \tag{6.28}$$

according to Eqs. (6.24) and (6.26).

Differentiating a second time, we have

$$\ddot r = -h\frac{d}{dt}\frac{du}{d\theta} = -h\dot\theta\frac{d^2u}{d\theta^2} = -h^2u^2\frac{d^2u}{d\theta^2} \tag{6.29}$$

From these values of r, $\dot\theta$, and $\ddot r$, we readily find that Eq. (6.22) transforms to

$$\frac{d^2u}{d\theta^2} + u = -\frac{1}{mh^2u^2}f(u^{-1}) \tag{6.30}$$

The above equation is the differential equation of the orbit of a particle moving under a central force: $f(r)\lambda_r$. The solution gives u (hence r) as a function of θ. Conversely, if one is given the polar equation of the orbit, namely, $r = r(\theta) = u^{-1}$, then the force function can be found by differentiating to get $d^2u/d\theta^2$ and inserting this into the differential equation.

EXAMPLE

Let us ascertain whether or not a spiral orbit given by

$$r = c\theta^2$$

is possible in a central-force field and, if so, determine the form of the force function. We have

$$u = \frac{1}{c\theta^2}$$

and

$$\frac{du}{d\theta} = \frac{-2}{c}\theta^{-3} \qquad \frac{d^2u}{d\theta^2} = \frac{6}{c}\theta^{-4} = 6cu^2$$

Then, from Eq. (6.30),

$$6cu^2 + u = -\frac{1}{mh^2u^2}f(u^{-1})$$

Hence

$$f(u^{-1}) = -mh^2(6cu^4 + u^3)$$

and

$$f(r) = -mh^2\left(\frac{6c}{r^4} + \frac{1}{r^3}\right)$$

Thus the spiral orbit $r = c\theta^2$ is possible if the force is a combination of an inverse fourth power and an inverse cube law.

6.7.   Energy in a Central Field

We have previously shown that an inverse-square force field is a conservative one. Let us now ascertain whether or not *any* central force $f(r)\lambda_r$ is conservative. We have

$$\lambda_r = \frac{\mathbf{r}}{r} = \frac{1}{r}(\mathbf{i}x + \mathbf{j}y + \mathbf{k}z)$$

and

$$f(r)\lambda_r = \frac{f(r)}{r}(\mathbf{i}x + \mathbf{j}y + \mathbf{k}z) \tag{6.31}$$

Hence the rectangular components of the force are

$$f_x = f(r)\frac{x}{r} \qquad f_y = f(r)\frac{y}{r} \qquad f_z = f(r)\frac{z}{r} \tag{6.32}$$

Applying the test for conservativeness, Eqs. [4.22(a)], we have

$$\frac{\partial f_x}{\partial y} = x\frac{d}{dr}\left(\frac{f(r)}{r}\right)\frac{\partial r}{\partial y}$$

$$\frac{\partial f_y}{\partial x} = y\frac{d}{dr}\left(\frac{f(r)}{r}\right)\frac{\partial r}{\partial x}$$

But

$$\frac{\partial r}{\partial x} = \frac{\partial}{\partial x}(x^2 + y^2 + z^2)^{1/2} = x(x^2 + y^2 + z^2)^{-1/2} = \frac{x}{r}$$

Similarly,

$$\frac{\partial r}{\partial y} = \frac{y}{r} \qquad \frac{\partial r}{\partial z} = \frac{z}{r}$$

Clearly, then,

$$\frac{\partial f_x}{\partial y} = \frac{xy}{r}\frac{d}{dr}\left(\frac{f(r)}{r}\right) = \frac{\partial f_y}{\partial x}$$

and similar equations exist for the pairs f_x, f_z and f_y, f_z. We conclude that any central force of the form $f(r)\lambda_r$ is conservative, provided that the function $f(r)$ is differentiable. We can therefore define a potential-energy function $V(r)$, as in Sec. 6.3, as follows:

$$V(r) = -\int_{\infty}^{r} f(r)\lambda_r \cdot d\mathbf{r} = -\int_{\infty}^{r} f(r)\, dr \qquad (6.33)$$

Now the square of the speed is given in polar coordinates by

$$v^2 = \dot{r}^2 + r^2\dot{\theta}^2$$

Thus the total energy $\frac{1}{2}mv^2 + V$ becomes

$$\frac{1}{2}m(\dot{r}^2 + r^2\dot{\theta}^2) + V(r) = E = \text{constant} \qquad (6.34)$$

We can also write the above equation in terms of the variable $u = 1/r$. From Eqs. (6.27) and (6.28) we obtain

$$\frac{1}{2}mh^2\left[\left(\frac{du}{d\theta}\right)^2 + u^2\right] + V(u^{-1}) = E \qquad (6.35)$$

In the above equation the only variables occurring are u and θ. We shall call this equation, therefore, *the energy equation of the orbit.*

EXAMPLE

In the example of the preceding section we had for the spiral orbit $r = c\theta^2$:

$$\frac{du}{d\theta} = \frac{-2}{c}\theta^{-3} = -2c^{1/2}u^{3/2}$$

so the energy equation of the orbit is

$$\frac{1}{2}mh^2(4cu^3 + u^2) + V = E$$

Thus

$$V(r) = E - \frac{1}{2}mh^2\left(\frac{4c}{r^3} + \frac{1}{r^2}\right)$$

This readily gives the force function of the example above, since $f(r) = -dV/dr$.

6.8. Orbits in an Inverse-Square Field

The most important type of central field is that in which the force varies inversely as the square of the radial distance:

$$f(r) = -\frac{k}{r^2} \tag{6.36}$$

In the above equation, since we have included a minus sign, the constant of proportionality k is positive for an attractive force, and vice versa. (As we have seen in Sec. 6.2, $k = GMm$ for a gravitational field.) The equation of the orbit [Eq. (6.30)] then becomes

$$\frac{d^2u}{d\theta^2} + u = \frac{k}{mh^2} \tag{6.37}$$

The general solution is clearly

$$u = A \cos (\theta - \epsilon) + \frac{k}{mh^2} \tag{6.38}$$

or

$$r = \frac{1}{A \cos (\theta - \epsilon) + k/mh^2} \tag{6.39}$$

The constants of integration A and ϵ are determined from the initial conditions. The value of ϵ merely determines the orientation of the orbit, so we can, without loss of generality in discussing the form of the orbit, choose $\epsilon = 0$. Then

$$r = \frac{1}{A \cos \theta + k/mh^2} \tag{6.40}$$

This is the polar equation of the orbit. It is the equation of a conic section (ellipse, parabola, or hyperbola) with the origin at a focus. The equation can be written in the forms

$$r = r_0 \frac{1 + e}{1 + e \cos \theta} \qquad r = \frac{L}{1 + e \cos \theta} \tag{6.41}$$

where

$$e = \frac{Amh^2}{k} \tag{6.42}$$

and

$$L = r_0(1 + e) = \frac{mh^2}{k} \tag{6.43}$$

The constant e is called the *eccentricity*, and L is known as the *semilatus rectum*. The different cases, illustrated in Fig. 6.6, are:

$$e < 1 \quad \text{ellipse}$$
$$e = 0 \quad \text{circle (special case of an ellipse)}$$
$$e = 1 \quad \text{parabola}$$
$$e > 1 \quad \text{hyperbola}$$

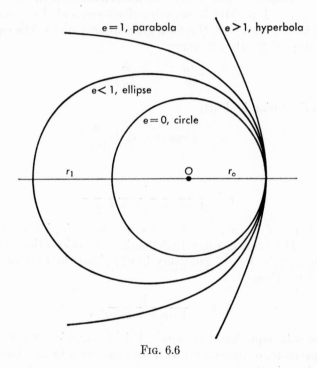

FIG. 6.6

From the first of Eqs. (6.41), r_o is the value of r for $\theta = 0$. The value of r for $\theta = \pi$ is given by

$$r_1 = r_o \frac{1 + e}{1 - e} \tag{6.44}$$

In reference to the elliptic orbits of the planets around the sun, the distance r_o is called the *perihelion* distance (closest to the sun) and the distance r_1 is called the *aphelion* distance (farthest from the sun). The corresponding distances for the orbit of the moon around the earth — and for the orbits of the earth's artificial satellites — are called the *perigee* and *apogee* distances, respectively.

The orbital eccentricities of the planets are quite small. (See Table 6.1 below.) For example, in the case of the earth's orbit $e = 0.017$, $r_o = 91,000,000$ miles, and $r_1 = 95,000,000$ miles. On the other hand, the comets generally have large orbital eccentricities (highly elongated orbits). Halley's comet, for instance, has an orbital eccentricity of 0.967 with a perihelion distance of only 55,000,000 miles, while at aphelion it is beyond the orbit of Neptune. Many comets (the nonrecurring type) have parabolic or hyperbolic orbits.

Orbital parameters from initial conditions. From Eq. (6.43) we find

$$e = \frac{mh^2}{kr_o} - 1 \qquad (6.45)$$

Let v_o be the speed of the particle at $\theta = 0$. Then, from the definition of the constant h, Eq. (6.24), we have

$$h = r^2\dot{\theta} = r_o^2\dot{\theta}_o = r_o v_o \qquad (6.46)$$

The eccentricity is then given by

$$e = \frac{mr_o v_o^2}{k} - 1 \qquad (6.47)$$

For a circular orbit ($e = 0$) we have then $k = mr_o v_o^2$ or

$$\frac{k}{r_o^2} = \frac{mv_o^2}{r_o} \qquad (6.48)$$

Now let us denote the quantity k/mr_o by v_c^2, so that if $v_o = v_c$, the orbit is a circle. The expression for the eccentricity, Eq. (6.47), can then be written

$$e = (v_o/v_c)^2 - 1 \qquad (6.49)$$

and the equation of the orbit, Eq. (6.41), is

$$r = r_o \frac{(v_o/v_c)^2}{1 + [(v_o/v_c)^2 - 1]\cos\theta} \qquad (6.50)$$

The value of r_1 is given by $\theta = \pi$, thus

$$r_1 = r_o \frac{(v_o/v_c)^2}{2 - (v_o/v_c)^2} \qquad (6.51)$$

EXAMPLE

A rocket satellite is going around the earth in a circular orbit of radius r_o. A sudden blast of the rocket motor increases the speed by 10 percent. Find the equation of the new orbit, and compute the apogee distance. Let v_c be the speed in the circular orbit, and let v_o be the new initial speed:

$$v_o = 1.1 \, v_c$$

Equation (6.50) of the new orbit then reads

$$r = r_o \frac{1.21}{1 + 0.21 \cos \theta}$$

and the apogee distance from Eq. (6.51) is

$$r_1 = r_o \frac{1.21}{2 - 1.21} = 1.53 \, r_o$$

The orbits are shown in Fig. 6.7.

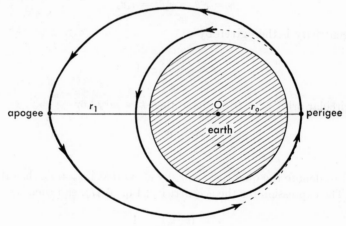

FIG. 6.7

6.9. Orbital Energies in the Inverse-Square Field

Since the potential-energy function $V(r)$ for an inverse-square force field is given by

$$V(r) = -\frac{k}{r} = -ku \qquad (6.52)$$

the energy equation of the orbit, Eq. (6.35), then reads

$$\frac{1}{2}mh^2\left[\left(\frac{du}{d\theta}\right)^2 + u^2\right] - ku = E \tag{6.53}$$

or, upon separating variables,

$$d\theta = \left(\frac{2E}{mh^2} + \frac{2ku}{mh^2} - u^2\right)^{-1/2} du \tag{6.54}$$

Upon integrating, we find

$$\theta = \sin^{-1}\left[\frac{mh^2 u - k}{(k^2 + 2Emh^2)^{1/2}}\right] + \epsilon \tag{6.55}$$

where ϵ is a constant of integration. If we let $\epsilon = -\pi/2$ and solve for u, we obtain

$$u = \frac{k}{mh^2}[1 + (1 + 2Emh^2k^{-2})^{1/2} \cos \theta]$$

or

$$r = \frac{mh^2k^{-1}}{1 + (1 + 2Emh^2k^{-2})^{1/2} \cos \theta} \tag{6.56}$$

This is the polar equation of the orbit. If we compare it with Eqs. (6.41) and (6.42), we see that the eccentricity is given by

$$e = (1 + 2Emh^2k^{-2})^{1/2} \tag{6.57}$$

The above expression for the eccentricity allows us to classify the orbits according to the total energy E as follows:

$$E < 0 \quad e < 1 \quad \text{closed orbits (ellipse or circle)}$$
$$E = 0 \quad e = 1 \quad \text{parabolic orbit}$$
$$E > 0 \quad e > 1 \quad \text{hyperbolic orbit}$$

Since $E = T + V$ and is constant, the closed orbits are those for which $T < |V|$, and the open orbits are those for which $T \geq |V|$.

EXAMPLE

A comet is observed to have a speed v_o when it is a distance r_o from the sun, and its direction of motion makes angle φ with the radius vector from the sun. Find the eccentricity of the comet's orbit.

In the sun's gravitational field $k = GMm$, where M is the mass of the sun, and m is the mass of the body. The total energy E is then given by

$$E = \frac{1}{2}mv^2 - \frac{GMm}{r} = \frac{1}{2}mv_o^2 - \frac{GMm}{r_o} = \text{constant}$$

and the orbit will be elliptic, parabolic, or hyperbolic, according to whether E is negative, zero, or positive. Accordingly, if v_o^2 is less than, equal to, or greater than $2GM/r_o$, the orbit will be an ellipse, a parabola, or a hyperbola, respectively. Now

$$h = |\mathbf{r} \times \mathbf{v}| = r_o v_o \sin \varphi$$

The eccentricity e, from Eq. (6.57), therefore has the value

$$e = \left[1 + \left(v_o^2 - \frac{2GM}{r_o} \right) \frac{r_o^2 v_o^2 \sin^2 \varphi}{G^2 M^2} \right]^{1/2}$$

The product GM may be expressed in terms of the earth's speed v_e and orbital radius r_e (assuming a circular orbit), namely,

$$GM = r_e v_e^2$$

[See Eq. (6.48).] The equation giving the eccentricity can then be written

$$e = \left[1 + \left(\frac{v_o^2}{v_e^2} - \frac{2r_e}{r_o} \right) \frac{r_o^2 v_o^2}{r_e^2 v_e^2} \sin^2 \varphi \right]^{1/2}$$

Limits of the radial motion. From the radial equation of the orbit, Eq. (6.56), we see that the values of r for $\theta = 0$, r_o, and for $\theta = \pi$, r_1, are given by

$$r_o = \frac{mh^2 k^{-1}}{1 + (1 + 2Emh^2 k^{-2})^{1/2}} \qquad r_1 = \frac{mh^2 k^{-1}}{1 - (1 + 2Emh^2 k^{-2})^{1/2}} \quad (6.58)$$

Now in the case of an elliptical orbit, E is negative, and the major axis $2a$ of the ellipse is given by

$$2a = r_o + r_1 = -\frac{k}{E} \tag{6.59}$$

Thus the value of a is determined entirely from the total energy.

In the case of a circular orbit of radius a, we have

$$V = -\frac{k}{a} = \text{constant} \qquad E = -\frac{k}{2a} = \text{constant}$$

Thus the *kinetic* energy is given by

$$T = \frac{1}{2} mv^2 = E - V = \frac{k}{2a}$$

It can be shown that the time average of the kinetic energy for elliptic motion in an inverse-square field is also $k/2a$, and that the time average of the potential energy is $-k/a$, where a is the semimajor axis of the ellipse. The proof is left as an exercise.

6.10. Periodic Time of Orbital Motion

In Sec. 6.5 we showed that the areal velocity $\dot{A}$ of a particle moving in any central field is constant. Consequently, the time t_{12} required for a particle to move from one point P_1 to any other point P_2 (Fig. 6.8) is, from Eqs. (6.21) and (6.25), given by

$$t_{12} = \frac{A_{12}}{\dot{A}} = A_{12}\frac{2m}{J} = A_{12}\frac{2}{h} \qquad (6.60)$$

where A_{12} is the area swept out by the radius vector between P_1 and P_2.

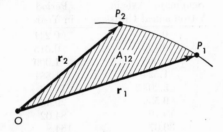

FIG. 6.8

Let us apply the above result to the case of an elliptic orbit of a particle in an inverse-square field. Since the area of an ellipse is πab, where a and b are the semimajor and the semiminor axes, respectively, then the time τ required for the particle to complete one orbital path is expressed by

$$\tau = \frac{2\pi ab}{h}$$

But for an ellipse

$$\frac{b}{a} = \sqrt{1 - e^2} = \sqrt{\frac{L}{a}}$$

where e is the eccentricity, and L is the semilatus rectum. Thus we may write

$$\tau = \frac{2\pi a^{3/2}L^{1/2}}{h} \qquad (6.61)$$

From the value of L given by Eq. (6.43), we finally obtain the following formula for the period:

$$\tau = 2\pi(m/k)^{1/2}a^{3/2} \qquad (6.62)$$

Thus, for a given field, the period depends only on the size of the major axis.

Since, for a planet of mass m moving in the sun's gravitational field, $k = GMm$, we can write for the period of orbital motion of a planet

$$\tau = ca^{3/2} \tag{6.63}$$

where $c = 2\pi(GM)^{-1/2}$. Clearly, c is the same for all planets. Equation (6.63) is a mathematical statement of Kepler's third law (Sec. 6.5). If a is expressed in astronomical units (93,000,000 miles $= a_{\text{earth}} = 1$ astronomical unit) and τ is in years, then the numerical value of c is unity. In Table 6.1 are listed the periods, semimajor axes in astronomical units, and the orbital eccentricities of the planets of the solar system.

Table 6.1

Planet	Semimajor Axis in Astronomical Units	Period in Years	Eccentricity
Mercury	0.387	0.241	0.206
Venus	0.723	0.615	0.007
Earth	1.000	1.000	0.017
Mars	1.524	1.881	0.093
Jupiter	5.203	11.86	0.048
Saturn	9.539	29.46	0.056
Uranus	19.19	84.02	0.047
Neptune	30.07	164.8	0.009
Pluto	39.46	247.7	0.249

6.11. Motion in an Inverse-Square Repulsive Field. Scattering of Atomic Particles

There is an important physical application involving motion of a particle in a central field in which the law of force is of the inverse-square repulsive type, namely the deflection of high-speed atomic particles (protons, alpha particles, etc.) by the positively charged nuclei of atoms. The basic investigations underlying our present knowledge of atomic and nuclear structure are scattering experiments, the first of which were carried out by the British physicist Lord Rutherford in the early part of this century.

Consider a particle of charge q and mass m (the incident high-speed particle) passing near a heavy particle of charge Q (the nucleus, assumed fixed). The incident particle is repelled with a force given by Coulomb's law:

$$f(r) = \frac{Qq}{r^2} \tag{6.64}$$

where the position of Q is taken to be the origin. (We shall use cgs electro-

static units for Q and q. Then r is in centimeters, and the force is in dynes.)
The differential equation of the orbit, Eq. (6.30), then takes the form

$$\frac{d^2u}{d\theta^2} + u = -\frac{Qq}{mh^2} \qquad (6.65)$$

and so the equation of the orbit is

$$u^{-1} = r = \frac{1}{A \cos (\theta - \epsilon) - Qq/mh^2} \qquad (6.66)$$

We can also write the equation of the orbit in the form given by Eq. (6.56),
namely,

$$r = \frac{mh^2Q^{-1}q^{-1}}{-1 + (1 + 2Emh^2Q^{-2}q^{-2})^{1/2} \cos (\theta - \epsilon)} \qquad (6.67)$$

since $k = -Qq$. The orbit is a hyperbola. This may be seen from the
physical fact that the energy E is always greater than zero in a repulsive
field of force. (In our case $E = 1/2\,mv^2 + Qq/r$.) Hence the eccentricity e,
the coefficient of $\cos (\theta - \epsilon)$ in Eq. (6.67), is greater than unity, which
means that the orbit must be hyperbolic.

The incident particle approaches along one asymptote and recedes
along the other, as shown in Fig. 6.9. We have chosen the direction of the

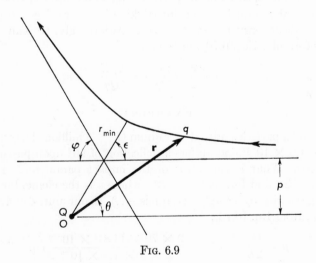

Fig. 6.9

polar axis such that the initial position of the particle is $\theta = 0, r = \infty$. It is
clear from either of the two equations of the orbit that r assumes its mini-
mum value when $\cos (\theta - \epsilon) = 1$, that is, when $\theta = \epsilon$. Since $r = \infty$ when

$\theta = 0$, then r is also infinite when $\theta = 2\epsilon$. Hence the angle between the two asymptotes of the hyperbolic path is 2ϵ, and the angle φ through which the incident particle is deflected is given by

$$\varphi = \pi - 2\epsilon \tag{6.68}$$

Furthermore, in Eq. (6.67) the denominator on the right vanishes at $\theta = 0$ and $\theta = 2\epsilon$. Thus,

$$-1 + (1 + 2Emh^2Q^{-2}q^{-2})^{1/2} \cos \epsilon = 0 \tag{6.69}$$

from which we readily find

$$\tan \epsilon = (2Em)^{1/2}hQ^{-1}q^{-1} = \cot \frac{\varphi}{2} \tag{6.70}$$

The last step follows from Eq. (6.68).

In applying the above equation to scattering problems, it is convenient to express the constant h in terms of another quantity p called the *impact parameter*. The impact parameter is the perpendicular distance from the origin (scattering center) to the initial line of motion of the particle, as shown in Fig. 6.9. We have then

$$h = |\mathbf{r} \times \mathbf{v}| = pv_o \tag{6.71}$$

where v_o is the initial speed of the particle. We know also that the energy E is constant and is equal to the initial kinetic energy $\frac{1}{2}mv_o^2$, because the initial potential energy is zero ($r = \infty$). Accordingly, we can write the scattering formula, Eq. (6.70), in the form

$$\cot \frac{\varphi}{2} = \frac{pmv_o^2}{Qq} = \frac{2pE}{Qq} \tag{6.72}$$

Examples

1. An alpha particle emitted by radium ($E = 5$ million electron volts $= 5 \times 10^6 \times 1.6 \times 10^{-12}$ erg) suffers a deflection of 90° upon passing near a gold nucleus. What is the value of the impact parameter? For alpha particles $q = 2e$, and for gold $Q = 79e$, where e is the elementary charge. (The charge carried by a single electron is $-e$.) In our units $e = 4.8 \times 10^{-10}$ esu. Thus, from Eq. (6.72),

$$p = \frac{Qq}{2E} \cot 45° = \frac{2 \times 79 \times (4.8)^2 \times 10^{-20}}{2 \times 5 \times 1.6 \times 10^{-6}} \text{ cm}$$

$$= 2.1 \times 10^{-12} \text{ cm}$$

2. Calculate the distance of closest approach of the alpha particle in the above problem. The distance of closest approach is given by the

equation of the orbit [Eq. (6.67)] for $\theta = \epsilon$, thus

$$r_{\min} = \frac{mh^2Q^{-1}q^{-1}}{-1 + (1 + 2Emh^2Q^{-2}q^{-2})^{1/2}} \qquad (6.73)$$

Upon using Eqs. (6.71) and (6.72), the above equation, after a little algebra, can be written

$$r_{\min} = \frac{p \cot \varphi/2}{-1 + (1 + \cot^2 \varphi/2)^{1/2}} = \frac{p \cos \varphi/2}{1 - \sin \varphi/2} \qquad (6.74)$$

Thus, for $\varphi = 90$ degrees, we find $r_{\min} = 2.41 \, p = 5.1 \times 10^{-12}$ cm.

Notice that Eqs. (6.73) and (6.74) become indeterminate when $h = p = 0$. In this case the particle is aimed directly at the nucleus. It approaches the nucleus along a straight line, and, being continually repelled by the coulomb force, its speed is reduced to zero when it reaches a certain point, $r_{\min}$, from which point it returns along the same straight line. The angle of deflection is 180 degrees. The value of $r_{\min}$ in this case is found by using the fact that the energy E is constant. At the turning point the potential energy is $Qq/r_{\min}$, and the kinetic energy is zero. Hence $E = \frac{1}{2}mv_o^2 = Qq/r_{\min}$, and

$$r_{\min} = \frac{Qq}{E} \qquad (6.75)$$

For radium alpha particles and gold nuclei we find $r_{\min} \simeq 10^{-12}$ cm when the angle of deflection is 180 degrees. The fact that such deflections are actually observed shows that the order of magnitude of the radius of the nucleus is at least as small as 10^{-12} cm.

★6.12. Motion in a Nearly Circular Orbit. Stability

A circular orbit is possible under any attractive central force, but not all central forces result in *stable* circular orbits. We wish to investigate the following question: If a particle traveling in a circular orbit suffers a slight disturbance, will the ensuing orbit remain close to the original circular path? In order to answer this query, we refer to the radial differential equation of motion [Eq. (6.22)]. Since $\dot{\theta} = h/r^2$, we can write the radial equation as follows:

$$m\ddot{r} - \frac{mh^2}{r^3} = f(r) \qquad (6.76)$$

Now for a circular orbit, r is constant, and $\ddot{r} = 0$. Thus, calling a the radius of the circular orbit, we have

$$-\frac{mh^2}{a^3} = f(a) \qquad (6.77)$$

for the force at $r = a$.

Now let us express the radial motion in terms of the variable x defined by

$$x = r - a \tag{6.78}$$

Equation (6.76) can then be written

$$m\ddot{x} - mh^2(x + a)^{-3} = f(x + a) \tag{6.79}$$

Expanding the two terms involving $x + a$ as power series in x, we obtain

$$m\ddot{x} - mh^2 a^{-3}\left(1 - 3\frac{x}{a} + \ldots\right) = f(a) + f'(a)x + \ldots \tag{6.80}$$

The above equation, by virtue of the relation shown in Eq. (6.77), reduces to

$$m\ddot{x} + \left[\frac{-3}{a}f(a) - f'(a)\right]x = 0 \tag{6.81}$$

if we neglect terms involving x^2 and higher powers of x. Now, if the coefficient of x (the quantity in brackets) in the above equation is positive, then the equation is the same as that of the simple harmonic oscillator. In this case the particle, if perturbed, oscillates harmonically about the circle $r = a$, so the circular orbit is a stable one. On the other hand, if the coefficient of x is negative in Eq. (6.81), the motion is non-oscillatory, and the result is that x eventually increases exponentially with time; the orbit is unstable. (If the coefficient of x is zero, then higher terms in the expansion must be included in order to determine the stability.) Hence we can state that a circular orbit of radius a is stable if

$$f(a) + \frac{a}{3}f'(a) < 0 \tag{6.82}$$

In particular, if the radial force function is a power law, namely,

$$f(r) = -cr^n \tag{6.83}$$

then the condition for stability reads

$$-ca^n - \frac{a}{3}cna^{n-1} < 0$$

which reduces to

$$n > -3 \tag{6.84}$$

Thus the inverse-square law ($n = -2$) gives stable circular orbits, as does the law of direct distance ($n = 1$). The latter case is that of the two-dimensional harmonic oscillator. For the inverse fourth power ($n = -4$) circular orbits are unstable. It can be shown that circular orbits are also unstable for the inverse cube law of force ($n = -3$). To show this it is necessary to include terms of higher power than one in the radial equation.

★6.13.   Apsides and Apsidal Angles for Nearly Circular Orbits

An *apsis*, or *apse*, is a point in an orbit at which the radius vector assumes an extreme value (maximum or minimum). The perihelion and aphelion points are the apsides of planetary orbits. The angle swept out by the radius vector between two consecutive apsides is called the *apsidal angle*. Thus the apsidal angle is π for elliptic orbits under the inverse square law of force.

In the case of motion in a nearly circular orbit, we have seen that r oscillates about the circle $r = a$ (if the orbit is stable). From equation (6.81) it follows that the period τ_r of this oscillation is given by

$$\tau_r = 2\pi \sqrt{\frac{m}{-\left[\frac{3}{a}f(a) + f'(a)\right]}} \tag{6.85}$$

The apsidal angle in this case is just the amount by which the polar angle θ increases during the time that r oscillates from a minimum value to the succeeding maximum value. This time is clearly $\frac{1}{2}\tau_r$. Now $\dot{\theta} = h/r^2$, therefore $\dot{\theta}$ remains approximately constant, and we can write

$$\dot{\theta} \simeq \frac{h}{a^2} = \left[-\frac{f(a)}{ma}\right]^{1/2} \tag{6.86}$$

The last step above follows from equation [6.77]. Hence the apsidal angle ψ is given by

$$\psi = \frac{1}{2}\tau_r\dot{\theta} = \pi\left[3 + a\frac{f'(a)}{f(a)}\right]^{-1/2} \tag{6.87}$$

Thus for the power law of force $f(r) = -cr^n$, we obtain

$$\psi = \pi(3 + n)^{-1/2} \tag{6.88}$$

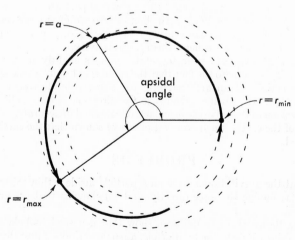

FIG. 6.10

The apsidal angle is independent of the size of the orbit in this case. The orbit is *re-entrant*, or repetitive, in the case of the inverse-square law ($n = -2$) for which $\psi = \pi$ and also in the case of the linear law ($n = 1$) for which $\psi = \pi/2$. If, however, say $n = 2$, then $\psi = \pi/\sqrt{5}$ which is an irrational multiple of π, and the motion does not repeat itself.

If the law of force departs slightly from the inverse-square law, then the apsides will either advance or regress steadily, depending on whether the apsidal angle is slightly greater or slightly less than π. (See Fig. 6.10) Let us suppose, for example, that the force is of the form

$$f(r) = -\frac{k}{r^2} - \frac{\epsilon}{r^4} \tag{6.89}$$

where ϵ is very small. (This is the form of the force function in the plane of a ring, as shown in Example 2, Sec. 6.3.) The apsidal angle, from Eq. (6.87), is

$$\psi = \pi\left(3 + a\frac{2ka^{-3} + 4\epsilon a^{-5}}{-ka^{-2} - \epsilon a^{-4}}\right)^{-1/2}$$

$$= \pi\left(\frac{1 - \epsilon k^{-1}a^{-2}}{1 + \epsilon k^{-1}a^{-2}}\right)^{-1/2}$$

$$\simeq \pi\left(1 + \frac{\epsilon}{ka^2}\right) \tag{6.90}$$

In the last step above we have neglected powers of the quantity ϵ/ka^2 higher than one. We see that the apsides advance if ϵ is positive, whereas they regress if ϵ is negative.

For a given planet, the gravitational perturbation owing to the other planets in the solar system is indeed approximated by a term of the form ϵ/r^4 in Eq. (6.89). [The cumulative effect of one planet may be considered to be approximately the same as if that planet were smeared out into a ring. [See Eq. (6.13).] For the innermost planet, Mercury, the calculated perturbations are such as to cause an advance of Mercury's perihelion of 531 sec of arc per century. The observed advance is 574 sec per century. The discrepancy of 43 sec per century is explained by Einstein's general theory of relativity.

The gravitational field near the earth departs slightly from the inverse-square law. This is due to the fact that the earth is not quite a true sphere. As a result, the perigee of an artificial satellite whose orbit lies near the earth's equatorial plane will advance steadily in the direction of the satellite's motion. The observation of this advance is, in fact, one method of accurately determining the shape of the earth. Such observations have shown that the earth is slightly pear-shaped.

PROBLEMS

1. Show that the gravitational force on a particle inside a thin spherical shell is zero by (a) finding the force directly, and (b) showing that the gravitational potential is constant.

2. Assuming the earth to be uniform, show that if a straight hole were drilled from the North Pole to the South Pole, a particle dropped into the hole would execute simple harmonic motion. Find the period of this motion.

3. Show that the motion is simple harmonic, with the same period as in Prob. 2, for a particle sliding in a straight smooth tube passing obliquely through the earth. Neglect effects of rotation.

4. Find the gravitational potential and the force on a particle of unit mass located on the axis of a thin ring of radius a and mass M. The test particle is a distance r from the center of the ring.

5. A particle moving in a central field describes the spiral orbit $r = ae^{k\theta}$. Find the law of force.

6. The orbit of a particle is a circle with the center of force on the circumference. What is the law of force?

7. A particle moves in an inverse-cube field of force. Determine the possible orbits.

8. A rocket satellite is traveling in a circular orbit close to the earth. It is desired to have the satellite go into a new orbit for which the apogee distance is equal to the radius of the moon's orbit around the earth (240,000 miles). (a) Find the increase in speed necessary to accomplish this. Assume that the radius of the original orbit is 4,000 miles. (b) Calculate also the apogee distance of the new orbit if the speed increase is 1 percent less than the value calculated above.

9. An asteroid has a speed v_a when it is a distance r_a from the sun, and its direction of motion makes an angle φ with the radius vector from the sun. What is the direction of the major axis of the elliptical orbit of the asteroid relative to the initial radius vector given?

10. Regarding the earth's orbit as circular, show that the maximum length of time that a comet, traveling in a parabolic orbit, can remain inside the earth's orbit is $2/3\pi$ of a year.

11. The major axis of the elliptic orbit of a certain comet is 100 astronomical units. (a) What is its period? (b) If its distance from the sun is $1/2$ astronomical unit at perihelion, what is the value of the eccentricity of the orbit? (c) What is the comet's speed at perihelion and at aphelion?

12. Show that for a particle describing an elliptic orbit of eccentricity ϵ and semi-major axis a in an inverse-square field, the values of r and θ may be expressed in terms of the time t as follows:

$$r = a \left(1 - \epsilon \cos \omega t + \frac{1}{2}\epsilon^2 - \frac{1}{2}\epsilon^2 \cos 2\omega t + \cdots \right)$$

$$\theta = \omega t + 2\epsilon \sin \omega t + \frac{5}{4}\epsilon^2 \sin 2\omega t + \cdots$$

where $2\pi/\omega$ is the periodic time.

13. Find the apsidal angle for nearly circular motion in a central field for which the law of force is $(-c/r^2)e^{-kr}$.

14. A particle moves in a central field for which the law of force is $-cr^{-2} - \epsilon r^{-3}$. Find the equation of the orbit and discuss the motion.

15. Prove the statement made in Sec. 6.9 that the time average of the potential energy of a particle describing an elliptic orbit in an inverse-square field is $-k/a$, where k is the force constant, and a is the semimajor axis of the ellipse.

16. Find the values of r for which motion in a circular orbit is stable if the law of force is $(-c/r^2)e^{-kr}$ and also if the law is $-cr^{-2} - \epsilon r^{-4}$.

7

Dynamics of a System of
Particles

In studying a system or collection of many free particles, we shall be mainly interested in the general features of the motion of such a system.

7.1.   Center of Mass and Linear Momentum

Our general system consists of n particles of masses $m_1, m_2, \ldots, m_n$ whose position vectors are, respectively, $\mathbf{r}_1, \mathbf{r}_2, \ldots, \mathbf{r}_n$. We define the *center of mass* of the system as the point whose position vector $\mathbf{r}_c$ (Fig. 7.1) is given by

$$\mathbf{r}_c = \frac{m_1\mathbf{r}_1 + m_2\mathbf{r}_2 + \cdots + m_n\mathbf{r}_n}{m_1 + m_2 + \cdots + m_n} = \frac{\Sigma\, m_i\mathbf{r}_i}{M} \qquad (7.1)$$

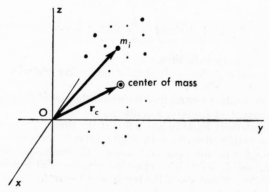

FIG. 7.1

where $M = \Sigma\, m_i$ is the total mass of the system. The above definition is clearly equivalent to the three equations

$$x_c = \frac{\Sigma\, m_i x_i}{M} \quad y_c = \frac{\Sigma\, m_i y_i}{M} \quad z_c = \frac{\Sigma\, m_i z_i}{M} \qquad [7.1(a)]$$

We define the *linear momentum* **p** of the system as the vector sum of the momenta of the individual particles, namely,

$$\mathbf{p} = \Sigma\, \mathbf{p}_i = \Sigma\, m_i \mathbf{v}_i \qquad (7.2)$$

From Eq. (7.1), by differentiating with respect to the time t, it follows that

$$\mathbf{p} = \Sigma\, m_i \mathbf{v}_i = M\mathbf{v}_c \qquad (7.3)$$

that is, the linear momentum of a system of particles is equal to the velocity of the center of mass multiplied by the total mass of the system.

Suppose now that there are external forces $\mathbf{F}_1, \mathbf{F}_2, \ldots, \mathbf{F}_i, \ldots, \mathbf{F}_n$, acting on the respective particles. In addition, there may be internal forces of interaction between any two particles of the system. We shall denote these internal forces by $\mathbf{F}_{ij}$, meaning the force exerted on particle i by particle j. The equation of motion of particle i is then

$$\mathbf{F}_i + \sum_{j=1}^{n}{}' \mathbf{F}_{ij} = m_i \ddot{\mathbf{r}}_i = \dot{\mathbf{p}}_i \qquad (7.4)$$

where $\mathbf{F}_i$ means the total external force acting on particle i. The second term in the above equation represents the vector sum of all the internal forces exerted on particle i by all other particles of the system. (The prime on the summation sign means that the term $j = i$ is excluded.) Adding Eqs. (7.4) for the n particles,

$$\sum_{i=1}^{n} \mathbf{F}_i + \sum_{i=1}^{n} \sum_{j=1}^{n}{}' \mathbf{F}_{ij} = \sum_{i=1}^{n} \dot{\mathbf{p}}_i \qquad (7.5)$$

In the double summation above, for every force $\mathbf{F}_{ij}$ there is also a force $\mathbf{F}_{ji}$, and these two forces are equal and opposite

$$\mathbf{F}_{ji} = -\mathbf{F}_{ji} \qquad (7.6)$$

from the law of action and reaction (Newton's third law). Consequently, the internal forces cancel in pairs, and the double sum vanishes. We can therefore write Eq. (7.5) in the following way:

$$\Sigma\, \mathbf{F}_i = \Sigma\, \dot{\mathbf{p}}_i = \dot{\mathbf{p}} = M\mathbf{a}_c \qquad (7.7)$$

In words: The acceleration of the center of mass of a system of particles is the same as that of a single particle having a mass equal to the total mass of the system and acted upon by the sum of the external forces.

Consider, for example, a swarm of particles moving in a uniform gravitational field. Then

$$\Sigma\, \mathbf{F}_i = \Sigma\, m_i \mathbf{g} = M\mathbf{g}$$

Hence

$$\mathbf{a}_c = \mathbf{g} \tag{7.8}$$

This is the equation for a single particle (projectile). Thus the center of mass of the shrapnel from an artillery shell that has burst in mid-air will follow the same parabolic path that the shell would have taken had it not burst.

In the special case in which there are *no* external forces acting on a system (or if $\Sigma\, \mathbf{F}_i = \mathbf{O}$), then $\mathbf{a}_c = \mathbf{O}$ and $\mathbf{v}_c = \text{constant}$. Thus the linear momentum of the system remains constant:

$$\Sigma\, \mathbf{p}_i = \mathbf{p} = M\mathbf{v}_c = \text{constant} \tag{7.9}$$

This is the *principle of conservation of linear momentum*. The constancy of the linear momentum of an isolated system is directly related to, and is in fact a consequence of, Newton's third law of motion.

7.2. Kinetic Energy of a System of Particles

The total kinetic energy T of a system of particles is given by the sum of the individual energies, namely,

$$T = \Sigma\, \frac{1}{2} m_i v_i^2 = \Sigma\, \frac{1}{2} m_i (\mathbf{v}_i \cdot \mathbf{v}_i) \tag{7.10}$$

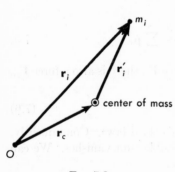

FIG. 7.2

As shown in Fig. 7.2, we can express each position vector $\mathbf{r}_i$ in the form

$$\mathbf{r}_i = \mathbf{r}_c + \mathbf{r}_i' \tag{7.11}$$

where $\mathbf{r}_i'$ is the position of particle i relative to the center of mass. Taking the derivative with respect to t, we have

$$\mathbf{v}_i = \mathbf{v}_c + \mathbf{v}_i' \tag{7.11(a)}$$

Here $\mathbf{v}_c$ is the velocity of the center of mass and $\mathbf{v}_i'$ is the velocity of particle i

relative to the center of mass. The expression for T can therefore be written

$$T = \Sigma \frac{1}{2}m_i(\mathbf{v}_c + \mathbf{v}_i') \cdot (\mathbf{v}_c + \mathbf{v}_i')$$

$$= \Sigma \frac{1}{2}m_i v_c^2 + \Sigma\, m_i(\mathbf{v}_c \cdot \mathbf{v}_i') + \Sigma \frac{1}{2}m_i v_i'^2$$

$$= \frac{1}{2}v_c^2 \Sigma\, m_i + \mathbf{v}_c \cdot \Sigma\, m_i\mathbf{v}_i' + \Sigma \frac{1}{2}m_i v_i'^2 \tag{7.12}$$

Now, from Eq. (7.11), we have

$$\Sigma\, m_i\mathbf{r}_i' = \Sigma\, m_i(\mathbf{r}_i - \mathbf{r}_c) = \Sigma\, m_i\mathbf{r}_i - M\mathbf{r}_c = \mathbf{0} \tag{7.13}$$

Similarly, we obtain

$$\Sigma\, m_i\mathbf{v}_i' = \mathbf{0} \tag{7.13(a)}$$

Therefore the expression for the kinetic energy reduces to

$$T = \frac{1}{2}M\,v_c^2 + \Sigma \frac{1}{2}m_i v_i'^2 \tag{7.14}$$

Thus the total kinetic energy of a system of particles is given by the sum of the kinetic energy of translation of the center of mass (the first term on the right) plus the kinetic energy of motion of the individual particles relative to the center of mass (the last term).

7.3. Angular Momentum of a System

As stated in Sec. 6.4, the angular momentum of a single particle is defined as the cross product $\mathbf{r} \times m\mathbf{v}$. The angular momentum $\mathbf{J}$ of a system of particles is defined accordingly, as the vector sum

$$\mathbf{J} = \sum_{i=1}^{n} (\mathbf{r}_i \times m_i\mathbf{v}_i)$$

Let us calculate the time derivative of the angular momentum:

$$\frac{d\mathbf{J}}{dt} = \sum_{i=1}^{n} (\mathbf{v}_i \times m_i\mathbf{v}_i) + \sum_{i=1}^{n} (\mathbf{r}_i \times m_i\mathbf{a}_i) \tag{7.15}$$

Now the first term on the right vanishes, and, since $m_i\mathbf{a}_i$ is equal to the total force acting on particle i, we can write

$$\frac{d\mathbf{J}}{dt} = \sum_{i=1}^{n} [\mathbf{r}_i \times (\mathbf{F}_i + \sum_{j=1}^{n}{}' \mathbf{F}_{ij})]$$

$$= \sum_{i=1}^{n} \mathbf{r}_i \times \mathbf{F}_i + \sum_{i=1}^{n}\sum_{j=1}^{n}{}' \mathbf{r}_i \times \mathbf{F}_{ij} \tag{7.16}$$

where, as in Sec. 7.1, $\mathbf{F}_i$ denotes the total external force on particle i, and $\mathbf{F}_{ij}$ denotes the (internal) force exerted on particle i by any other particle j. Now the double summation on the right consists of pairs of terms of the form

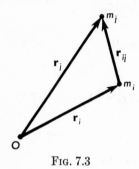

$$(\mathbf{r}_i \times \mathbf{F}_{ij}) + (\mathbf{r}_j \times \mathbf{F}_{ji}) \qquad (7.17)$$

Denoting the vector displacement of particle j relative to particle i by $\mathbf{r}_{ij}$, we see from the triangle shown in Fig. 7.3 that

$$\mathbf{r}_{ij} = \mathbf{r}_j - \mathbf{r}_i \qquad (7.18)$$

Therefore, since $\mathbf{F}_{ij} = -\mathbf{F}_{ji}$, the sum (7.17) reduces to

$$-\mathbf{r}_{ij} \times \mathbf{F}_{ij}$$

Fig. 7.3

which clearly vanishes if the internal forces are central (that is, if they act along the lines connecting pairs of particles). Hence the double sum in Eq. (7.16) vanishes. Now, as defined in Sec. 1.13, the cross product $\mathbf{r}_i \times \mathbf{F}_i$ is the moment of the external force $\mathbf{F}_i$. The sum $\sum_{i=1}^{n} \mathbf{r}_i \times \mathbf{F}_i$ is therefore the total moment of all the external forces acting on the system. If we denote the total external moment by $\mathbf{L}$, then Eq. (7.16) takes the form

$$\frac{d\mathbf{J}}{dt} = \mathbf{L} \qquad (7.19)$$

That is, the time rate of change of the angular momentum of a system is equal to the total moment of all the external forces acting on the system.

If a system is isolated, then $\mathbf{L} = \mathbf{O}$, and the angular momentum remains constant in both magnitude and direction:

$$\mathbf{J} = \Sigma \, \mathbf{r}_i \times m_i \mathbf{v}_i = \text{constant} \qquad (7.20)$$

This is a statement of the *principle of conservation of angular momentum*. It is a generalization of Eq. (6.11) for a single particle in a central field.

7.4.   Motion of Two Interacting Bodies.   The Reduced Mass

Let us consider the motion of a system consisting of two bodies (treated as particles) that interact with one another by a central force. We shall assume the system is isolated, and hence the center of mass moves with constant velocity. For simplicity, we shall take the center of mass as the origin. We have then

$$m_1 \mathbf{r}_1' + m_2 \mathbf{r}_2' = \mathbf{0} \tag{7.21}$$

where, as shown in Fig. 7.4, m_1 and m_2 are the respective masses of the two particles, and the vectors $\mathbf{r}_1'$ and $\mathbf{r}_2'$ represent their positions relative to the center of mass. As shown in the figure, the vector $\mathbf{R}$ is the position of particle m_1 relative to particle m_2. That is

$$\mathbf{R} = \mathbf{r}_1' - \mathbf{r}_2' = \mathbf{r}_1'\left(1 + \frac{m_1}{m_2}\right) \tag{7.22}$$

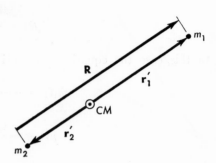

Fɪɢ. 7.4

The last step above follows from Eq. (7.21).

The differential equations of motion of the two particles are

$$m_1 \ddot{\mathbf{r}}_1' = \mathbf{F} = f(R)\frac{\mathbf{R}}{R} \tag{7.23}$$

$$m_2 \ddot{\mathbf{r}}_2' = -\mathbf{F} = -f(R)\frac{\mathbf{R}}{R} \tag{7.23(a)}$$

where $f(R)$ is the magnitude of the mutual force exerted by one particle on the other. By using the relation between $\mathbf{r}_1'$ and $\mathbf{R}$ expressed by Eq. (7.22), we can write the equation of motion of m_1 [Eq. (7.23)] in either of the following ways:

$$m_1 \ddot{\mathbf{r}}_1' = f(cr_1)\frac{\mathbf{r}_1}{r_1} \tag{7.24}$$

$$\mu \ddot{\mathbf{R}} = f(R)\frac{\mathbf{R}}{R} \tag{7.25}$$

where $c = 1 + m_1/m_2$, and

$$\mu = \frac{m_1}{c} = \frac{m_1 m_2}{m_1 + m_2} \tag{7.26}$$

The quantity μ is called the *reduced mass*. Equation (7.24) gives the motion of m_1 relative to the center of mass of the two particles. Equation (7.25) is the equation of motion of m_1 relative to m_2. According to the latter, we can regard m_2 as the center of motion if we change the value of m_1 to the reduced mass μ. If the bodies are of equal mass m, then $\mu = m/2$. On the other hand, if m_2 is very much greater than m_1, so that m_1/m_2 is very small, then μ is nearly equal to m_1.

For two bodies attracting one another by gravitation, we have

$$f(R) = -\frac{Gm_1m_2}{R^2}$$

In this case the equations of motion, Eqs. (7.24) and (7.25), become

$$m_1\ddot{\mathbf{r}}_1 = -\frac{Gm_1m_2c^{-2}}{r_1^2}\left(\frac{\mathbf{r}_1}{r_1}\right) \tag{7.27}$$

$$\mu\ddot{\mathbf{R}} = -\frac{Gm_1m_2}{R^2}\left(\frac{\mathbf{R}}{R}\right) \tag{[7.27(a)]}$$

The two equations are identical except for constants. They are the same as the equation of a single particle in an inverse-square central field (as treated in Sec. 6.8). Since the choice of subscripts is arbitrary, we conclude that the orbit of either particle is a central conic with the center of mass as a focus. Furthermore, from Eq. [7.27(a)], we see that either particle describes a central conic about the other as a focus. Thus, regarding the earth and the moon as an isolated system, both the moon and the earth describe an ellipse with the center of mass of the earth-moon system as a focus. The moon also describes an ellipse about the center of the earth as a focus, and the earth describes an ellipse about the center of the moon as a focus.

7.5. Collisions

When two bodies undergo a collision with one another, the force each exerts on the other during the contact is an *internal* force (regarding the two bodies as the system). The total momentum is therefore unchanged by the collision, and we can write

$$\mathbf{p}_{1i} + \mathbf{p}_{2i} = \mathbf{p}_{1f} + \mathbf{p}_{2f}$$

or

$$m_1\mathbf{v}_{1i} + m_2\mathbf{v}_{2i} = m_1\mathbf{v}_{1f} + m_2\mathbf{v}_{2f} \tag{7.28}$$

where the subscripts i and f indicate the quantities before and after the collision, respectively, and the subscripts 1 and 2 refer to the two bodies. The above equation is perfectly general. It applies to any two bodies regardless of their shapes, rigidity, etc.

Let us consider a special case, namely the direct collision of two spherical bodies (Fig. 7.5). We shall choose the x axis to be along the line of centers, so we have

$$m_1\dot{x}_{1i} + m_2\dot{x}_{2i} = m_1\dot{x}_{1f} + m_2\dot{x}_{2f} \qquad [7.28(a)]$$

All other velocity components are zero.

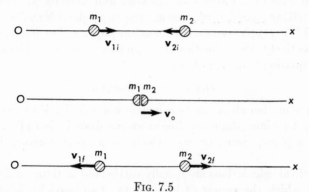

FIG. 7.5

If we wish to know the values of the components after the collision, given the values before the collision, we need another equation. This equation is given by the *coefficient of restitution* ϵ which is defined as the ratio of the speed of separation to the speed of approach, namely,

$$\epsilon = \frac{\dot{x}_{2f} - \dot{x}_{1f}}{\dot{x}_{1i} - \dot{x}_{2i}} \qquad (7.29)$$

The numerical value of ϵ depends primarily on the compositions of the bodies; it also depends, to a small extent, on their sizes. A perfectly elastic collision is one for which $\epsilon = 1$, while for a perfectly inelastic collision $\epsilon = 0$. For ivory or glass spheres, ϵ may be as high as 0.95. For clay or putty, the value of ϵ is, of course, zero. The value of ϵ may also depend on the speed of approach, as in the case of the silicone compound known as "nutty putty."

From Eq. [7.28(a)] and (7.29) we readily find

$$\dot{x}_{1f} = \frac{(m_1 - \epsilon m_2)\dot{x}_{1i} + (m_2 + \epsilon m_2)\dot{x}_{2i}}{m_1 + m_2} \qquad (7.30)$$

$$\dot{x}_{2f} = \frac{(m_1 + \epsilon m_1)\dot{x}_{1i} + (m_2 - \epsilon m_1)\dot{x}_{2i}}{m_1 + m_2} \qquad [7.30(a)]$$

If the special case $\epsilon = 1$ and $m_1 = m_2$, we find that

$$\dot{x}_{1f} = \dot{x}_{2i} \qquad \dot{x}_{2f} = \dot{x}_{1i} \qquad (7.31)$$

In other words, the two bodies just exchange velocities.

7.6. Oblique Collisions. Comparison of Laboratory and Center-of-Mass Coordinate Systems

Let us now turn to the more general case of collisions in which the motion is not confined to a single straight line. We shall, however, consider the special case of a particle of mass m_1 and velocity v_{1i} (the *incident* particle) striking a particle of mass m_2 (the *target* particle) which is initially at rest. This is a typical situation in nuclear physics. Letting v_{1f} and v_{2f} denote, respectively, the velocities of m_1 and m_2 after the collision, the momentum equation [Eq. (7.28)] reads

$$m_1 v_{1i} = m_1 v_{1f} + m_2 v_{2f} \qquad (7.32)$$

The above equation allows us to calculate one velocity if we are given the other two. One immediate conclusion we can draw is that all three velocities lie in a plane, since any one velocity is a linear combination of the other two.

Theoretical calculations are usually carried out in terms of a coordinate system in which the center of mass of the two particles is at rest, the center-of-mass system. On the other hand, the observations of scattering angles, etc., are done in the laboratory coordinate system. It is of interest, therefore, to see how to convert from one system to the other.

From the definition of the center of mass, the momentum in the center-of-mass system is zero both before and after the collision. Hence we can write

$$m_1 v'_{1i} + m_2 v'_{2i} = O = m_1 v'_{1f} + m_2 v'_{2f} \qquad (7.33)$$

where the primes indicate velocities in the center-of-mass system. The velocity vectors in the laboratory system and in the center-of-mass system are shown in Fig. 7.6. In the figure, φ_1 is the angle of deflection of the

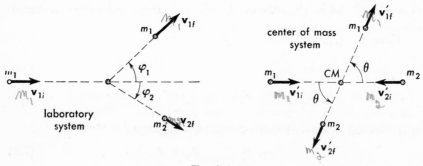

FIG. 7.6

incident particle, and φ_2 is the angle which the line of motion of the target particle makes with the line of motion of the incident particle, both angles being measured in the laboratory system. In the center-of-mass system both particles approach the center of mass, collide, and then recede from the center of mass. The angle θ denotes the angle of deflection of either particle in the center-of-mass system, as shown.

The relationships among the velocity vectors $\mathbf{v}'_{1f}$, $\mathbf{v}_{1f}$, and $\mathbf{v}_c$ are shown in Fig. 7.7, where $\mathbf{v}_c$ denotes the velocity of the center of mass. From a study of the figure we see that we can write

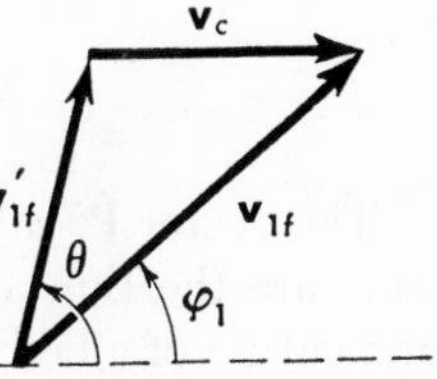

$$\tan \varphi_1 = \frac{v'_{if} \sin \theta}{v_c + v'_{1f} \cos \theta} = \frac{\sin \theta}{a + \cos \theta} \quad (7.34)$$

where $a = v_c/v'_{1f}$. But

FIG. 7.7

$$\mathbf{v}_c = \frac{m_1 \mathbf{v}_{1i} + \mathbf{0}}{m_1 + m_2} \quad (7.35)$$

From Eqs. (7.33) and (7.35) we have

$$a = \frac{v_c}{v'_{1f}} = \frac{m_1 v_{1i}}{(m_1 + m_2)v'_{1f}} = \frac{m_1 v_{1i}}{m_2(v'_{1f} + v'_{2f})} = \frac{m_1 v_{1i}}{m_2 v_r} \quad (7.36)$$

where v_r is the relative speed of the two particles after the collision.

In particular, if the collision is perfectly elastic, then $v_r = v_{1i}$ and so $a = m_1/m_2$. Furthermore, if the bodies are of equal mass so that $a = 1$, then

$$\tan \varphi_1 = \frac{\sin \theta}{1 + \cos \theta} = \tan \frac{\theta}{2}$$

or

$$\phi_1 = \frac{\theta}{2}$$

That is, the angle of deflection in the laboratory coordinate system is just half that in the center-of-mass system.

7.7. Impulse

Forces of extremely short duration, such as those exerted by bodies undergoing collisions, are called *impulsive forces*. For a given body, regarded here as a particle, the component equations of motion are

$$\frac{d}{dt}(m\dot{x}) = F_x, \quad \frac{d}{dt}(m\dot{y}) = F_y, \quad \frac{d}{dt}(m\dot{z}) = F_z \quad (7.37)$$

Taking the time integral over the interval $t = t_1$ to $t = t_2$ (the interval during which the force acts), we have

$$\Delta(m\dot{x}) = \int_{t_1}^{t_2} F_x \, dt \quad \Delta(m\dot{y}) = \int_{t_1}^{t_2} F_y \, dt \quad \Delta(m\dot{z}) = \int_{t_1}^{t_2} F_z \, dt \quad (7.38)$$

The above three equations can be written as one vector equation, namely,

$$\Delta(m\mathbf{v}) = m\mathbf{v}_2 - m\mathbf{v}_1 = \int_{t_2}^{t_2} \mathbf{F} \, dt = \hat{\mathbf{P}} \qquad (7.39)$$

The vector $\hat{\mathbf{P}}$, called the *impulse*, is defined as the vector whose components are the time integrals in Eq. (7.38). In words: The change in the momentum of a body under the action of an impulsive force is equal to the impulse (time integral) of that force. We can think of an ideal impulse as one that produces an instantaneous change of momentum but no change in position, that is, the integral of an "infinitely" large force lasting for an "infinitesimal" time.

Let us apply the concept of impulse to the case of the direct collision of two spherical bodies (treated in Sec. 7.5). We shall divide the impulse into two parts, namely, the impulse of compression, $\hat{P}_c$, and the impulse of restitution, $\hat{P}_r$. (We are concerned only with components along the line of centers.) Therefore, for the compression we can write

$$m_1\dot{x}_o - m_1\dot{x}_{1i} = \hat{P}_c \qquad (7.40)$$

$$m_2\dot{x}_o - m_2\dot{x}_{2i} = -\hat{P}_c \qquad (7.41)$$

where $\dot{x}_o$ is the *common* velocity of both particles at the instant their relative speed is zero. Similarly, for the restitution, we have

$$m_1\dot{x}_{1f} - m_2\dot{x}_o = \hat{P}_r \qquad (7.42)$$

$$m_2\dot{x}_{2f} - m_2\dot{x}_o = \hat{P}_r \qquad (7.43)$$

Upon eliminating $\dot{x}_o$ from Eqs. (7.40) and (7.41) and from Eqs. (7.42) and (7.43), we obtain

$$m_1m_2(\dot{x}_{2i} - \dot{x}_{1i}) = \hat{P}_c(m_1 + m_2) \qquad (7.44)$$

and

$$m_1m_2(\dot{x}_{1f} - \dot{x}_{2f}) = \hat{P}_r(m_1 + m_2) \qquad (7.45)$$

Dividing Eq. (7.45) by Eq. (7.44) yields

$$\frac{\dot{x}_{2f} - \dot{x}_{1f}}{\dot{x}_{1i} - \dot{x}_{2i}} = \frac{\hat{P}_r}{\hat{P}_c} \qquad (7.46)$$

From the definition of the coefficient of restitution ϵ, Eq. (7.29), we then have

$$\epsilon = \frac{\hat{P}_r}{\hat{P}_c} \tag{7.47}$$

The coefficient of restitution is thus equal to the ratio of the impulse of restitution to the impulse of compression.

7.8.   Motion of a Body of Variable Mass. Rockets

In the case of the motion of a body whose mass is changing, one must be careful in setting up the differential equations of motion. The concept of impulse can be conveniently employed for this type of problem.

Let us consider the motion of a rocket-propelled body. We shall let m_o denote the mass of the empty rocket, and m_f the mass of the unburned fuel. The total mass of the moving rocket at any instant is then $m_o + m_f$. Now if the *external* force acting on the rocket is $\mathbf{F}$, then the change of momentum of the system (rocket plus fuel) during a time interval Δt is equal to the impulse

$$\mathbf{F}\,\Delta t$$

The initial momentum of the system is $(m_o + m_f)\mathbf{v}$. The momentum at the end of the interval Δt is the sum of *two* momenta, namely the momentum of the rocket proper

$$(m_o + m_f - \Delta m)\,(\mathbf{v} + \Delta\mathbf{v})$$

and the momentum of the ejected fuel

$$\Delta m(\mathbf{v} + \mathbf{v}_e)$$

where $\mathbf{v}_e$ is the velocity of the exhaust gases relative to the rocket, and Δm is the mass of the ejected fuel. Thus the total change of momentum is given by

$$\mathbf{F}\,\Delta t = \Delta\mathbf{p} = [(m_o + m_f - \Delta m)(\mathbf{v} + \Delta\mathbf{v}) + \Delta m(\mathbf{v} + \mathbf{v}_e)] - (m_o + m_f)\mathbf{v}$$

After carrying out the obvious cancellations and dividing by Δt, we find in the limit as Δt approaches zero

$$\mathbf{F} - \mathbf{v}_e \dot{m} = (m_o + m_f)\dot{\mathbf{v}} \tag{7.48}$$

The term $-\mathbf{v}_e \dot{m}$ is the thrust of the rocket motor.

If the fuel is ejected at a constant rate $c\ (=\dot{m}\ )$, then

$$m_f = M - ct \tag{7.49}$$

where M is the initial mass of the fuel. Suppose, in particular, that the external force $\mathbf{F}$ is negligibly small, and let the direction of motion be in the positive x direction. Then the velocity $\mathbf{v}_e$ of the ejected fuel is in the negative x direction, and we can write

$$cv_e = (m_o + M - ct)\ddot{x} \tag{7.50}$$

where c is the rate of fuel ejection, and v_e is the speed of the exhaust gases. Separating variables and integrating, we obtain

$$\dot{x} = \dot{x}_o + \int_o^t \frac{v_e c\, dt}{(m_o + M - ct)} = \dot{x}_o + v_e \ln \left[\frac{m_o + M}{m_o + M - ct} \right] \tag{7.51}$$

The maximum increase in speed attainable (after all of the fuel is exhausted) is given by the last term in the above equation with $M = ct$, namely,

$$v_e \ln \left[1 + \frac{M}{m_o} \right]$$

It is therefore necessary to have a very large fuel-payload ratio M/m_o in order to reach speeds much in excess of v_e, owing to the nature of the logarithmic function.

PROBLEMS

1. A gun of mass M fires a bullet of mass m. Find the velocity of the bullet and the recoil velocity of the gun in terms of the energy E of the explosive charge.
2. An artillery shell is fired at an angle of elevation of 45° with a muzzle velocity v_o. At the uppermost part of the trajectory, the shell bursts into two equal fragments, one of which moves directly downward. (a) Find the initial velocity (speed and direction) of the other fragment if the energy of the explosion of the shell is one half the initial kinetic energy. (b) Where does the second fragment hit the ground?
3. A bullet of mass m and speed v_o is fired into a block of wood of mass M resting on a rough horizontal table. If μ is the coefficient of sliding friction between the block and the table, how far will the block slide before coming to rest?
4. A rocket satellite is going in a circular orbit of radius r_o. A small explosive charge separates the rocket into two equal parts. If the energy of the explosion is 1 percent of the initial kinetic energy of the system, and if one part is shot directly forward, the other backward, find the resulting orbits of the two parts and make a plot of the orbits.
5. Show that the kinetic energy of a two-particle system is $\frac{1}{2}(m_1 + m_2)v_c^2 + \frac{1}{2}\mu V^2$, where v_c is the speed of the center of mass, μ is the reduced mass, and V is the relative speed of the two particles.
6. Show that the constant c in Eq. (6.43) for the period of a planet should be $2\pi(GM + Gm)^{-1/2}$, rather than $2\pi(GM)^{-1/2}$, where m is the mass of the planet and M is the mass of the sun.

7. If two bodies undergo a direct collision, show that the loss in kinetic energy is equal to $\frac{1}{2}\mu V_o^2(1 - \epsilon^2)$, where μ is the reduced mass, V_o is the relative speed before impact, and ϵ is the coefficient of restitution.

8. Three particles of equal mass m lie on a straight line, along which the particles move. Initially, the particles are located at the points 0, a, and $2a$, and their velocities are $2v_o$, v_o, and $1/2\,v_o$, respectively. Find the final velocity of each particle, assuming that all collisions are perfectly elastic.

9. The binding energy of a certain diatomic molecule is E_b. (This is the energy required to separate the two atoms.) If the two atoms are identical and of atomic weight M, what is the least energy an incident proton must have in order to dissociate the molecule? (Take the atomic weight as the ratio of the mass of the atom to the mass of the proton.)

10. Show that the angular momentum of a two-particle system is $(m_1 + m_2)$ $(\mathbf{r}_c \times \mathbf{v}_c) + \mu \mathbf{R} \times \dot{\mathbf{R}}$, where μ is the reduced mass, $\mathbf{r}_c$ is the position of the center of mass, and $\mathbf{R}$ is the position of particle 1 relative to particle 2.

11. A rocket is fired vertically upward. Find the equation of motion assuming g to be constant. What is the ratio of fuel to payload in order to achieve a final speed equal to the escape speed from the earth (7 miles per sec) if the speed of the exhaust gas is (a) 1/2 mile per sec and (b) 2 miles per sec? Assume that the rate of fuel loss per second is constant and is equal to 1 percent of the initial mass of fuel.

12. A uniform heavy chain of length a hangs initially with a part of length b hanging over the edge of a table. The remaining part, of length a-b, is coiled up at the edge of the table. If the chain is released, show that the speed of the chain when the last link leaves the end of the table is $[2g(a^3 - b^3)/3a^2]^{1/2}$.

13. A ball is dropped from a height h onto a horizontal pavement. If the coefficient of restitution is ϵ, show that the total vertical distance the ball goes before the rebounds cease is $h(1 + \epsilon^2)/(1 - \epsilon^2)$.

14. (a) Find the equation of motion of a raindrop falling through a mist, collecting mass as it falls. Assume that the drop remains spherical and that the rate of accretion is proportional to the area of the drop. (b) Show that the acceleration is constant if the drop starts from rest when it is infinitely small, and find the value of this acceleration.

15. A particle of mass m_1 with kinetic energy T_{1i} strikes a particle of mass m_2 which is at rest. The incident particle is observed to undergo a deflection φ_1, and its kinetic energy after the collision is T_{1f}. (a) Find the kinetic energy of the target particle m_2 after the collision, and thereby obtain the loss Q of energy in the collision. (b) Show that if $m_1 = m_2$, then Q is zero if the final velocities of the two particles are at right angles to each other.

8

Mechanics of Rigid Bodies. Motion in a Plane

A rigid body may be defined as a system of particles whose *relative* positions are fixed, or, in other words, the distance between any two particles is constant. This definition of a rigid body is idealized. In the first place, as pointed out in the definition of a particle, there are no true particles in nature. Secondly, real extended bodies are not strictly rigid; they become more or less deformed (stretched, compressed, or bent) when external forces are applied. We shall for the present, however, neglect such deformations.

8.1. Center of Mass of a Rigid Body

We have already defined the center of mass (Sec. 7.1) of a system of particles as the point (x_c, y_c, z_c) where

$$x_c = \frac{\Sigma\, x_i m_i}{\Sigma\, m_i} \quad y_c = \frac{\Sigma\, y_i m_i}{\Sigma\, m_i} \quad z_c = \frac{\Sigma\, z_i m_i}{\Sigma\, m_i}$$

For a rigid extended body, we can replace the summation by an integration over the volume of the body, namely,

$$x_c = \frac{\displaystyle\int_v \rho x\, dv}{\displaystyle\int_v \rho\, dv} \quad y_c = \frac{\displaystyle\int_v \rho y\, dv}{\displaystyle\int_v \rho\, dv} \quad z_c = \frac{\displaystyle\int_v \rho z\, dv}{\displaystyle\int_v \rho\, dv} \tag{8.1}$$

where ρ is the density, and dv is the element of volume.

If a rigid body is in the form of a thin shell, the equations for the center of mass become

$$x_c = \frac{\int_s \rho x \, ds}{\int_s \rho \, ds} \qquad y_c = \frac{\int_s \rho y \, ds}{\int_s \rho \, ds} \qquad z_c = \frac{\int_s \rho z \, ds}{\int_s \rho \, ds} \qquad (8.2)$$

where ds is the element of area, and ρ is the mass per unit area, the integration extending over the area of the body.

Similarly, if the body is in the form of a thin wire, we have

$$x_c = \frac{\int_l \rho x \, dl}{\int_l \rho \, dl} \qquad y_c = \frac{\int_l \rho y \, dl}{\int_l \rho \, dl} \qquad z_c = \frac{\int_l \rho z \, dl}{\int_l \rho \, dl} \qquad (8.3)$$

In this case ρ is the mass per unit length, and dl is the element of length.

For uniform homogeneous bodies, the density factors ρ are constant in each case and therefore may be canceled out in each equation above.

If a body is composite, that is, if it consists of two or more parts whose centers of mass are known, then it is clear, from the definition of the center of mass, that we can write

$$x_c = \frac{x_1 M_1 + x_2 M_2 + \cdots}{M_1 + M_2 + \cdots} \qquad (8.4)$$

with similar equations for y_c and z_c. Here (x_1, y_1, z_1) is the center of mass of the part M_1, etc.

Symmetry considerations. If a body possesses symmetry, it is possible to take advantage of that symmetry in locating the center of mass. Thus, if the body has a plane of symmetry, that is, if each particle m_i has a mirror image of itself m_i' relative to some plane, then the center of mass lies in that plane. To prove this, let us suppose that the xy plane is a plane of symmetry. We have then

$$z_c = \frac{\Sigma \, (z_i m_i + z_i' m_i')}{\Sigma \, (m_i + m_i')}$$

But $m_i = m_i'$ and $z_i = -z_i'$. Hence the terms in the numerator cancel in pairs, and so $z_c = 0$; that is, the center of mass lies in the xy plane.

Similarly, if the body has a line of symmetry, it is easy to show that the center of mass lies on that line. The proof is left as an exercise.

Solid hemisphere.   To find the center of mass of a solid homogeneous hemisphere of radius a, we know from symmetry that the center of mass lies on the radius that is normal to the plane face. Choosing coordinate axes as shown in Fig. 8.1, we have that the center of mass lies on the z axis. To calculate z_c we use a circular element of volume of thickness dz and radius $(a^2 - z^2)^{1/2}$, as shown. Thus

$$dv = \pi(a^2 - z^2)\, dz$$

Therefore

$$z_c = \frac{\int_o^a \rho\pi z(a^2 - z^2)\, dz}{\int_o^a \rho\pi(a^2 - z^2)\, dz} = \frac{3}{8}a \tag{8.5}$$

Hemispherical shell.   For a hemispherical shell of radius a we use the same axes as in the previous problem (Fig. 8.1). Again, from symmetry,

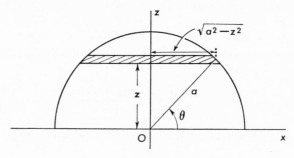

Fig. 8.1

the center of mass is located on the z axis. For our element of surface we choose a circular strip of width $a\, d\theta$. Hence we can write

$$ds = 2\pi(a^2 - z^2)^{1/2}a\, d\theta$$

But $\theta = \sin^{-1}(z/a)$, so $d\theta = (a^2 - z^2)^{-1/2}\, dz$. Therefore

$$ds = 2\pi a\, dz$$

The location of the center of mass is accordingly given by

$$z_c = \frac{\int_o^a \rho 2\pi a z\, dz}{\int_o^a \rho 2\pi a\, dz} = \frac{1}{2}a \tag{8.6}$$

Semicircle.   To find the center of mass of a thin wire bent into the form of a semicircle of radius a, we use axes as shown in Fig. 8.2. We have

$$dl = a\, d\theta$$

and

$$z = a \sin \theta$$

Hence

$$z_c = \frac{\displaystyle\int_o^\pi \rho(a \sin \theta)\, a\, d\theta}{\displaystyle\int_o^\pi \rho\, a\, d\theta} = \frac{2}{\pi}\, a \qquad (8.7)$$

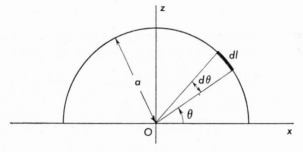

FIG. 8.2

In the case of a uniform semicircular lamina, the center of mass is on the z axis (Fig. 8.2). It is left as a problem to show that

$$z_c = \frac{4}{3\pi}\, a \qquad (8.8)$$

8.2.   Static Equilibrium of a Rigid Body

We have found (Sec. 7.1) that the acceleration of the center of mass of a system is equal to the vector sum of the external forces divided by the mass. In particular, if the system is a rigid body, and if the sum of all the external forces vanishes

$$\mathbf{F}_1 + \mathbf{F}_2 + \cdots = \mathbf{0} \qquad (8.9)$$

then the center of mass, if initially at rest, will remain at rest. Thus equation (8.9) expresses the condition for *translational equilibrium* of a rigid body.

Similarly, the vanishing of the total moment of all the applied forces

$$\mathbf{r}_1 \times \mathbf{F}_1 + \mathbf{r}_2 \times \mathbf{F}_2 + \cdots = \mathbf{O} \tag{8.10}$$

means that the angular momentum of the body does not change (Sec. 7.3). This is the condition for *rotational equilibrium* of a rigid body — that is, the condition that the body, if initially at rest, will not start to rotate. Equations (8.9) and (8.10) together constitute the necessary conditions for complete equilibrium of a rigid body.

Equilibrium in a uniform gravitational field.   Let us consider a rigid body in a uniform gravitational field, say at the surface of the earth. Since the sum of the gravitational forces $\Sigma\, m_i \mathbf{g}$ is equal to $M\mathbf{g}$ where M is the mass of the body, we can write the condition for translational equilibrium as

$$\mathbf{F}_1 + \mathbf{F}_2 + \cdots + M\mathbf{g} = \mathbf{O} \tag{8.11}$$

where $\mathbf{F}_1$, $\mathbf{F}_2$, etc., are all the external forces other than gravity.

Similarly, the condition for rotational equilibrium may be written

$$\mathbf{r}_1 \times \mathbf{F}_1 + \mathbf{r}_2 \times \mathbf{F}_2 + \cdots + \sum_i \mathbf{r}_i \times m_i \mathbf{g} = \mathbf{O} \tag{8.12}$$

But $\mathbf{g}$ is a constant vector, so we can write

$$\sum_i \mathbf{r}_i \times m_i \mathbf{g} = \left(\sum_i m_i \mathbf{r}_i \right) \times \mathbf{g} = M\mathbf{r}_c \times \mathbf{g} = \mathbf{r}_c \times M\mathbf{g} \tag{8.13}$$

The above equation states that the moment of the force of gravity about any point is the same as that of a single force $M\mathbf{g}$ acting at the center of mass.* The equation for rotational equilibrium then becomes

$$\mathbf{r}_1 \times \mathbf{F}_1 + \mathbf{r}_2 \times \mathbf{F}_2 + \cdots + \mathbf{r}_c \times M\mathbf{g} = \mathbf{O} \tag{8.14}$$

Equilibrium under coplanar forces.   If the lines of action of a set of forces acting on a rigid body are coplanar, that is, if they all lie in a plane, then we can write $\mathbf{F}_1 = \mathbf{i}X_1 + \mathbf{j}Y_1$, etc. The component forms of the equations of equilibrium [Eqs. (8.9) and (8.10)] (which the student will recall from elementary physics) are then

Translational equilibrium:

$$X_1 + X_2 + \cdots = 0 \quad Y_1 + Y_2 + \cdots = 0 \tag{8.15}$$

Rotational equilibrium:

$$x_1 Y_1 - y_1 X_1 + x_2 Y_2 - y_2 X_2 + \cdots = 0 \tag{8.16}$$

*The apparent center of gravitational force is called the *center of gravity*. In a uniform gravitational field such as we are considering, the center of mass and the center of gravity coincide.

8.3.   Rotation of a Rigid Body about a Fixed Axis.   Moment of Inertia

The simplest type of rigid-body motion, other than pure translation, is that in which the body is constrained to rotate about a fixed axis. Let us choose the z axis of an appropriate coordinate system as the axis of rotation. The path of a representative particle m_i located at the point (x_i, y_i, z_i) is then a circle of radius $(x_i^2 + y_i^2)^{1/2} = R_i$ centered on the z axis. A representative cross section parallel to the xy plane is shown in Fig. 8.3.

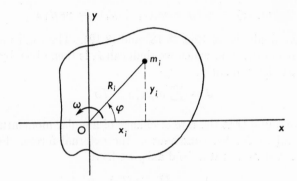

Fɪɢ. 8.3

The speed v_i of particle i is given by

$$v_i = R_i\omega = (x_i^2 + y_i^2)^{1/2}\omega \tag{8.17}$$

where ω is the angular speed of rotation. From a study of the figure, we see that the velocity has components as follows:

$$\dot{x}_i = -v_i \sin \varphi = -\omega y_i \tag{8.18}$$

$$\dot{y}_i = v_i \cos \varphi = \omega x_i \tag{8.19}$$

$$\dot{z}_i = 0 \tag{8.20}$$

where φ is defined as shown in the figure. The above equations can also be obtained by taking the components of

$$\mathbf{v}_i = \boldsymbol{\omega} \times \mathbf{r}_i \tag{8.21}$$

where $\boldsymbol{\omega} = \mathbf{k}\omega$.

Let us calculate the kinetic energy of rotation of the body. We have

$$T = \sum_i \frac{1}{2}m_i v_i^2 = \frac{1}{2}(\sum_i m_i R_i^2)\omega^2 = \frac{1}{2}I\omega^2 \tag{8.22}$$

where

$$I = \sum_i m_i R_i^2 = \sum_i m_i(x_i^2 + y_i^2) \tag{8.23}$$

The quantity I, defined by the above equation, is of particular importance in the study of the motion of rigid bodies. It is called the *moment of inertia*.

To show how the moment of inertia further enters the picture, let us next calculate the angular momentum about the axis of rotation. Since the angular momentum of a single particle is, by definition, $\mathbf{r}_i \times m_i \mathbf{v}_i$, the z component is

$$m_i(x_i\dot{y}_i - y_i\dot{x}_i) = m_i(x_i^2 + y_i^2)\omega = m_i R_i^2 \omega \tag{8.24}$$

where we have made use of Eqs. (8.18) and (8.19). The total z component of the angular momentum, which we shall call J, is then given by summing over all the particles, namely,

$$J = \sum_i m_i^2 R_i^2 \omega = I\omega \tag{8.25}$$

In Sec. 7.3 we found that the rate of change of angular momentum for any system is equal to the total moment of the external forces. For a body constrained to rotate about a fixed axis, we have

$$L = \frac{dJ}{dt} = \frac{d(I\omega)}{dt} \tag{8.26}$$

where L is the total moment of all the applied forces about the axis of rotation (the component of $\mathbf{L}$ along the axis). If the body is rigid, then I is constant, and we can write

$$L = I\frac{d\omega}{dt} \tag{8.27}$$

The analogy between the equations for translation and for rotation about a fixed axis is shown below:

Translation		*Rotation*	
Linear momentum	$p = mv$	Angular momentum	$J = I\omega$
Force	$F = m\dot{v}$	Torque	$L = I\dot{\omega}$
Kinetic energy	$T = \frac{1}{2}mv^2$	Kinetic energy	$T = \frac{1}{2}I\omega^2$

Thus the moment of inertia is analogous to mass; it is a measure of the rotational inertia of a body relative to some fixed axis of rotation, just as mass is a measure of translational inertia of a body

8.4.   Calculation of the Moment of Inertia

In actual calculations of the moment of inertia $\Sigma\, mR^2$ for extended bodies, we can replace the summation by an integration over the body, just as we did in calculation of the center of mass. Thus we may write

$$I = \int R^2\, dm \tag{8.28}$$

where dm, the element of mass, is given by a density factor multiplied by an appropriate differential (volume, area, or length). It is important to remember that R is the perpendicular distance from the element of mass to the axis of rotation.

In the case of a composite body, it is clear, from the definition of the moment of inertia, that we may write

$$I = I_1 + I_2 + \cdots \tag{8.29}$$

where I_1, I_2, etc., are the moments of inertia of the various parts about the particular axis chosen.

Let us calculate the moments of inertia for some important special cases.

Thin rod.   For a thin uniform rod of length a and mass M, we have, for an axis perpendicular to the rod at one end [Fig. 8.4(a)],

$$I = \int_{o}^{a} x^2\rho\, dx = \frac{1}{3}\rho a^3 = \frac{1}{3}Ma^2 \tag{8.30}$$

The last step follows from the fact that $M = \rho a$.

If the axis is taken at the center of the rod [Fig. 8.4(b)], we have

$$I = \int_{-a/2}^{a/2} x^2\rho\, dx = \frac{1}{12}\rho a^3 = \frac{1}{12}Ma^2 \tag{8.31}$$

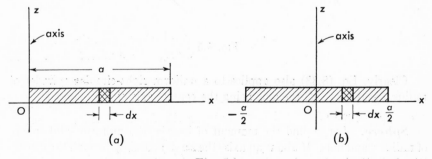

FIG. 8.4

Hoop or cylindrical shell. In the case of a thin circular hoop or cylindrical shell, for the central or symmetry axis all particles lie at the same distance from the axis. Thus

$$I = Ma^2 \tag{8.22}$$

where a is the radius, and M is the mass.

Circular disc. To calculate the moment of inertia of a uniform circular disc of radius a and mass M, we shall use polar coordinates. The element of mass, a thin ring of radius r and thickness dr, is given by

$$dm = \rho 2\pi r dr$$

where ρ is the mass per unit area. The moment of inertia about an axis through the center of the disc normal to the plane faces (Fig. 8.5) is obtained as follows:

$$I = \int_o^a \rho(r^2)(2\pi r \, dr) = 2\pi \rho \frac{a^4}{4} = \frac{1}{2}Ma^2 \tag{8.33}$$

The last step results from the relation $M = \rho \pi a^2$.

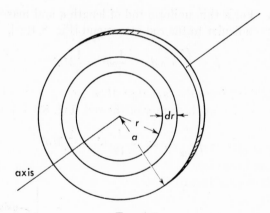

FIG. 8.5

Clearly, Eq. (8.33) also applies to a uniform right-circular cylinder of radius a and mass M, the axis being the central axis of the cylinder.

Sphere. Let us find the moment of inertia of a uniform solid sphere of radius a and mass M about an axis (the z axis) passing through the center. We shall divide the sphere into thin circular discs, as shown in Fig. 8.6.

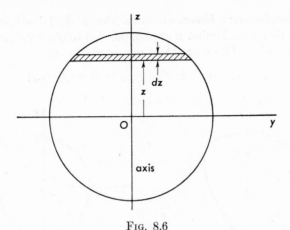

Fig. 8.6

The moment of inertia of a representative disc of radius y, from Eq. (8.33), is $1/2\, y^2\, dm$. But $dm = \rho\pi y^2\, dz$, hence

$$I = \int_{-a}^{a} \frac{1}{2}\pi\rho y^4\, dz = \int_{-a}^{a} \frac{1}{2}\pi\rho(a^2 - z^2)^2\, dz = \frac{8}{15}\pi\rho a^5 \qquad (8.34)$$

The last step above should be filled in by the student. Since the mass M is given by

$$M = \frac{4}{3}\pi a^3 \rho$$

we have

$$I = \frac{2}{5}Ma^2 \qquad (8.35)$$

Spherical shell. The moment of inertia of a thin uniform spherical shell can be found very simply by application of Eq. (8.34). If we differentiate with respect to a, namely,

$$\frac{8}{3}\pi\rho a^4\, da$$

the result is the moment of inertia of a shell of thickness da and radius a. The mass of the shell is $4\pi a^2\rho\, da$. Hence we can write

$$I = \frac{2}{3}Ma^2 \qquad (8.36)$$

for the moment of inertia of a thin shell of radius a and mass M. The student should verify the above result by direct integration.

Perpendicular-axis theorem.   Consider a rigid body which is in the form of a thin plane lamina of any shape. Let us place the lamina in the xy plane (Fig. 8.7). The moment of inertia about the z axis is given by

$$I_z = \sum_i m_i(x_i^2 + y_i^2) = \sum_i m_i x_i^2 + \sum_i m_i y_i^2$$

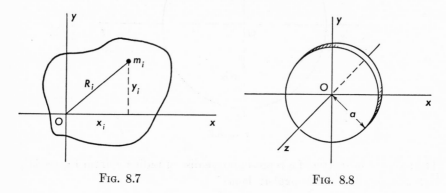

FIG. 8.7   FIG. 8.8

But the sum $\sum_i m_i x_i^2$ is just the moment of inertia I_y about the y axis, because z_i is zero for all particles. Similarly, $\sum_i m_i y_i^2$ is the moment of inertia I_x about the x axis. The above equation can therefore be written

$$I_z = I_x + I_y \tag{8.37}$$

This is the perpendicular-axis theorem. In words: The moment of inertia of any plane lamina about an axis normal to the plane of the lamina is equal to the sum of the moments of inertia about any two mutually perpendicular axes passing through the given axis and lying in the plane of the lamina.

As an example of the use of this theorem, let us consider a thin circular disc in the xy plane (Fig. 8.8). From Eq. (8.33) we have

$$I_z = \frac{1}{2}Ma^2 = I_x + I_y$$

In this case, however, we know from symmetry that $I_x = I_y$. Therefore we must have

$$I_x = I_y = \frac{1}{4}Ma^2 \tag{8.38}$$

for the moment of inertia about any axis in the plane of the disc passing through the center. Equation (8.38) can also be obtained by direct integration.

Parallel-axis theorem. Consider the equation for the moment of inertia about some axis, say the z axis,

$$I = \sum_i m_i(x_i^2 + y_i^2)$$

Now we can express x_i and y_i in terms of the coordinates of the center of mass (x_c, y_c, z_c) and the coordinates *relative* to the center of mass (x_i', y_i', z_i') (Fig. 8.9) as follows:

$$x_i = x_c + x_i'$$
$$y_i = y_c + y_i' \tag{8.39}$$

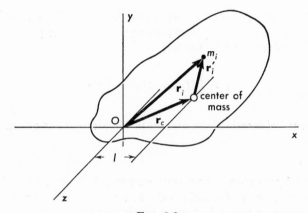

FIG. 8.9

We have, therefore, after substituting and collecting terms,

$$I = \sum_i m_i(x_i'^2 + y_i'^2) + \sum_i m_i(x_c^2 + y_c^2) + 2x_c \sum_i m_i x_i' + 2y_c \sum_i m_i y_i' \tag{8.40}$$

The first sum on the right is just the moment of inertia about an axis parallel to the z axis and passing through the center of mass. We shall call it I_c. The second sum is clearly equal to the mass of the body multiplied by the square of the distance between the center of mass and the z axis. Let us call this distance l. That is, $l^2 = x_c^2 + y_c^2$.

Now, from the definition of the center of mass,

$$\sum_i m_i x_i' = \sum_i m_i y_i' = 0$$

Hence, the last two sums on the right of Eq. (8.40) vanish. The final result may be written

$$I = I_c + Ml^2 \tag{8.41}$$

This is the parallel-axis theorem. It is applicable to any rigid body, solid as well as laminar. The theorem states, in effect, that the moment of inertia of a rigid body about any axis is equal to the moment of inertia about a parallel axis passing through the center of mass plus the product of the mass of the body and the square of the distance between the two axes.

Applying the above theorem to a circular disc, we have, from Eqs. (8.33) and (8.41),

$$I = \frac{1}{2}Ma^2 + Ma^2 = \frac{3}{2}Ma^2 \qquad (8.42)$$

for the moment of inertia of a uniform circular disc about an axis perpendicular to the plane of the disc and passing through the edge. Furthermore, from Eqs. (8.38) and (8.41), we find

$$I = \frac{1}{4}Ma^2 + Ma^2 = \frac{5}{4}Ma^2 \qquad (8.43)$$

for the moment of inertia about an axis in the plane of the disc and tangent to the edge.

Radius of gyration. For some purposes it is convenient to express the moment of inertia of a rigid body in terms of a distance k called the *radius of gyration*, where k is defined by the equation

$$I = Mk^2 \quad \text{or} \quad k = \sqrt{\frac{I}{M}} \qquad (8.44)$$

For example, we find for the radius of gyration of a thin rod about an axis passing through one end [refer to Eq. (8.33)]

$$k = \sqrt{\frac{\frac{1}{3}Ma^2}{M}} = \frac{a}{\sqrt{3}}$$

Moments of inertia for various objects can be tabulated simply by listing the squares of their radii of gyration, as in the table on opposite page.

Table 8-1
Values of k^2 of Various Bodies
(Moment of inertia = mass $\times$ k^2)

Body	Axis	k^2
Thin rod, length a	Normal to rod at its center	$\dfrac{a^2}{12}$
	Normal to rod at one end	$\dfrac{a^2}{3}$
Thin rectangular lamina, sides a and b	Through the center, parallel to side b	$\dfrac{a^2}{12}$
	Through the center, normal to the lamina	$\dfrac{a^2 + b^2}{12}$
Thin circular disc, radius a	Through the center, in the plane of the disc	$\dfrac{a^2}{4}$
	Through the center, normal to the disc	$\dfrac{a^2}{2}$
Thin hoop (or ring) radius a	Through the center, in the plane of the loop	$\dfrac{a^2}{2}$
	Through the center, normal to the plane of the hoop	a^2
Thin cylindrical shell, radius a, length b	Central longitudinal axis	a^2
Uniform solid right circular cylinder, radius a, length b	Central longitudinal axis	$\dfrac{a^2}{2}$
	Through center, perpendicular to longitudinal axis	$\dfrac{a^2}{4} + \dfrac{b^2}{12}$
Thin spherical shell, radius a	Any diameter	$\dfrac{2}{3}a^2$
Uniform solid sphere, radius a	Any diameter	$\dfrac{2}{5}a^2$
Uniform solid rectangular parallelepiped, sides a, b, and c	Through center, normal to face ab, parallel to edge c	$\dfrac{a^2 + b^2}{12}$

8.5.   The Physical Pendulum

A rigid body which is free to swing under its own weight about a fixed horizontal axis of rotation is known as a *physical pendulum* or *compound pendulum*. A physical pendulum is shown in Fig. 8.10, where O represents the location of the axis of rotation, and C is the center of mass. The distance between O and C is l, as shown.

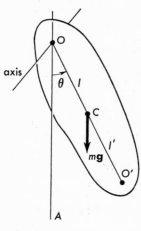

Denoting the angle between the line OC and the vertical line OA by θ, the moment of the force $M\mathbf{g}$ (acting at C) about the axis of rotation is of magnitude

$$Mgl \sin \theta$$

The fundamental equation of motion

$$L = I\dot{\omega}$$

then takes the form

$$-Mgl \sin \theta = I\ddot{\theta}$$

or

FIG. 8.10

$$\ddot{\theta} + \frac{Mgl}{I} \sin \theta = 0 \qquad (8.45)$$

The above equation is identical in form to the equation of motion of a simple pendulum. For small oscillations, as in the case of the simple pendulum, we can replace $\sin \theta$ by θ:

$$\ddot{\theta} + \frac{Mgl}{I} \theta = 0 \qquad (8.46)$$

The solution is

$$\theta = \theta_o \cos (2\pi ft + \epsilon) \qquad (8.47)$$

where θ_o is the amplitude and ϵ is a phase angle. The frequency of oscillation f is given by

$$f = \frac{1}{2\pi} \sqrt{\frac{Mgl}{I}} \qquad (8.48)$$

(To avoid confusion, we shall not use a specific symbol to designate the angular frequency $2\pi f$.)

The period T is therefore given by

$$T = \frac{1}{f} = 2\pi \sqrt{\frac{I}{Mgl}} \tag{8.49}$$

We can also express the period in terms of the radius of gyration k, namely,

$$T = 2\pi \sqrt{\frac{k^2}{gl}} \tag{8.50}$$

Thus the period is the same as that of a simple pendulum of length $\sqrt{k^2/l}$.

As an example, a thin uniform rod of length a swinging as a physical pendulum about one end ($k^2 = a^2/3$) has a period

$$T = 2\pi \sqrt{\frac{2a}{3g}}$$

Center of oscillation. By use of the parallel-axis theorem, we can express the radius of gyration k in terms of the radius of gyration about the center of mass k_c, as follows:

$$I = I_c + Ml^2$$

or

$$Mk^2 = Mk_c^2 + Ml^2$$

Canceling the M's, we get

$$k^2 = k_c^2 + l^2 \tag{8.51}$$

Equation (8.50) can therefore be written as

$$T = 2\pi \sqrt{\frac{k_c^2 + l^2}{gl}} \tag{8.52}$$

Suppose that the axis of rotation of a physical pendulum is shifted to a different position O' at a distance l' from the center of mass C, as shown in Fig. 8.10. The period of oscillation T' about this new axis is given by

$$T' = 2\pi \sqrt{\frac{k_c^2 + l'^2}{gl'}}$$

It follows that the periods of oscillation about O and about O' will be equal, provided

$$\frac{k_c^2 + l^2}{l} = \frac{k_c^2 + l'^2}{l'}$$

The above equation readily reduces to

$$ll' = k_c^2 \tag{8.53}$$

The point O', related to O by the above equation, is called the *center of oscillation* for the point O. It is clear that O is also the center of oscillation for O'. Thus, for a rod of length a swinging about one end, we have $k_c^2 = a^2/12$ and $l = a/2$. Hence, from Eq. (8.53), $l' = a/6$, and so the rod will have the same period when swinging about an axis located a distance $a/6$ from the center as it does for an axis passing through one end.

8.6.   A General Theorem Concerning Angular Momentum

In order to study the more general case of rigid-body motion, that in which the axis of rotation is *not* fixed, we need to develop a fundamental theorem about angular momentum. In Sec. 7.3 we showed that the time rate of change of angular momentum of any system is equal to the applied torque:

$$\dot{\mathbf{J}} = \mathbf{L} \tag{8-54}$$

or, explicitly

$$\frac{d}{dt} \sum_i (\mathbf{r}_i \times m_i \mathbf{v}_i) = \sum_i (\mathbf{r}_i \times \mathbf{F}_i) \tag{8.55}$$

In the above equation all quantities are referred to some inertial coordinate system.

Let us now introduce the center of mass by expressing the position vector of each particle $\mathbf{r}_i$ in terms of the position of the center of mass $\mathbf{r}_c$ and the position vector of particle i relative to the center of mass $\mathbf{r}_i'$ (as in Sec. 7.2), namely,

$$\mathbf{r}_i = \mathbf{r}_c + \mathbf{r}_i'$$

and

$$\mathbf{v}_i = \mathbf{v}_c + \mathbf{v}_i'$$

Equation (8.55) then becomes

$$\frac{d}{dt} \sum_i [(\mathbf{r}_c + \mathbf{r}_i') \times m_i(\mathbf{v}_c + \mathbf{v}_i')] = \sum_i (\mathbf{r}_c + \mathbf{r}_i') \times \mathbf{F}_i \tag{8.56}$$

Upon expanding and using the fact that $\Sigma \, m_i \mathbf{r}_i'$ and $\Sigma \, m_i \mathbf{v}_i'$ both vanish, we find that Eq. (8.56) reduces to

$$\mathbf{r}_c \times \sum_i m_i \mathbf{a}_c + \frac{d}{dt} \sum_i \mathbf{r}_i' \times m_i \mathbf{v}_i' = \mathbf{r}_c \times \sum_i \mathbf{F}_i + \sum_i \mathbf{r}_i' \times \mathbf{F}_i \tag{8.57}$$

where $\mathbf{a}_c = \dot{\mathbf{v}}_c = \ddot{\mathbf{r}}_c$.

In Sec. 7.1 we showed that the translation of the center of mass of any system of particles obeys the equation

$$\sum_i \mathbf{F}_i = \sum_i m_i \mathbf{a}_c = M \mathbf{a}_c \qquad (8.58)$$

Consequently, the first term on the left of Eq. (8.57) cancels the first term on the right. The final result is

$$\frac{d}{dt} \sum_i \mathbf{r}_i' \times m_i \mathbf{v}_i' = \sum_i \mathbf{r}_i' \times \mathbf{F}_i \qquad (8.59)$$

The sum on the left in the above equation is just the angular momentum of the system about the center of mass, and the sum on the right is the total moment of the external forces about the center of mass. Calling these quantities $\mathbf{J}'$ and $\mathbf{L}'$, respectively, we have

$$\dot{\mathbf{J}}' = \mathbf{L}' \qquad (8.60)$$

This important result states that the time rate of change of angular momentum about the center of mass of any system is equal to the total moment of the external forces about the center of mass. This is true even if the center of mass is accelerating. If we choose any point *other* than the center of mass as a reference point for the $\dot{\mathbf{J}} = \mathbf{L}$ relationship, then that point must be at rest in an inertial coordinate system (except for certain special cases which we shall not attempt to discuss). An example of the use of the above theorem is given in Sec. 8.8.

8.7. Laminar Motion of a Rigid Body

If the motion of a body is such that all particles move parallel to some fixed plane, then that motion is called *laminar*. In laminar motion the axis of rotation may change position, but it does not change in direction. (Rotation about a fixed axis is a special case of laminar motion.) The rolling of a cylinder on a plane surface is an example of laminar motion.

If a body undergoes a laminar displacement, that displacement can be specified as follows: Choose some reference point of the body, for example, the center of mass. The reference point undergoes some displacement $\Delta \mathbf{r}$. In addition, the body rotates about the reference point through some angle $\Delta \varphi$. It can be shown that any laminar displacement can be so specified. Consequently, laminar motion can be specified by giving the translational velocity of a convenient reference point together with the angular velocity.

The fundamental equation governing translation of a rigid body is

$$\mathbf{F} = M \ddot{\mathbf{r}}_c = M \dot{\mathbf{v}}_c = M \mathbf{a}_c \qquad (8.61)$$

where **F** represents the sum of all the external forces acting on the body, M is the mass, and $\mathbf{a}_c$ is an acceleration of the center of mass.

Application of Eq. (8.25) to the case of laminar motion of a rigid body yields

$$J' = I_c\omega \tag{8.62}$$

for the magnitude of the angular momentum about an axis C passing through the center of mass where ω is the angular speed of rotation about that axis. The fundamental equation governing the rotation of the body [Eq. (8.60)] then becomes

$$\dot{J}' = I_c\dot{\omega} = L' \tag{8.63}$$

where L' is the total moment of the applied forces about the axis C.

8.8. Body Rolling down an Inclined Plane

As an illustration of laminar motion, we shall study the motion of a round object (cylinder, ball, etc.) rolling down an inclined plane. As shown in Fig. 8.11, there are three forces acting on the body. These are (1) the

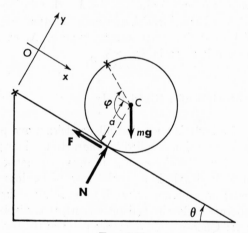

Fig. 8.11

downward force of gravity $M\mathbf{g}$, (2) the normal reaction of the plane **N**, and (3) the frictional force parallel to the plane **F**. Choosing axes as shown, the component equations of the translation of the center of mass are

$$M\ddot{x}_c = Mg \sin \theta - F \tag{8.64}$$

$$M\ddot{y}_c = -Mg \cos \theta + N \tag{8.65}$$

where θ is the inclination of the plane to the horizontal. Since the body remains in contact with the plane, we have

$$y_c = \text{constant}$$

Hence

$$\ddot{y}_c = 0$$

Therefore, from Eq. (8.65),

$$N = Mg \cos \theta \qquad (8.66)$$

The only force which exerts a moment about the center of mass is the frictional force $\mathbf{F}$. The magnitude of this moment is Fa where a is the radius of the body. Hence the rotational equation [Eq. (8.63)] becomes

$$I_c \dot{\omega} = Fa \qquad (8.67)$$

To discuss the problem further, we need to make some assumptions regarding the contact between the plane and the body. We shall solve the equations of motion for two cases.

CASE A. NO SLIPPING. If the contact is perfectly rough so that no slipping can occur, we have the following relations:

$$x_c = a\varphi \qquad [8.68(a)]$$

$$\dot{x}_c = a\dot{\varphi} = a\omega \qquad [8.68(b)]$$

$$\ddot{x}_c = a\ddot{\varphi} = a\dot{\omega} \qquad [8.68(c)]$$

where φ is the angle of rotation. Equation (8.67) can then be written

$$\frac{I_c}{a^2}\ddot{x}_c = F \qquad (8.69)$$

Substituting the above value for F into Eq. (8.64) yields

$$M\ddot{x}_c = Mg \sin \theta - \frac{I_c}{a^2}\ddot{x}_c$$

Solving for $\ddot{x}_c$, we find

$$\ddot{x}_c = \frac{Mg \sin \theta}{M + (I_c/a^2)} = \frac{g \sin \theta}{1 + (k_c^2/a^2)} \qquad (8.70)$$

where k_c is the radius of gyration about the center of mass. The body therefore rolls down the plane with constant linear acceleration and also with constant angular acceleration by virtue of Eq. [8.68(c)].

For example, the acceleration of a uniform cylinder ($k_c^2 = a^2/2$) down the plane is

$$\frac{g \sin \theta}{1 + \frac{1}{2}} = \frac{2}{3}g \sin \theta$$

whereas that of a uniform sphere ($k_c^2 = 2a^2/5$) is

$$\frac{g \sin \theta}{1 + \frac{2}{5}} = \frac{5}{7}g \sin \theta$$

Energy considerations. The above results can also be obtained from energy considerations. In a uniform gravitational field the potential energy V of a rigid body is given by the sum of the potential energies of the individual particles, namely,

$$V = \Sigma \, (m_i g z_i) = M g z_c$$

where z_c is the vertical distance of the center of mass from some (arbitrary) reference plane. Now if the forces, other than gravity, acting on the body do no work, then the motion is conservative, and we can write

$$T + V = T + M g z_c = E = \text{constant}$$

where T is the kinetic energy.

In the case of the body rolling down the inclined plane, the kinetic energy of translation is $\frac{1}{2}M\dot{x}^2$ and that of rotation is $\frac{1}{2}I_c\omega^2$, hence the energy equation reads

$$\frac{1}{2}M\dot{x}^2 + \frac{1}{2}I_c\omega^2 + M g z_c = E$$

But $\omega = \dot{x}/a$ and $z_c = -Mgx \sin \theta$.

Hence

$$\frac{1}{2}M\dot{x}^2 + \frac{1}{2}Mk_c^2\frac{\dot{x}^2}{a^2} - Mgx \sin \theta = E$$

Differentiating with respect to t and collecting terms yields

$$M\dot{x}\ddot{x}\left(1 + \frac{k_c^2}{a^2}\right) - Mg\dot{x} \sin \theta = 0$$

Canceling the common factor $\dot{x}$ (assuming, of course, that $\dot{x} \neq 0$) and solving for $\ddot{x}$, we find the same result as that obtained above using forces and moments [Eq. (8.70)].

CASE B. OCCURRENCE OF SLIPPING. Let us now consider the case in which the contact with the plane is not perfectly rough but has a certain coefficient of sliding friction μ. If slipping occurs, then the magnitude of the frictional force **F** is given by

$$F = F_{\max} = \mu N = \mu M g \cos\theta \tag{8.71}$$

The equation of translation [Eq. (8.64)] then becomes

$$M\ddot{x}_c = Mg \sin\theta - \mu M g \cos\theta \tag{8.72}$$

and the rotational equation, Eq. (8.67), is

$$I_c\dot{\omega} = \mu M g a \cos\theta \tag{8.73}$$

From Eq. (8.72) we see that again the center of mass undergoes constant acceleration:

$$\ddot{x}_c = g(\sin\theta - \mu \cos\theta) \tag{8.74}$$

and, at the same time, the angular acceleration is constant:

$$\dot{\omega} = \frac{\mu M g a \cos\theta}{I_c} = \frac{\mu g a \cos\theta}{k_c^2} \tag{8.75}$$

Let us integrate these two equations with respect to t, assuming that the body starts from rest, that is, at $t = 0$, $\dot{x}_c = 0$, $\dot{\varphi} = 0$. We obtain

$$\dot{x}_c = g(\sin\theta - \mu \cos\theta)t$$

$$\omega = \dot{\varphi} = g(\mu a \cos\theta/k_c^2)t \tag{8.76}$$

Consequently, the linear speed and the angular speed have a constant ratio, and we can write

$$\dot{x}_c = (\text{constant})\, a\omega = \gamma a\omega$$

where

$$\gamma = \frac{\sin\theta - \mu \cos\theta}{\mu a^2 \cos\theta/k_c^2} = \frac{k_c^2}{a^2}\left(\frac{\tan\theta}{\mu} - 1\right) \tag{8.77}$$

Now $\dot{x}_c$ cannot be greater than $a\omega$, so γ cannot be greater than unity. The limiting case, that for which we have pure rolling, is given by $\dot{x}_c = a\omega$, that is,

$$\gamma = 1$$

Solving for μ in Eq. (8.77) with $\gamma = 1$, we find that the critical value of μ is given by

$$\mu = \frac{\tan\theta}{1 + (a/k_c)^2} \tag{8.78}$$

If μ is greater than that given above, then the body rolls without slipping.

For example, if a ball is placed on a 45° plane, it will roll without slipping provided μ is greater than $\tan 45°/(1 + 5/2)$ or 2/7.

8.9. Motion of a Rigid Body under an Impulsive Force

In Sec. 7.6 we introduced the concept of an impulsive force or impulse acting on a particle. We shall now extend the concept to include the laminar motion of an extended rigid body.

First, if the body is constrained to rotate about a fixed axis, then the fundamental equation of motion is

$$L = \dot{J} = I\dot{\omega}$$

Let us assume that the applied torque L is zero except for a very short interval of time $(t_2 - t_1)$. We can integrate with respect to t as follows:

$$\int_{t_1}^{t_2} L\, dt = J_2 - J_1 = I(\omega_2 - \omega_1) \tag{8.79}$$

We shall call the integral $\int L\, dt$ the *impulsive torque*, and we shall use the symbol $\hat{J}$ to designate this quantity. We can then write the above equation as

$$\int L\, dt = \hat{J} = \Delta J = I\, \Delta\omega \tag{8.80}$$

If the impulsive torque is produced by a single force F whose line of action is a distance b from the axis, then

$$L = Fb$$

and so

$$\int L\, dt = b \int F\, dt$$

that is

$$\hat{J} = \hat{P}b \tag{8.81}$$

where $\hat{P} = \int F\, dt$ is the impulse.

Similarly, if we consider the general case of laminar motion under an impulsive force, we have the translational equation

$$\mathbf{F} = M\dot{\mathbf{v}}_c$$

which yields after integragation with respect to t,

$$\hat{\mathbf{P}} = M\, \Delta\mathbf{v}_c \tag{8.82}$$

Likewise, the rotational equation

$$L' = I_c\dot{\omega}$$

gives

$$\hat{J}' = I_c\, \Delta\omega \tag{8.83}$$

where, as shown in Sec. 8.7, the moments are to be taken with respect to the center of mass.

Equations (8.82) and (8.83) state that the effect of an impulsive force (or forces) on a rigid body in laminar motion is (1) to produce a sudden change in the velocity of the center of mass — translational effect, and (2) to produce a sudden change in the angular velocity of the body — rotational effect.

Impulse applied to a rod.   As an illustration of impulsive motion of a rigid body, let us consider a uniform rod of length a and mass M constrained to rotate about one end (Fig. 8.12). Let an impulse $\hat{\mathbf{P}}$ be applied in a direction perpendicular to the rod a distance b from the axis of rotation. If the rod is initially at rest, then, from Eqs. (8.80) and (8.81), the angular speed ω acquired by the rod is given by

$$\omega = \frac{\hat{P}b}{I} = \hat{p}\frac{3b}{Ma^2} \qquad (8.84)$$

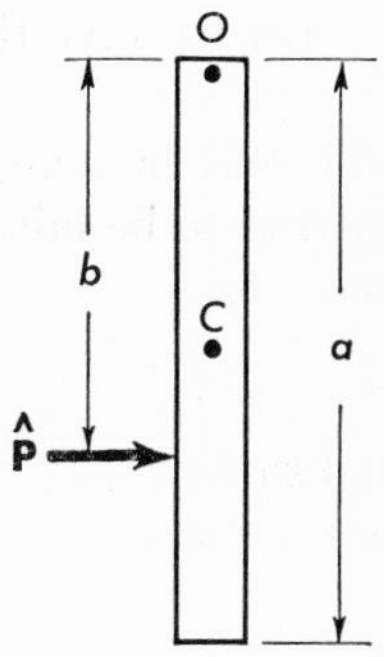

The initial velocity $\mathbf{v}_c$ of the center of mass is in the direction of $\hat{\mathbf{P}}$, and, since the body is constrained to rotate about O, the magnitude of $\mathbf{v}_c$ is given by

$$v_c = \frac{a}{2}\omega = \frac{a}{2}\hat{P}\frac{3b}{Ma^2} = \hat{P}\frac{3b}{2Ma} \qquad (8.85)$$

Fig. 8.12

Now, according to Eq. (8.82), the velocity of the center of mass is $\hat{P}/M$. The apparent disagreement may seem puzzling. The reason that $\mathbf{v}_c$ is not equal to $\hat{\mathbf{P}}/M$ in this case is that there is another impulse which acts on the rod, namely the reaction (impulse) of the axis at O. Let us call this reactive impulse $\hat{\mathbf{P}}_o$. (From the law of action and reaction, the impulse exerted on the axis by the rod is $-\hat{\mathbf{P}}_o$.) The total impulse received by the rod is then the vector sum $\hat{\mathbf{P}} + \hat{\mathbf{P}}_o$, and the velocity of the center of mass is given by

$$M\mathbf{v}_c = \hat{\mathbf{P}} + \hat{\mathbf{P}}_o \qquad (8.86)$$

Upon use of Eq. (8.85), we have

$$\hat{\mathbf{P}}\frac{3b}{2a} = \hat{\mathbf{P}} + \hat{\mathbf{P}}_o$$

Solving for $\hat{\mathbf{P}}_o$, we obtain

$$\hat{\mathbf{P}}_o = \hat{\mathbf{P}}\left(\frac{3b}{2a} - 1\right) \qquad (8.87)$$

Thus the reactive impulse $\hat{\mathbf{P}}_o$ vanishes if

$$\frac{3b}{2a} - 1 = 0$$

that is, if

$$b = \frac{2}{3}a \tag{8.88}$$

That point of application of an impulse for which there is no reaction at the axis is known as the *center of percussion*. The center of percussion of a rod about the end O is then a point $2a/3$ from O. As a matter of fact, this turns out to be the same point as the center of oscillation (Sec. 8.5).

Let us solve the problem now for the case in which the rod, instead of being constrained to rotate about some axis, is free to move in a plane; that is, it may be lying on a smooth horizontal surface. Again we shall consider the rod to be initially motionless. The equation of translation Eq. (8.82), becomes

$$\hat{\mathbf{P}} = M\mathbf{v}_c$$

and so

$$\mathbf{v}_c = \frac{\hat{\mathbf{P}}}{M} \tag{8.89}$$

since there is no impulse other than $\hat{\mathbf{P}}$.

In writing the equation of rotation, Eq. (8.83), we must remember to take moments about the center of mass. Thus

$$\hat{J}' = l\hat{P} \tag{8.90}$$

where l is the distance from the center of mass to the line of action of the impulse $\hat{\mathbf{P}}$. The rotation is then given by

$$l\hat{P} = I_c\omega \tag{8.91}$$

or

$$\omega = \hat{P}\frac{l}{I_c} \tag{8.92}$$

If the impulse is applied a distance b from the end of the rod, as in the previous case, then $l = b - a/2$. Also, the moment of inertia I_c is equal to $Ma^2/12$. The final result is

$$\omega = \hat{P}\frac{6(2b - a)}{Ma^2} \tag{8.93}$$

Collisions. In problems involving collisions of extended rigid bodies, we make use of the fact that the impulsive forces which the bodies exert on one another are equal and opposite, and so the principles of conservation of linear momentum and angular momentum apply. The concepts of impulsive force and impulsive torque are often helpful in collision problems.

Consider, as an example, the impact of a small object of mass m with a uniform rod of length a and mass M. Suppose that the rod is initially at rest on a smooth horizontal plane, as above, and that the point of impact is a distance l from the center (Fig. 8.13). Equations (8.89) and (8.92) give the velocity $\mathbf{v}_c$ of the center of mass and the angular speed ω of the rod after the impact, where $\hat{\mathbf{P}}$ is the impulse delivered to the rod by the impact. We know also that the impulse received by the object from the impact is $-\hat{\mathbf{P}}$. Hence we can write

$$m\, \Delta \mathbf{v} = m(\mathbf{v}_f - \mathbf{v}_o) = -\hat{\mathbf{P}} \qquad (8.94)$$

where $\mathbf{v}_o$ and $\mathbf{v}_f$ are, respectively, the velocities of the object before and after the impact.

We can show that Eqs. (8.89) and (8.94) together yield conservation of linear momentum, for, upon eliminating $\hat{\mathbf{P}}$, we obtain

$$M\mathbf{v}_c + m\mathbf{v}_f = m\mathbf{v}_o \qquad (8.95)$$

or, taking x components for axes as shown,

$$M\dot{x}_c + m\dot{x}_f = m\dot{x}_o \qquad (8.96)$$

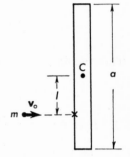

FIG. 8.13

The y components are all zero in the present case. Also, from Eqs. (8.91) and (8.94), we obtain

$$I_c\omega + lm\dot{x}_f = lm\dot{x}_o \qquad (8.97)$$

which states that the angular momentum about C is the same before and after the impact.

If we are given $\dot{x}_o$ and are required to find $\dot{x}_f$, $\dot{x}_c$, and ω, we need another equation, namely, the equation for the coefficient of restitution ϵ (defined in Sec. 7.5):

$$\epsilon \text{ (speed of approach)} = \text{speed of separation}$$

The speed of approach is just $\dot{x}_o$. To find the speed of separation immediately after impact, we need to know the speed of the rod at the point of impact. This is given by the sum of the translational speed of the center of mass of the rod in the forward direction, $\dot{x}_c$, and the rotational speed (relative to the center) at the point of impact, $l\omega$. Hence the speed of separation just after impact is $\dot{x}_c + l\omega - \dot{x}_f$. Therefore we may write

$$\epsilon \dot{x}_o = \dot{x}_c + l\omega - \dot{x}_f \tag{8.98}$$

The values of $\dot{x}_f$, $\dot{x}_c$, and ω are now determined from the three equations, Eqs. (8.96), (8.97), and (8.98). Setting $I_c = Ma^2/12$, we finally obtain

$$\dot{x}_c = \dot{x}_o \left(\frac{\epsilon + 1}{\dfrac{M}{m} + \dfrac{12l^2}{a^2} + 1} \right) \tag{8.99}$$

$$\dot{x}_f = \dot{x}_o - \frac{M}{m} \dot{x}_c = \dot{x}_o \left(1 - \frac{\epsilon + 1}{1 + \dfrac{m}{M} + \dfrac{12\, ml^2}{Ma^2}} \right) \tag{8.100}$$

$$\omega = \frac{\dot{x}_c}{l} \frac{12l^2}{a^2} = \frac{\dot{x}_o}{l} \left(\frac{\epsilon + 1}{1 + \dfrac{a^2}{12l^2} + \dfrac{Ma^2}{12ml^2}} \right) \tag{8.101}$$

The student should verify the above results.

PROBLEMS

1. Find the center of mass of each of the following homogeneous laminae:
    (a) A sector of a circle of radius a, the angle of the sector being θ
    (b) A quadrant of an ellipse whose semiaxes are a and b
    (c) A triangle
    (d) The area bounded by the parabola $y = ax^2$ and the line $y = b$
2. Find the center of mass of each of the following homogeneous solids:
    (a) A right-circular cone of height h
    (b) An octant of an ellipsoid of semiaxes a, b, and c
    (c) One half of a torus of principal radii a and b
    (d) The volume bounded by the parabola of revolution $z = a(x^2 + y^2)$ and the plane $z = b$
3. Find the center of mass of a solid hemispherical body of radius a whose density varies linearly with the distance from the center, the density being zero at the center and ρ_o at the outside.
4. A solid uniform sphere of radius a has a spherical cavity of radius $(1/2)a$ centered at a point $(1/2)a$ from the center of the sphere. Find the center of mass.
5. A solid uniform hemisphere rests in limiting equilibrium against a smooth vertical wall. The contact with the floor is rough, with coefficient of friction μ. Find the angle between the plane face of the hemisphere and the floor.
6. How far up a ladder of length l and weight w can a man of weight W climb before slipping occurs if the ladder rests against a rough vertical wall? The angle between the ladder and the floor is θ. Assume that the coefficient of friction μ is the same between the ladder and wall and between the ladder and floor.

7. Given that a set of forces $F_1, F_2, \ldots$ acting on a rigid body is (a) in translational equilibrium and (b) in rotational equilibrium about some point O. Prove that the set of forces is also in rotational equilibrium about any other point O'.

8. Show that the moments of inertia of a solid uniform rectangular parallelepiped, elliptic cylinder, and ellipsoid are, respectively, $(m/3)(a^2 + b^2)$, $(m/4)(a^2 + b^2)$, and $(m/5)(a^2 + b^2)$, where m is the mass, and $2a$ and $2b$ are the principal diameters of the solid at right angles to the axis of rotation, the axis being through the center in each case.

9. Show that the moment of inertia of a solid uniform octant of a sphere of radius a is $\frac{2}{5}ma^2$ about an axis along one of the straight edges, where m is the mass of the octant. (NOTE: This is the same formula as that for a sphere of mass m.)

10. Find the moment of inertia of a uniform solid right-circular cone of mass m about the axis.

11. Find the moment of inertia of a uniform semicircular lamina about an axis passing through the center of mass and perpendicular to the plane of the lamina.

12. A thin rod AB of length l and mass m has a small object of mass m' fastened at end B. Find the period of oscillation of the rod if it swings as a physical pendulum about end A.

13. A square plate of side a swings as a physical pendulum about one corner. Find the period of oscillation and the center of oscillation if the axis of rotation is (a) normal to the plate, and (b) in the plane of the plate.

14. Show that the period of a physical pendulum is equal to $2\pi(d/2g)^{1/2}$, where d is the distance between the point of suspension O and the center of oscillation O'.

15. A uniform solid ball has a few turns of light string wound around it. If the end of the string is held steady, and the ball is allowed to fall under gravity, what is the acceleration of the center of the ball?

16. Two men are holding the ends of a uniform plank of length l and mass m. Show that if one man suddenly lets go, the load supported by the other man suddenly drops from $mg/2$ to $mg/4$.

17. Two weights of mass m_1 and m_2 are tied to the ends of a light inextensible cord. The cord passes over a pulley of radius a and moment of inertia I. Find the accelerations of the weights, assuming $m_1 > m_2$ and neglecting friction in the axle of the pulley.

18. A uniform right-circular cylinder of radius a is balanced on the top of a perfectly rough fixed cylinder of radius $b(b > a)$, the axes of the two cylinders being parallel. If the balance is slightly disturbed, find the point at which the rolling cylinder leaves the fixed one.

19. A long uniform rod of length l stands vertically on a rough floor. The rod is slightly disturbed and falls to the floor. (a) Find the horizontal and vertical components of the reaction at the floor as functions of the angle θ between the rod and the vertical at any instant. (b) Find also the angle at which the rod begins to slip and in what direction the slipping occurs. Let μ be the coefficient of friction between the rod and the floor.

20. A ball is initially projected, without rotation, at a speed v_o up a rough inclined plane of inclination θ and coefficient of friction μ. Find the position of the ball as a function of time, and determine the position of the ball when pure rolling begins. [Assume that μ is greater than $(2/7) \tan \theta$.]

21.   A uniform circular disc rests on a smooth horizontal surface. If it is struck tangentially at a point on the circumference, about what point does the disc begin to rotate?

22.   A ballistic pendulum is made of a long plank of length l and mass m. It is free to swing about one end O, and is initially at rest in a vertical position. A bullet of mass m' is fired horizontally into the pendulum at a distance l' from O, the bullet coming to rest in the plank. If the resulting amplitude of oscillation of the pendulum is θ_o, find the speed of the bullet.

23.   Two uniform rods AB and BC of equal mass m and equal length l are smoothly joined at B. The system is initially at rest on a smooth horizontal surface, the points A, B, and C lying in a straight line. If an impulse $\hat{\mathbf{P}}$ is applied at A at right angles to the rod, find the initial motion of the system. (HINT: Isolate the rods.)

9

General Motion of a Rigid Body

In the motion of a rigid body constrained either to rotate about a fixed axis or to move parallel to a fixed plane, the direction of the axis of rotation does not change. In the more general cases of rigid-body motion, the direction of the axis of rotation varies. The situation here is considerably more complicated. In fact, even in the case of a body on which no external forces whatever are acting, the motion is not simple.

9.1. Angular Momentum of a Rigid Body. Products of Inertia

Because of the fact that angular momentum is of central importance in the study of the dynamics of rigid bodies, we shall begin with a derivation of the general expression for angular momentum of a rigid body. As defined in Sec. 7.3, the angular momentum $\mathbf{J}$ of any system of particles is the vector sum of the individual angular momenta of all the particles, namely,

$$\mathbf{J} = \sum_i (\mathbf{r}_i \times m\mathbf{v}_i) \qquad (9.1)$$

We shall first calculate the angular momentum of a rigid body which is rotating about a single fixed point. In this case we can imagine a coordinate system fixed in the body with origin O at the fixed point (Fig. 9.1).

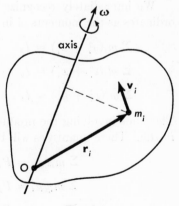

FIG. 9.1

Referring to Sec. 5.4, Eq. (5.25), we see that the velocity $\mathbf{v}_i$ of any constituent particle of the body is given by

$$\mathbf{v}_i = \boldsymbol{\omega} \times \mathbf{r}_i \qquad (9.2)$$

where $\boldsymbol{\omega}$ is the angular velocity of the body, and $\mathbf{r}_i$ is the position vector of the representative particle i. Consequently,

$$\mathbf{J} = \sum_i [m_i \mathbf{r}_i \times (\boldsymbol{\omega} \times \mathbf{r}_i)] \qquad (9.3)$$

Now the x component of the triple cross product

$$\mathbf{r}_i \times (\boldsymbol{\omega} \times \mathbf{r}_i)$$

is given by

$$[\mathbf{r}_i \times (\boldsymbol{\omega} \times \mathbf{r}_i)]_x = \omega_x(y_i^2 + z_i^2) - \omega_y x_i y_i - \omega_z x_i z_i \qquad (9.4)$$

as may easily be shown by expansion of the determinant form of the cross product. (The student should do this as an exercise.)

The x component of the angular momentum is therefore given by

$$
\begin{aligned}
J_x &= \sum m_i[\omega_x(y_i^2 + z_i^2) - \omega_y x_i y_i - \omega_z x_i z_i] \\
&= \omega_x \sum m_i(y_i^2 + z_i^2) - \omega_y \sum m_i x_i y_i - \omega_z \sum m_i x_i z_i \qquad (9.5)
\end{aligned}
$$

Analogous expressions hold for J_y and J_z:

$$J_y = -\omega_x \sum m_i y_i x_i + \omega_y \sum m_i(x_i^2 + z_i^2) - \omega_z \sum m_i y_i z_i \qquad (9.6)$$

$$J_z = -\omega_x \sum m_i z_i x_i - \omega_y \sum m_i z_i y_i + \omega_z \sum m_i(x_i^2 + y_i^2) \qquad (9.7)$$

We immediately recognize the sums involving the squares of the coordinates as the moments of inertia of the body about the coordinate axes:

$$\sum m_i(y_i^2 + z_i^2) = I_x \qquad \text{moment of inertia about the } x \text{ axis}$$

$$\sum m_i(z_i^2 + x_i^2) = I_y \qquad \text{moment of inertia about the } y \text{ axis}$$

$$\sum m_i(x_i^2 + y_i^2) = I_z \qquad \text{moment of inertia about the } z \text{ axis}$$

The sums involving the products of the coordinates are called *products of inertia*. These quantities will be designated as follows:

$$\sum m_i x_i y_i = P_{xy} \qquad xy \text{ product of inertia}$$

$$\sum m_i y_i z_i = P_{yz} \qquad yz \text{ product of inertia}$$

$$\sum m_i z_i x_i = P_{zx} \qquad zx \text{ product of inertia}$$

It is clear that $P_{xy} = P_{yx}$, etc.*

Using the above notation for the moments and products of inertia, we have

$$\mathbf{J} = \mathbf{i}(I_x\omega_x - P_{xy}\omega_y - P_{xz}\omega_z)$$
$$+ \mathbf{j}(-P_{yx}\omega_x + I_y\omega_y - P_{yz}\omega_z)$$
$$+ \mathbf{k}(-P_{zx}\omega_x - P_{zy}\omega_y + I_z\omega_z) \qquad (9.8)$$

It is apparent that the angular momentum $\mathbf{J}$ is not necessarily in the same direction as the instantaneous axis of rotation (the direction of $\boldsymbol{\omega}$). For instance, if the z axis is the axis of rotation, then $\omega_x = \omega_y = 0$ and $\omega_z = \omega$. Then we have, from Eq. (9.8),

$$J_x = -P_{xz}\omega \qquad J_y = -P_{yz}\omega \qquad J_z = I_z\omega$$

Thus $\mathbf{J}$ may have components (J_x and J_y) perpendicular to the axis of rotation. The component J_z in the direction of the axis of rotation, however, is $I_z\omega$, in agreement with Eq. (8.25).

9.2. Principal Axes of a Rigid Body

In order to calculate the moments and products of inertia of an extended rigid body, we replace the summations by integrations over the volume, as we have done previously:

$$I_x = \int (y^2 + z^2)\, dm \quad I_y = \int (z^2 + x^2)\, dm \quad I_z = \int (x^2 + y^2)\, dm \quad (9.9)$$
$$P_{xy} = \int xy\, dm \quad P_{yz} = \int yz\, dm \quad P_{zx} = \int zx\, dm \qquad (9.10)$$

We have already calculated the moments of inertia for a number of simple cases in Sec. 8.4.

Let us now consider the products of inertia. First, in the case of a laminar body, if the xy plane is the plane of the lamina, then $z = 0$ for all particles. Consequently,

$$P_{yz} = P_{zz} = 0 \qquad (9.11)$$

*The set of nine quantities

$$
\begin{matrix}
I_x & -P_{xy} & -P_{xz} \\
-P_{yx} & I_y & -P_{yz} \\
-P_{zx} & -P_{zy} & I_z
\end{matrix}
$$

is required to specify completely the rotational properties of a rigid body about a given point. There are many other cases which arise in physics in which a set of nine quantities is required for the description of some physical property at a point. Such sets are called *tensors*. The above set is known as the *inertia tensor* of the body.

If, in addition, the lamina has an axis of symmetry, say the x axis as shown in Fig. 9.2, then the xy product of inertia $\int xy\, dm$ consists of two parts of equal magnitude and opposite sign. Therefore

$$P_{xy} = 0 \qquad\qquad (9.12)$$

and so *all* three products of inertia vanish. The coordinate axes are said to be *principal axes for the body at the origin* if the products of inertia all vanish.

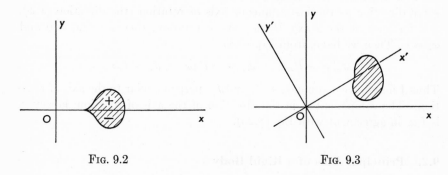

FIG. 9.2   FIG. 9.3

We can see from the definition of the products of inertia that the coordinate axes will be principal axes if the coordinate planes are planes of symmetry. There are also other types of symmetry which give principal axes. A body does not have to be symmetric, however, in order for the products of inertia to vanish.

Consider, for example, a plane lamina of any shape (Fig. 9.3). If the xy plane is the plane of the lamina, then, as we have shown above, the two products P_{yz} and P_{zx} are both zero. Now, relative to a given origin O in the plane of the lamina, we can prove that it is always possible to find a set of axes $Ox'y'$ such that

$$P_{x'y'} = \int x'y'\, dm = 0$$

To show this, we observe that the integral $\int xy\, dm$ changes sign as we rotate the Oxy system through an angle of 90°, because

$$x \rightarrow -y \quad\quad y \rightarrow x$$

Consequently, the integral must vanish for some angle between 0° and 90°. This angle defines the x' axis, and the $Ox'y'z$ axes are therefore principal axes at O, since

$$P_{x'y'} = P_{x'z} = P_{y'z} = 0$$

It can be shown that there *always* exists a set of principal axes for any rigid body at a given point. A general method of finding principal axes will be discussed in Sec. 9.4.

The moments of inertia of a rigid body, taken with respect to three principal axes at a given point, are called the *principal moments of inertia* of the body at that point. If the coordinate axes are principal axes, the expression for angular momentum [Eq. (9.8)] reduces to

$$\mathbf{J} = \mathbf{i}I_x\omega_x + \mathbf{j}I_y\omega_y + \mathbf{k}I_z\omega_z \qquad (9.13)$$

where I_x, I_y, and I_z are the principal moments of inertia.

Now suppose that the axis of rotation is a principal axis, say the z axis. Then $\omega_x = \omega_y = 0$ and $\omega_z = \omega$. Thus

$$\mathbf{J} = \mathbf{k}I_z\omega \qquad (9.14)$$

In this case the angular momentum is parallel to the axis of rotation. We have therefore the following important fact: $\mathbf{J}$ is either in the same direction as the axis of rotation, or is not, depending on whether or not the rotation is about a principal axis.

Dynamic balancing. The above principle finds application in the case of a rotating device such as a flywheel or fan blade. If the device is *statically balanced*, the center of mass lies on the axis of rotation. To be *dynamically balanced* the axis of rotation must also be a principal axis so that, as the body rotates, the angular momentum vector $\mathbf{J}$ will lie along the axis. Otherwise, if the rotational axis is not a principal one, the angular momentum vector varies in direction: it describes a cone as the body rotates. Then, since $\dot{\mathbf{J}}$ is equal to the applied torque, there must be a torque exerted on the body. The direction of this torque is at right angles to the axis (Fig. 9.4). The result is a reaction on the bearings. Thus in the case of a dynamically unbalanced rotator, there may be violent vibration and wobbling, even if the rotator is statically balanced.

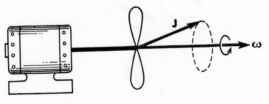

Fɪɢ. 9.4

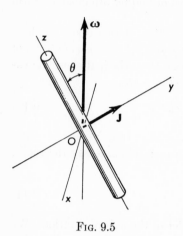

FIG. 9.5

EXAMPLE

A thin rod of length $2a$ and mass M is constrained to rotate with constant angular speed ω about an axis passing through the center making an angle θ with the rod (Fig. 9.5). Let us find the direction of the angular momentum **J**. We shall choose axes fixed on the rod as shown in the figure. These axes are clearly principal axes, and $I_x = I_y = 1/3\,Ma^2$, $I_z = 0$.

The axis of rotation (direction of ω) lies in the yz plane. Hence $\omega_x = 0$, $\omega_y = \omega \sin \theta$, $\omega_z = \omega \cos \theta$. Applying Eq. (9.13), we find

$$\mathbf{J} = \mathbf{j}\,\frac{1}{3}Ma^2\omega \sin \theta \qquad (9.15)$$

Thus **J** is in the y direction, as shown, and rotates (with the body) around ω.

9.3.   Moment of Inertia of a Rigid Body about an Arbitrary Axis

Let us apply the fundamental definition

$$I = \Sigma\, m_i R_i^2 \qquad (9.16)$$

to find the moment of inertia of a rigid body about any axis. In the above formula R_i is the perpendicular distance from the representative particle m_i to the axis OL, as shown in Fig. 9.6.

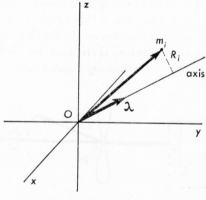

FIG. 9.6

Suppose we designate the direction of the axis OL by the unit vector λ. Then

$$R_i = |\mathbf{r}_i \times \lambda| \tag{9.17}$$

where

$$\mathbf{r}_i = \mathbf{i}x_i + \mathbf{j}y_i + \mathbf{k}z_i \tag{9.18}$$

is the position vector of the particle. We shall let l, m, and n be the direction cosines of the axis; that is

$$\lambda = \mathbf{i}l + \mathbf{j}m + \mathbf{k}n \tag{9.19}$$

Therefore

$$R_i^2 = |\mathbf{r}_i \times \lambda|^2 = (ny_i - mz_i)^2 + (lz_i - nx_i)^2 + (mx_i - ly_i)^2$$
$$= l^2(y_i^2 + z_i^2) + m^2(z_i^2 + x_i^2) + n^2(x_i^2 + y_i^2)$$
$$- 2nmy_iz_i - 2lnz_ix_i - 2mlx_iy_i \tag{9.20}$$

The above result, substituted into Eq. (9.16), yields

$$I = l^2 I_x + m^2 I_y + n^2 I_z - 2nm P_{yz} - 2ln P_{zx} - 2ml P_{xy} \tag{9.21}$$

for the moment of inertia of a rigid body about any line in terms of the direction cosines (l,m,n) of that line and the moments and products of inertia $(I_x, P_{xy},$ etc.$)$ of the body for some arbitrary coordinate system with origin on the line.

If the coordinate axes are principal axes for the body, Eq. (9.21) reduces to the simpler formula

$$I = l^2 I_x + m^2 I_y + n^2 I_z \tag{9.22}$$

EXAMPLE

Let us find the moment of inertia I of a uniform rectangular lamina about a diagonal. If we choose our origin at the center with axes as shown in Fig. 9.7(a), then it is clear from symmetry that the axes are principal axes. If the sides of the rectangle are a and b, as shown, then the principal moments of inertia at the center are

$$I_x = \frac{Mb^2}{12} \qquad I_y = \frac{Ma^2}{12} \qquad I_z = \frac{M(a^2 + b^2)}{12} \tag{9.23}$$

where M is the mass.

The direction cosines of the diagonal are

$$l = a/(a^2 + b^2)^{1/2} \qquad m = b/(a^2 + b^2)^{1/2} \qquad n = 0 \tag{9.24}$$

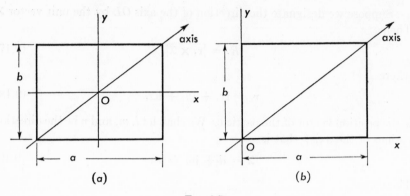

(a)   (b)

FIG. 9.7

These values substituted into Eq. (9.22) yield

$$I = \frac{Mb^2a^2}{12(a^2 + b^2)} + \frac{Ma^2b^2}{12(a^2 + b^2)} = \frac{Ma^2b^2}{6(a^2 + b^2)} \qquad (9.25)$$

Suppose we had chosen axes along two edges, as shown in Fig. 9.7(b). Then, although

$$P_{zx} = P_{zy} = 0$$

the xy product of inertia is not zero, but

$$P_{xy} = \int xy \, dm = \int_0^b \int_0^a \rho xy \, dx \, dy = \rho\frac{a^2b^2}{4} \qquad (9.26)$$

or, since $M = \rho ab$, we have

$$P_{xy} = \frac{Mab}{4} \qquad (9.27)$$

Thus the Oxy axes are not principal axes. We know, however, that

$$I_x = \frac{Mb^2}{3} \qquad I_y = \frac{Ma^2}{3} \qquad I_z = \frac{M(a^2 + b^2)}{3} \qquad (9.28)$$

The direction cosines of the diagonal are again given by Eqs. (9.25). Applying Eq. (9.21), we find

$$I = \frac{a^2}{a^2 + b^2}\frac{Mb^2}{3} + \frac{b^2}{a^2 + b^2}\frac{Ma^2}{3} - \frac{2ab}{a^2 + b^2}\frac{Mab}{4} = \frac{Ma^2b^2}{6(a^2 + b^2)}$$

which agrees with the previous result, Eq. (9.25).

9.4. The Momental Ellipsoid. Existence of Principal Axes

A very useful geometric interpretation of the general expression for the moment of inertia [Eq. (9.21)] may be obtained in the following way. Consider an arbitrary axis of rotation OL, and let us define a point Q on the axis (Fig. 9.8) such that the distance OQ is equal (numerically) to the reciprocal of the square root of the moment of inertia about OL:

$$OQ = \frac{1}{\sqrt{I}} \tag{9.29}$$

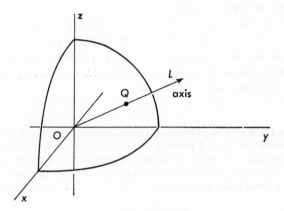

FIG. 9.8

If x, y, and z are the coordinates of the point Q, and l, m, and n are the direction cosines of the line OL, then

$$l = \frac{x}{OQ} = x\sqrt{I}$$

$$m = \frac{y}{OQ} = y\sqrt{I} \tag{9.30}$$

$$n = \frac{z}{OQ} = z\sqrt{I}$$

Equation (9.21) then becomes

$$x^2 I_x + y^2 I_y + z^2 I_z - 2yzP_{yz} - 2zxP_{zx} - 2xyP_{xy} = 1 \tag{9.31}$$

The above equation is the equation of a surface — the locus of points Q as we vary the direction of the axis OL. It is the equation of a general quadric surface in three dimensions. Since I is never zero for any extended body, the surface is bounded and must therefore be an ellipsoid.* It is called the *momental ellipsoid of the body at the point O.*

If the coordinate axes are principal axes, the equation of the momental ellipsoid is

$$x^2 I_x + y^2 I_y + z^2 I_z = 1 \qquad (9.32)$$

Thus, the principal axes of the body coincide with the principal axes of the momental ellipsoid. Since there are always at least three principal axes for every ellipsoid, it follows that there always exist at least three principal axes for a body at a given point.

If two of the three principal moments of inertia are equal, then the ellipsoid of inertia is one of revolution. If all three principal moments are equal at a point O, the momental ellipsoid is a sphere, and it follows that the moment of inertia is the same for any line passing through O, no matter what its direction may be.

★*Determination of the principal axes.* Suppose we are given the moments and products of inertia at a point O of a body in terms of an arbitrarily chosen coordinate system with origin at O, and we wish to find the principal axes at O. In order to solve this problem, we use the fact that the angular momentum $\mathbf{J}$ is parallel to the angular velocity $\boldsymbol{\omega}$ when the body is rotating about a principal axis:

$$\Phi \boldsymbol{\omega} = \mathbf{J}$$

or, in components

$$\Phi \omega_x = J_x = I_x \omega_x - P_{xy} \omega_y - P_{xz} \omega_z$$

$$\Phi \omega_y = J_y = -P_{xy} \omega_x + I_y \omega_y - P_{yz} \omega_z \qquad (9.33)$$

$$\Phi \omega_z = J_z = -P_{xz} \omega_x - P_{yz} \omega_y + I_z \omega_z$$

Here the constant Φ is one of the principal moments of inertia. Rearranging terms, we have

$$(I_x - \Phi) \omega_x - P_{xy} \omega_y - P_{xz} \omega_z = 0$$

$$-P_{xy} \omega_x + (I_y - \Phi) \omega_y - P_{yz} \omega_z = 0 \qquad (9.34)$$

$$-P_{xz} \omega_x - P_{yz} \omega_y + (I_z - \Phi) \omega_z = 0$$

---

*In the case of an infinitely thin straight body, the moment of inertia about the axis of the body is zero. The momental ellipsoid degenerates into a cylinder in this case.

In order that there be a nontrivial solution, the determinant of the coefficients of the ω's must vanish:

$$\begin{vmatrix} I_x - \Phi & -P_{xy} & -P_{xz} \\ -P_{xy} & I_y - \Phi & -P_{yz} \\ -P_{xz} & -P_{yz} & I_z - \Phi \end{vmatrix} = 0 \qquad (9.35)$$

The above equation is a cubic in Φ, namely,

$$-\Phi^3 + A\Phi^2 + B\Phi + C = 0$$

where A, B, and C are determined from the moments and products of inertia. The three roots Φ_1, Φ_2, and Φ_3 are the three principal moments of inertia at O, and the direction of any one principal axis is given by the ratios $\omega_x{:}\omega_y{:}\omega_z$ satisfying Eqs. (9.34) when Φ is placed equal to one of the three values Φ_1, Φ_2, or Φ_3.

★*One principal axis known.*   The above-outlined method allows us, in principle, to find the principal axes of any rigid body. In many cases, however, the body exhibits some symmetry so that at least one principal axis can be found by inspection.

If one principal axis is known, say the z axis, then the directions of the other two principal axes in the xy plane may be determined very simply as follows: Since the z axis is a principal one, we have

$$P_{zx} = P_{zy} = 0$$

The first two of Eqs. (9.34) then reduce to

$$(I_x - \Phi)\omega_x - P_{xy}\omega_y = 0$$
$$-P_{xy}\omega_x + (I_y - \Phi)\omega_y = 0 \qquad (9.37)$$

Now let $\tan\theta = \omega_y/\omega_x$, that is, θ is the angle between the principal axis and the x axis. Equations (9.37) become

$$I_x - \Phi - P_{xy}\tan\theta = 0$$
$$-P_{xy} + (I_y - \Phi)\tan\theta = 0 \qquad (9.38)$$

Upon eliminating Φ and using the identity $\tan 2\theta = 2\tan\theta/(1 - \tan^2\theta)$ we obtain

$$\tan 2\theta = \frac{2P_{xy}}{I_y - I_x} \qquad (9.39)$$

The two values of θ (between 0 and π) which satisfy the above equation give the directions of the two principal axes in the xy plane.

For instance, the directions of the principal axes in the plane of a rectangular lamina, of sides a and b, at a corner [Fig. 9.7(b)] are given by

$$\tan 2\theta = \frac{2(Mab/4)}{(Ma^2/3) - (Mb^2/3)} = \frac{3ab}{2(a^2 - b^2)}$$

9.5.   Rotational Kinetic Energy of a Rigid Body

Let us calculate the kinetic energy of a rigid body which is turning about a fixed point with angular velocity $\boldsymbol{\omega}$. For the velocity $\mathbf{v}_i$ of a representative particle i, we have

$$\mathbf{v}_i = \boldsymbol{\omega} \times \mathbf{r}_i$$

where $\mathbf{r}_i$ is the position vector of the particle relative to the fixed point. The kinetic energy T is therefore given by the equation

$$T = \sum_i \frac{1}{2} m_i \mathbf{v}_i \cdot \mathbf{v}_i = \frac{1}{2} \sum_i [(\boldsymbol{\omega} \times \mathbf{r}_i) \cdot (m_i \mathbf{v}_i)] \qquad (9.40)$$

Now in the triple scalar product we can exchange the dot and the cross. (See Sec. 1.16.) Hence we can write

$$T = \frac{1}{2} \sum_i \boldsymbol{\omega} \cdot (\mathbf{r}_i \times m_i \mathbf{v}_i) = \frac{1}{2} \boldsymbol{\omega} \cdot \left[\sum_i \mathbf{r}_i \times m_i \mathbf{v}_i \right] \qquad (9.41)$$

But $\sum_i \mathbf{r}_i \times m_i \mathbf{v}_i$ is, by definition, the angular momentum $\mathbf{J}$. Thus

$$T = \frac{1}{2} \boldsymbol{\omega} \cdot \mathbf{J} \qquad (9.42)$$

The above equation gives the rotational kinetic energy T of a rigid body in terms of the angular velocity $\boldsymbol{\omega}$ and the angular momentum $\mathbf{J}$. It is analogous to the equation $T = \frac{1}{2} \mathbf{v}_c \cdot \mathbf{p}_c$ giving the translational kinetic energy of a system in terms of the linear momentum $\mathbf{p}_c$ and the velocity $\mathbf{v}_c$ of the center of mass.

Expressing the dot product $\boldsymbol{\omega} \cdot \mathbf{J}$ explicitly in terms of the components of $\boldsymbol{\omega}$ and $\mathbf{J}$, we can write

$$2T = \boldsymbol{\omega} \cdot \mathbf{J} = \omega_x J_x + \omega_y J_y + \omega_z J_z \qquad (9.43)$$

Also, from Eq. (9.8) which gives the components of $\mathbf{J}$, we have

$$2T = I_x \omega_x^2 + I_y \omega_y^2 + I_z \omega_z^2 - 2P_{yz}\omega_y\omega_z - 2P_{zx}\omega_z\omega_x - 2P_{xy}\omega_x\omega_y \qquad (9.44)$$

If we employ principal axes, the terms involving the products of inertia vanish, and we get

$$2T = I_x \omega_x^2 + I_y \omega_y^2 + I_z \omega_z^2 \qquad (9.45)$$

where I_x, I_y, and I_z are principal moments of inertia. It should be pointed out that Eq. (9.44) or (9.45) can be obtained by starting with

$$2T = I\omega^2 \qquad (9.46)$$

and using the general expressions for the moment of inertia I as given by Eq. (9.21) or (9.22) together with the relations

$$\omega_x = l\omega \qquad \omega_y = m\omega \qquad \omega_z = n\omega \qquad (9.47)$$

where l, m, and n are the direction cosines of the axis of rotation. The steps are left as an exercise.

9.6. Euler's Equations

Consider the fundamental equation governing the rotation of a rigid body about a point:

$$\mathbf{L} = \dot{\mathbf{J}} \qquad (9.48)$$

We have seen that $\mathbf{J}$ is most simply expressed if the coordinate axes are principal axes for the body, namely,

$$\mathbf{J} = \mathbf{i}\omega_x I_x + \mathbf{j}\omega_y I_y + \mathbf{k}\omega_z I_z \qquad (9.49)$$

where I_x, I_y, and I_z are the principal moments of inertia of the body at the point of rotation. Now in order that Eq. (9.49) remain valid as the body rotates, our coordinate system must, in general, rotate with the body. Thus the angular velocity of the body and the coordinate system are one and the same, namely ω.* The time rate of change of $\mathbf{J}$ is therefore given by

$$\dot{\mathbf{J}} = [\dot{\mathbf{J}}] + \omega \times \mathbf{J} \qquad (9.50)$$

according to the results of Sec. 5.4, Eq. (5.26).

Written out in components, the equation $\mathbf{L} = \dot{\mathbf{J}}$ then becomes

$$L_x = [\dot{\mathbf{J}}_x] + (\omega \times \mathbf{J})_x = I_x\dot{\omega}_x + \omega_y\omega_z(I_z - I_y) \qquad (9.51)$$

$$L_y = [\dot{\mathbf{J}}_y] + (\omega \times \mathbf{J})_y = I_y\dot{\omega}_y + \omega_z\omega_x(I_x - I_z) \qquad (9.52)$$

$$L_z = [\dot{\mathbf{J}}_z] + (\omega \times \mathbf{J})_z = I_z\dot{\omega}_z + \omega_x\omega_y(I_y - I_x) \qquad (9.53)$$

These are known as *Euler's equations* for the motion of a rigid body.

Body constrained to rotate about a fixed axis. As an application of Euler's equations, consider the special case of a rigid body constrained to rotate about a fixed axis with constant angular velocity: ω = constant.

---

*If two of the principal moments of inertia are equal so that the momental ellipsoid is one of revolution, the coordinate axes need not be fixed in the body to be principal axes. (See Sec. 9.8.)

Euler's equations then reduce to

$$L_x = \omega_y\omega_z(I_z - I_y)$$
$$L_y = \omega_z\omega_x(I_x - I_z) \tag{9.54}$$
$$L_z = \omega_x\omega_y(I_y - I_x)$$

These give the components of the torque exerted on the body by the constraining support.

In particular, if the axis of rotation is a principal axis, then two of the three components of $\boldsymbol{\omega}$ are equal to zero. Consequently, all *three* components of the torque **L** vanish, in agreement with the previous statement concerning dynamic balancing (Sec. 9.2).

9.7. Motion of a Rigid Body under No Torques: Free Rotation

Let us apply Euler's equations to the case of a rigid body that is free to rotate in any direction around a certain point O about which there is no torque exerted on the body. This is the case, for example, when a body is supported on a smooth pivot at its center of mass. Another case in point is that of a body moving freely under no forces or else in a uniform gravitational field (such as a body tossed into the air), the point O being the center of mass.

The equation of motion is then

$$\mathbf{L} = \dot{\mathbf{J}} = \mathbf{O} \tag{9.55}$$

and Euler's equations become

$$I_x\dot{\omega}_x + \omega_y\omega_z(I_z - I_y) = 0$$
$$I_y\dot{\omega}_y + \omega_z\omega_x(I_x - I_z) = 0 \tag{9.56}$$
$$I_z\dot{\omega}_z + \omega_x\omega_y(I_y - I_x) = 0$$

Suppose we multiply the first equation by ω_x, the second by ω_y, and the third by ω_z. If we then add the three equations together, the terms involving the differences $I_z - I_y$, etc., cancel in pairs. The result is

$$I_x\omega_x\dot{\omega}_x + I_y\omega_y\dot{\omega}_y + I_z\omega_z\dot{\omega}_z = 0 \tag{9.57}$$

or

$$\frac{d}{dt}(I_x\omega_x^2 + I_y\omega_y^2 + I_z\omega_z^2) = 2\frac{dT}{dt} = 0 \tag{9.58}$$

Hence, the kinetic energy

$$T = \frac{1}{2}(I_x\omega_x^2 + I_y\omega_y^2 + I_z\omega_z^2) = \text{constant} \qquad (9.59)$$

as we should expect.

Another similar equation can be obtained by multiplying the first of Euler's equations, Eq. (9.56), by $I_x\omega_x$, the second by $I_y\omega_y$, and the third by $I_z\omega_z$. Adding again, we find

$$I_x^2\omega_x\dot{\omega}_x + I_y^2\omega_y\dot{\omega}_y + I_z^2\omega_z\dot{\omega}_z = 0 \qquad (9.60)$$

or

$$\frac{d}{dt}(I_x^2\omega_x^2 + I_y^2\omega_y^2 + I_z^2\omega_z^2) = 0 \qquad (9.61)$$

Now the quantity in parentheses in the above equation is just $\mathbf{J} \cdot \mathbf{J}$ or J^2. Thus we can write

$$J^2 = I_x^2\omega_x^2 + I_y^2\omega_y^2 + I_z^2\omega_z^2 = \text{constant} \qquad (9.62)$$

In words, the magnitude of the angular momentum remains constant for a body rotating freely under no torques, a result we already knew.

Now we know that if there are no torques, then the angular momentum $\mathbf{J}$ is constant in magnitude *and direction* from the point of view of an observer *outside* the body. Also, from the relation $2T = \boldsymbol{\omega} \cdot \mathbf{J}$, we have

$$\boldsymbol{\omega} \cdot \mathbf{J} = \text{constant} \qquad (9.63)$$

Thus the projection of $\boldsymbol{\omega}$ on $\mathbf{J}$ remains constant as the body rotates. This fact is illustrated in Fig. 9.9. The point O represents the fixed point — the

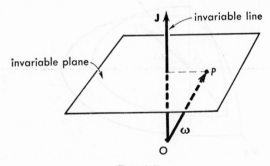

FIG. 9.9

center of mass of the body. The vector $\mathbf{J}$ defines a line OL called the *invariable line*. The extremity P of the angular velocity vector $\boldsymbol{\omega}$ moves in a plane, called the *invariable plane*, which is normal to the invariable line.

We have shown that the components of $\boldsymbol{\omega}$ must satisfy simultaneously the two equations, Eqs. (9.59) and (9.62). To see what this implies, from the point of view of an observer moving with the body, let us, for the moment, set

$$\omega_x = x \qquad \omega_y = y \qquad \omega_z = z$$

$$I_x = A \qquad I_y = B \qquad I_z = C$$

Then Eqs. (9.59) and (9.62) become

$$Ax^2 + By^2 + Cz^2 = \text{constant} \tag{9.64}$$

$$A^2x^2 + B^2y^2 + C^2z^2 = \text{constant} \tag{9.65}$$

These are the equations of two ellipsoids. As the body rotates, the extremity of the angular velocity vector — the point $P(x,y,z)$ in our notation — therefore describes a curve which is the intersection of these two ellipsoids. The principal axes of both ellipsoids coincide with the principal axes of the body. The first ellipsoid [Eq. (9.64)] is known as the *Poinsot ellipsoid*. It is similar to the momental ellipsoid, for its principal diameters are in the ratios $A^{-1/2}: B^{-1/2}: C^{-1/2}$. The second ellipsoid [Eq. (9.65)], which we shall call the J^2 ellipsoid, has principal diameters in the ratios $A^{-1}: B^{-1}: C^{-1}$. The intersecting ellipsoids are illustrated in Fig. 9.10. (It is left as a problem for the student to show that the Poinsot ellipsoid is tangent to the invariable plane at the point P.)

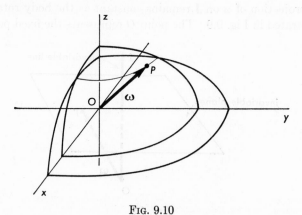

FIG. 9.10

Relative to our coordinate system fixed in the body, the angular velocity vector $\boldsymbol{\omega}$ traces out a cone, called the *body cone*. Also, relative to a coordinate system fixed in space, the angular velocity vector traces out another cone called the *space cone*. Now the instantaneous axis of rotation coincides with ω, hence the actual motion at any instant can be visualized as a rolling of the body cone on the space cone.

★9.8.   Free Rotation of Rigid Body with an Axis of Symmetry

Although the description of free rotation of a rigid body, given in the preceding section, is helpful in visualizing the motion of a rigid body under no torques, the method does not give the actual values of the components of ω as functions of the time. To find these it is necessary to solve Euler's equations [Eqs. (9.56)]. We shall solve Euler's equations for the special case in which the body possesses an axis of symmetry, so that two of the three principal moments of inertia at the center of mass are equal.*

We shall choose the z axis as the symmetry axis. Let us use the following notation:

$$I_s = I_z \text{ (moment of inertia about the symmetry axis)}$$

$$I = I_x = I_y \text{ (moment about axes normal to the symmetry axis)}$$

Euler's equations, Eqs. (9.56), then become

$$I\dot{\omega}_x + \omega_y\omega_z(I_s - I) = 0 \tag{9.66}$$

$$I\dot{\omega}_y + \omega_z\omega_x(I - I_s) = 0 \tag{9.67}$$

$$I_s\dot{\omega}_z = 0 \tag{9.68}$$

From the last equation it follows that

$$J_z = I_s\omega_z = \text{constant} \tag{9.69}$$

and

$$\omega_z = \text{constant} \tag{9.70}$$

If we adopt the abbreviation

$$\gamma = \frac{(I_s - I)\omega_z}{I} \tag{9.71}$$

then Eqs. (9.66) and (9.67) may be written

$$\dot{\omega}_x + \gamma\omega_y = 0 \tag{9.72}$$

$$\dot{\omega}_y - \gamma\omega_x = 0 \tag{9.73}$$

In order to separate the variables in the above pair of differential equations, we differentiate the first equation with respect to t:

$$\ddot{\omega}_x + {}_y\dot{\omega}\gamma = 0$$

*Actually, all that is required is that the momental ellipsoid have an axis of symmetry, not the body itself.

Solving for $\dot{\omega}_y$ and inserting the result into Eq. (9.73), we find

$$\ddot{\omega}_x + \gamma^2 \omega_x = 0 \tag{9.74}$$

The solution is

$$\omega_x = \omega_1 \cos(\gamma t + \epsilon) \tag{9.75}$$

where ω_1 and ϵ are constants of integration. To find ω_y we differentiate Eq. (9.75) with respect to t:

$$\dot{\omega}_x = -\gamma \omega_1 \sin(\gamma t + \epsilon)$$

Upon substituting the above value of $\dot{\omega}_x$ into Eq. (9.72) and solving for ω_y, we obtain

$$\omega_y = \omega_1 \sin(\gamma t + \epsilon) \tag{9.76}$$

It follows from Eqs. (9.75) and (9.76) (upon squaring and adding) that

$$\omega_x^2 + \omega_y^2 = \omega_1^2 = \text{constant} \tag{9.77}$$

Thus the component ω_1 of the angular velocity $\boldsymbol{\omega}$ in the xy plane remains constant.

We can summarize the above results as follows: The angular velocity $\boldsymbol{\omega}$ describes a *conical* motion about the z axis, or, in other words, the axis of rotation precesses about the axis of symmetry. The angular frequency of this precession is the constant γ. Hence the period T_p of the precession is

$$T_p = \frac{2\pi}{\gamma} = \frac{2\pi I}{\omega_z(I_s - I)} \tag{9.78}$$

During this precession, the magnitude of $\boldsymbol{\omega}$ remains constant, since

$$\omega^2 = \omega_x^2 + \omega_y^2 + \omega_z^2 = \omega_1^2 + \omega_z^2 \tag{9.79}$$

and both ω_1 and ω_z are constant.

If we call α the angle between the axis of rotation (the direction of $\boldsymbol{\omega}$) and the z axis (Fig. 9.11), then we have

$$\omega_z = \omega \cos \alpha \tag{9.80}$$

$$\omega_1 = \omega \sin \alpha \tag{9.81}$$

★*Free precession of a disc.* In particular, in the case of a circular disc (or any symmetric laminar body) we have $I_z = I_x + I_y$ so that

$$I_s = 2I \tag{9.82}$$

Consequently,

$$\gamma = \frac{(2I - I)\omega_z}{I} = \omega_z$$

in this case, and so the period of free precession T_p of the disc is given by

$$T_p = \frac{2\pi}{\gamma} = \frac{2\pi}{\omega_z} = \frac{2\pi}{\omega \cos \alpha} \tag{9.83}$$

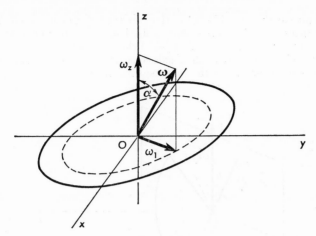

FIG. 9.11

★*Free precession of the earth.* In the case of the earth, it is known that the axis of rotation is very slightly inclined to the axis of symmetry, the angle α being about $0.2''$ (shown exaggerated in Fig. 9.12). The observed period of precession of the earth's axis of rotation about its symmetry axis is about 440 days. It is also known that the ratio $(I_s - I)/I$ is very nearly 0.00327, as determined from the period of the precession of the equinoxes — the gyroscopic precession. Consequently, the value of T_p, calculated from Eq. (9.78), is

$$T_p = \frac{2\pi I}{\omega_z(I_s - I)} = \frac{1 \text{ day}}{0.00327} = 305 \text{ days}$$

The disagreement between this and the observed value of 440 days is due not to an inaccurate knowledge of $(I_s - I)/I$ but rather to the fact that the earth is not perfectly rigid.

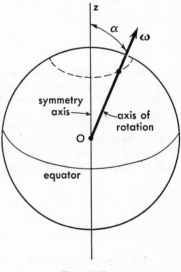

FIG. 9.12

★*Free rotation of a rigid body relative to a fixed reference system.* In the foregoing analysis of the free rotation of a rigid body, the precessional motion of the angular velocity ω is relative to a coordinate system fixed in the body. In order to study the motion relative to an observer outside the body, we shall employ axes as shown in Fig. 9.13. Here the $OXYZ$ system has a fixed orientation in space, and the $Oxyz$ system is fixed in the body and rotates with it. We shall use an auxiliary system $Ox'y'z'$ (which is fixed neither in the body nor in space) defined as follows: The z' axis coincides with the z axis, and the x' axis is the line of intersection of the xy plane with the XY plane.

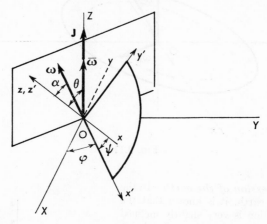

FIG. 9.13

The angle between the X axis and the x' axis is denoted by φ, and the angle between the x axis and the x' axis is called ψ. The angle between the Z axis and the z axis (or z' axis) is denoted by θ. The three angles φ, ψ, and θ are called the *Eulerian angles*.

Now there are no torques acting on the body, hence the angular momentum **J** is constant in magnitude and direction. We shall choose the Z axis as the direction of **J** (the invariable line). From the figure we see that the components of **J** in the $Ox'y'z'$ system are given by

$$J_{x'} = 0$$

$$J_{y'} = J \sin \theta \tag{9.84}$$

$$J_{z'} = J \cos \theta$$

Let us restrict ourselves again to the case of a body with an axis of symmetry (the z axis). In this case the momental ellipsoid is one of revolution, and the moments of inertia I_x, I_y, $I_{x'}$, and $I_{y'}$ are all equal. Thus the $Ox'y'z'$ axes are principle axes at O, as well as the $Oxyz$ axes. We have then, from the first of Eqs. (9.84), that $\omega_{x'} = 0$. Hence ω lies in the $y'z'$ plane. Let α denote the angle between ω and the symmetry axis Oz'. Then

$$\omega_{z'} = \omega \cos \alpha$$

$$\omega_{y'} = \omega \sin \alpha \tag{9.85}$$

and

$$J_{x'} = I_{x'}\omega_{x'} = 0$$

$$J_{y'} = I_{y'}\omega_{y'} = I\omega \sin \alpha \tag{9.86}$$

$$J_{z'} = I_{z'}\omega_{z'} = I_s\omega \cos \alpha$$

It readily follows that

$$\frac{J_{y'}}{J_{z'}} = \tan \theta = \frac{I}{I_s} \tan \alpha \tag{9.87}$$

According to the above result
(1) $\theta < \alpha$ if $I < I_s$ (flattened or pancake-shaped body)
(2) $\theta > \alpha$ if $I > I_s$ (elongated or cigar-shaped body)
Thus the angular momentum vector lies between the symmetry axis and the axis of rotation in the case of a flattened body, whereas, in the case of an elongated body, the axis of rotation lies between the axis of symmetry and the angular momentum vector. The two cases are illustrated in Fig. 9.14.

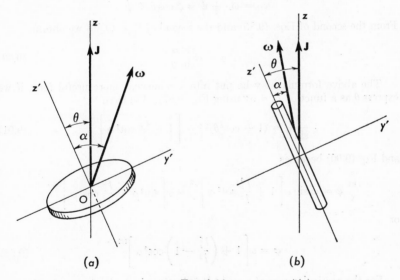

(a)   (b)

Fɪɢ. 9.14

We showed in the preceding section [Eq. (9.69)] that the component J_z of the angular momentum along the symmetry axis is constant. Then, since the magnitude J of the angular momentum is constant, it follows that θ is constant, and, from Eq. (9.87), the angle α is also constant. Thus, as the body rotates, the axis of symmetry (the z' axis) describes a conical motion (precesses) about $\mathbf{J}$. At the same time, since the angular velocity $\boldsymbol{\omega}$ lies in the $y'z'$ plane, the axis of rotation (direction of $\boldsymbol{\omega}$) precesses about $\mathbf{J}$ with the same frequency. Let us now determine the frequency of this precession.

Referring to Fig. 9.13, we see that the angular speed of rotation of the $y'z'$ plane about the Z axis is equal to the time rate of change of the angle φ. Thus $\dot{\varphi}$ is just the (angular) frequency of the precession discussed in the above paragraph. Our problem, then, is to determine the value of $\dot{\varphi}$.

We must now introduce the symbol $\bar{\omega}$ to denote the angular velocity of the $Ox'y'z'$ coordinate system. Refering to Fig. 9.13, we see that $\bar{\omega}$ has the following components:

$$\bar{\omega}_{x'} = \dot{\theta} = 0$$

$$\bar{\omega}_{y'} = \dot{\varphi} \sin\theta \tag{9.88}$$

$$\bar{\omega}_{z'} = \dot{\varphi} \cos\theta$$

Accordingly, the components of ω (the angular velocity of the body or the $Oxyz$ system) in the primed system are as follows:

$$\omega_{x'} = \bar{\omega}_{x'} = 0$$

$$\omega_y' = \bar{\omega}_{y'} = \dot{\varphi} \sin\theta \tag{9.89}$$

$$\omega_{z'} = \bar{\omega}_{z'} + \dot{\psi} = \dot{\varphi} \cos\theta + \dot{\psi}$$

From the second of Eqs. (9.85) and the second of Eqs. (9.89) we obtain

$$\dot{\varphi} = \omega \frac{\sin\alpha}{\sin\theta} \tag{9.90}$$

The above formula may be put into a somewhat more useful form if we express θ as a function of α by using Eq. (9.87). We have

$$\frac{1}{\sin\theta} = (1 + \cot^2\theta)^{1/2} = \left[1 + \frac{I_s^2}{I^2} \cot^2\alpha \right]^{1/2} \tag{9.91}$$

and Eq. (9.90) becomes

$$\dot{\varphi} = \omega \sin\alpha \left[1 + \frac{I_s^2}{I^2} \cot^2\alpha \right]^{1/2} = \omega \left[\sin^2\alpha + \frac{I_s^2}{I^2} \cos^2\alpha \right]^{1/2}$$

or

$$\dot{\varphi} = \omega \left[1 + \left(\frac{I_s^2}{I^2} - 1 \right) \cos^2\alpha \right]^{1/2} \tag{9.92}$$

For the particular case of a symmetric laminar body (such as a circular disc or square plate) we have [Eq. (9.81)] $I_s/I = 2$. Thus the angular frequency of precession of the symmetry axis about $\mathbf{J}$ is

$$\dot{\varphi} = \omega(1 + 3\cos^2\alpha)^{1/2} \tag{9.93}$$

In the case of the earth, the value of $\cos\alpha$ is very nearly unity. Thus Eq. (9.92) becomes

$$\dot{\varphi} = \omega \frac{I_s}{I} = \omega(1.00327)$$

The period of precession of the earth's axis about **J** is then

$$\frac{2\pi}{\dot{\varphi}} = \frac{2\pi}{\omega}\frac{1}{1.00327} \simeq 0.997 \text{ day}$$

This free precession of the earth's axis is superimposed upon a very much longer gyroscopic precession of 26,000 years, the latter resulting from the fact that there is actually a torque exerted on the earth (because of its oblateness) by the sun and the moon. The fact that the gyroscopic precession is so much longer than the free precession justifies the neglect of the external torques in calculating the period of the free precession.

9.9.   Gyroscopic Precession.   Motion of a Top

In this section we shall study the motion of a symmetrical rigid body which is free to turn about a fixed point and on which there is exerted a torque, instead of no torque, as in the case of free precession. The case is exemplified by a simple gyroscope (or top).

The notation for our coordinate axes is shown in Fig. 9.15(a). For clarity, only the Z, y', and z' axes are shown in Fig. 9.15(b), the x' axis being normal to the paper. The origin O is the fixed point about which the body turns.

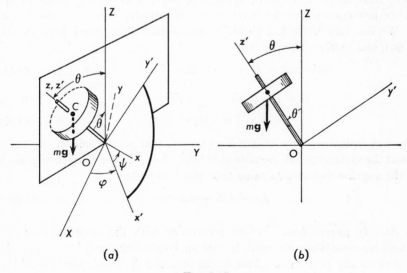

(a)   (b)

FIG. 9.15

The applied moment **L** resulting from the weight mg is of magnitude $mgh \sin \theta$, where h is the distance from O to the center of gravity C. The direction of **L** is along the x' axis, that is

$$L_{x'} = mgh \sin \theta \qquad L_{y'} = 0 \qquad L_{z'} = 0 \tag{9.94}$$

Denoting the angular velocity of the primed coordinate system by $\bar{\omega}$ (as in the previous section), we have the following fundamental equation of motion

$$\mathbf{L} = \dot{\mathbf{J}} = [\dot{\mathbf{J}}] + \bar{\omega} \times \mathbf{J} \tag{9.95}$$

Now the components of $\bar{\omega}$ are

$$\bar{\omega}_{x'} = \dot{\theta}$$
$$\bar{\omega}_{y'} = \dot{\varphi} \sin \theta \tag{9.96}$$
$$\bar{\omega}_{z'} = \dot{\varphi} \cos \theta$$

[These are the same as Eqs. (9.88), except that $\dot{\theta}$ is no longer necessarily constant.] Thus the angular momentum **J** has the following components:

$$J_{x'} = I_{x'}\bar{\omega}_{x'} = I\dot{\theta}$$
$$J_{y'} = I_{y'}\bar{\omega}_{y'} = I\dot{\varphi} \sin \theta \tag{9.97}$$
$$J_{z'} = I_{z'}(\bar{\omega}_{z'} + \dot{\psi}) = I_s(\dot{\varphi} \cos \theta + \dot{\psi}) = I_s S$$

where, again, $I = I_{x'} = I_{y'}$ is the moment of inertia normal to the symmetry axis, and $I_s = I_{z'}$ is the moment of inertia about the symmetry axis. In the last equation we let S (the spin) denote the quantity $\dot{\varphi} \cos \theta + \dot{\psi}$.

We can now write Eq. (9.95) in component form, using Eqs. (9.94), (9.96), and (9.97). The result is

$$mgh \sin \theta = I\ddot{\theta} + I_s S\dot{\varphi} \sin \theta - I\dot{\varphi}^2 \cos \theta \sin \theta \tag{9.98}$$

$$0 = I \frac{d}{dt} (\dot{\varphi} \sin \theta) - I_s S\dot{\theta} + I\dot{\theta} \cos \theta \tag{9.99}$$

$$0 = I_s \dot{S} \tag{9.100}$$

The last equation shows that S is constant, that is, the spin of the body about the symmetry axis remains constant. Also, of course, the component of the angular momentum along that axis is constant:

$$J_{z'} = I_s S = \text{constant} \tag{9.101}$$

Steady precession. Before proceeding with the integration of the remaining equations, we shall discuss an interesting special case, namely that of steady precession. This is the situation in which the axis of the gyroscope or top describes a right-circular cone about the vertical (Z axis).

In this case $\dot\theta = \ddot\theta = 0$, and Eq. (9.98), after canceling the common factor $\sin\theta$, reduces to

$$mgh = I_s S\dot\varphi - I\dot\varphi^2 \cos\theta$$

or, solving for S, we find

$$S = \frac{mgh}{I_s\dot\varphi} + \frac{I}{I_s}\dot\varphi\cos\theta \qquad (9.102)$$

as the condition for steady precession. Here $\dot\varphi$ is the angular frequency of the precession, that is, the angular frequency of the motion of the symmetry or spin axis about the vertical. In particular, if $\dot\varphi$ is very small, then S is large. (This is the usual case for a top or gyroscope.) Then the second term on the right in Eq. (9.102) may be ignored, and we may write approximately

$$S \simeq \frac{mgh}{I_s\dot\varphi} \qquad (9.103)$$

which is the familiar result of elementary gyroscopic theory given in most general physics textbooks.

★**The energy equation.** If we multiply Eq. (9.98) by $\dot\theta$, Eq. (9.99) by $\dot\varphi\sin\theta$, and Eq. (9.100) by $\dot S$, then, after adding the three together, we find

$$mgh\dot\theta\sin\theta = I\dot\theta\ddot\theta + I(\dot\varphi\sin\theta)\frac{d}{dt}(\dot\varphi\sin\theta) + I_s S\dot S \qquad (9.104)$$

We can now integrate with respect to t to get

$$\frac{1}{2}I\dot\theta^2 + \frac{1}{2}I(\dot\varphi\sin\theta)^2 + \frac{1}{2}I_s S^2 + mgh\cos\theta = E = \text{constant} \qquad (9.105)$$

We can identify the first three terms with the kinetic energy and the term $mgh\cos\theta$ with the potential energy, since, from Eqs. (9.97), the above equation may be written

$$\frac{1}{2}I_{x'}\bar\omega_{x'}^2 + \frac{1}{2}I_{y'}\bar\omega_{y'}^2 + \frac{1}{2}I_s S^2 + mgh\cos\theta = E \qquad (9.106)$$

Equation (9.105) [or (9.106)] is called the energy equation of the system.

In order to proceed further with the integration of the energy equation, we must find a way of eliminating $\dot\varphi$. To do this we make use of the fact that the applied moment **L** has no component about the vertical or Z axis. Thus the component of **J** along the Z axis is constant, namely,

$$J_Z = J_{y'}\sin\theta + J_{z'}\cos\theta = \text{constant} = B \qquad (9.107)$$

From the values of $J_{y'}$ and $J_{z'}$ given by Eqs. (9.97), the above equation may be written

$$J_Z = I\dot\varphi\sin^2\theta + I_s S\cos\theta = B \qquad (9.108)$$

Solving for $\dot{\varphi}$, we have

$$\dot{\varphi} = \frac{B - I_s S \cos\theta}{I \sin^2\theta} \tag{9.109}$$

We can now write the energy equation, Eq. (9.105), entirely in terms of θ as follows:

$$\frac{1}{2}I\dot{\theta}^2 + \frac{(B - I_s S \cos\theta)^2}{2I \sin^2\theta} + \frac{1}{2}I_s S^2 + mgh\cos\theta = E \tag{9.110}$$

★*Limits of the θ motion. Nutation.* Equation (9.110) allows us to find θ as a function of t by integration. Let us make the following substitution:

$$u = \cos\theta \tag{9.111}$$

Then $\dot{u} = -\sin\theta \, \dot{\theta} = -(1 - u^2)^{1/2}\dot{\theta}$, and Eq. (9.110) becomes

$$\frac{1}{2}I\frac{\dot{u}^2}{1 - u^2} + \frac{(B - I_s S u)^2}{2I(1 - u^2)} + mghu = E - \frac{1}{2}I_s S^2 \tag{9.112}$$

If we introduce the abbreviations

$$a = \frac{B}{I}$$

$$b = \frac{I_s S}{I}$$

$$c = \frac{2E - I_s S^2}{I} \tag{9.113}$$

$$d = \frac{2mgh}{I}$$

we can write

$$\dot{u}^2 = -(a - bu)^2 + (c - du)(1 - u^2) = f(u) \tag{9.114}$$

from which u (hence θ) can be found as a function of t by integration:

$$\frac{du}{dt} = \sqrt{f(u)} \qquad t = \int \frac{du}{\sqrt{f(u)}} \tag{9.115}$$

Now $f(u)$ is a cubic polynomial, hence the integration can be carried out in terms of elliptic functions.

We need not actually perform the integration, however, to discuss the general properties of the motion. We see that $f(u)$ must be positive in order that t be real. Hence the limits of the motion in θ are determined by the roots of the equation $f(u) = 0$. Since θ must lie between 0 and 90 degrees, then u must take values between 0 and $+1$. A plot of $f(u)$ is shown in Fig. 9.16 for the case in which there are two distinct roots u_1 and u_2 between 0 and $+1$. The corresponding values of θ, namely θ_1, and θ_2 are then the limits of the vertical motion. The axis of the top oscillates back and forth between these two values

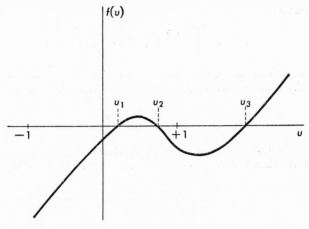

FIG. 9.16

of θ as the top precesses about the vertical (Fig. 9.17). This oscillation is called *nutation*. If we have a double root, that is, if $u_1 = u_2$, then there is no nutation and the top precesses steadily.

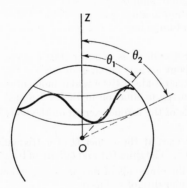

FIG. 9.17

★*Sleeping top.* Anyone who has played with a top knows that, if it is spinning sufficiently fast and started in a vertical position, the axis of the top will remain fixed in the vertical direction, a condition called *sleeping*. In terms of the above analysis, we see that sleeping must correspond to a double root at $u = +1$. In this case, since $\theta = \dot{\theta} = 0$, $E = mgh + 1/2I_sS^2$ [Eq. (9.105)]. Consequently, $c = 2mgh/I = d$ [Eqs. (9.113)]. Also $B = I_sS$ [Eq. (9.108)], so that $a = I_sS/I = b$. The equation

$$f(u) = 0$$

then becomes

$$(1 - u)^2 \left[\frac{2mgh}{I}(1 + u) - \frac{(I_s S)^2}{I^2} \right] = 0 \qquad (9.116)$$

and we do, indeed, have a double root at $u = +1$. Now setting the bracketed term in the above equation equal to zero gives us a third root u_3. We find

$$u_3 = \frac{I_s^2 S^2}{2Imgh} - 1 \qquad (9.117)$$

If the root u_3 does not correspond to a physically possible value of θ, that is, if u_3 is greater than 1, then the vertical sleeping motion will be stable. This gives

$$S^2 > \frac{4Imgh}{I_s^2 S^2} \qquad (9.118)$$

as the criterion for stability of the sleeping top. If the top slows down through friction so that the above condition no longer holds, then it will begin to undergo nutation and will eventually topple over.

PROBLEMS

1. A uniform rectangular lamina of mass m and sides a and b spins about a diagonal with constant angular speed ω. Find the direction and magnitude of the angular momentum about (a) the center, and (b) a corner (on the axis of rotation.)

2. A uniform circular disc of mass m and radius a is constrained to rotate with angular speed ω about an axis making an angle α with the disc's axis. Find the direction and magnitude of the angular momentum.

3. Find the kinetic energy of rotation in Probs. 1 and 2.

4. Find the magnitude of the torque exerted on the body by the supporting axis in Probs. 1 and 2.

5. Find the principle axes at the corner O of a triangular lamina AOB where the angle AOB is $90°$. The sides OA and OB are of length a and b, respectively.

6. Make a sketch of the ellipsoids of inertia of the following:
   (a) A uniform circular disc of radius a
   (b) A solid right-circular cylinder of radius a and length b, where $b = 8a$.
   (c) A solid rectangular parallelepiped of sides a, $2a$, and $3a$

7. In Prob. 6(b), what must be the ratio of radius to length in order that the ellipsoid of inertia at the center is a sphere?

8. A lamina rotates freely under no torques. (a) Show by means of Euler's equations that the component of the angular velocity in the plane of the lamina is constant in magnitude. (b) Under what conditions is the component of the angular velocity normal to the plane of the lamina constant in magnitude also?

9. A rigid body having an axis of symmetry rotates freely about a fixed point under no torques. If α is the angle between the axis of symmetry and the

instantaneous axis of rotation, show that the angle between the axis of rotation and the invariable line (the **J** vector) is

$$\tan^{-1}\left[\frac{(I_s - I)\tan\alpha}{I_s + I\tan^2\alpha}\right]$$

where I_s (the moment of inertia about the symmetry axis) is greater than I (the moment of inertia about an axis normal to the symmetry axis). Show that this angle cannot exceed $\tan^{-1}(8^{-1/2})$.

10. A rigid body rotates freely about its center of mass. There are no torques. Show by means of Euler's equations that, if all three principal moments of inertia are different, then the body will rotate stably about either the axis of greatest moment of inertia or the axis of least moment of inertia, but that rotation about the axis of intermediate moment of inertia is unstable. (This can be demonstrated by tossing a book into the air. Put an elastic band around the book.)

11. A circular disc is rotating freely under no torques. If α is the angle between the angular velocity ω and the axis of symmetry, what is the time in which the axis of symmetry describes a cone about the invariable line?

12. A space platform in the form of a thin circular disc of radius a and mass m is rotating with angular speed ω about its symmetry axis. A meteorite strikes the platform at the edge, inparting an impulse $\hat{\mathbf{P}}$ to the platform. The direction of $\hat{\mathbf{P}}$ is parallel to the axis of the platform. Find the resulting motion of the platform.

13. A rigid body having an axis of symmetry rotates with angular velocity ω in three-dimensional motion about its center of mass. There is a frictional torque $-c\omega$ exerted on the body, such as might be produced by air drag. (a) Show that the component of ω in the direction of the symmetry axis decreases exponentially with time. (b) Show also that the angle between the angular velocity ω and the symmetry axis steadily decreases if the moment of inertia about the symmetry axis is the largest principal moment.

14. A simple gyroscope consists of a heavy disc of mass 100g and radius 5 cm mounted at the center of a light rod of length 10 cm. It is set spinning rapidly and is observed to precess once in 5 sec. Find the approximate spin in revolutions per second.

15. Prove the statement made at the end of Sec. 9.7, namely, that the Poinsot ellipsoid is tangent to the invariable plane at the point P.

10

Lagrange's Equations

Instead of the direct application of Newton's laws to the motion of simple systems, we shall now consider a general, more sophisticated approach — a very elegant and useful method for finding the equations of motion for all dynamical systems, invented by the French mathematician Joseph Louis Lagrange.

10.1. Generalized Coordinates

We have seen that the position of a particle in space can be specified by three coordinates. These may be Cartesian, spherical, cylindrical, or, in fact, any three suitably chosen parameters. If the particle is constrained to move in a plane or on a fixed surface, only two coordinates are needed to specify the particle's position, whereas if the particle moves on a straight line or on a fixed curve, then one coordinate is sufficient.

In the case of a system of N particles we need, in general, $3N$ coordinates to specify completely the simultaneous positions of all the particles — the *configuration* of the system. If there are constraints imposed on the system, however, the number of coordinates actually needed to specify the configuration is less than $3N$. For instance, if the system is a rigid body, we need give only the position of some convenient reference point of the body (for example, the center of mass) and the orientation of the body in space in order to specify the configuration. In this case only six coordinates are needed — three for the reference point and three more (say the Eulerian angles) for the orientation.

In general, a certain minimum number n of coordinates is required to specify the configuration of a given system. We shall designate these coordinates by the symbols

$$q_1, q_2, \cdots q_n$$

called *generalized coordinates.* A given coordinate q_k may be either an angle or a distance. If, in addition to specifying the configuration of the system, each coordinate can vary independently of the others, the system is said to be *holonomic.* The number of coordinates n in this case is also the number of *degrees of freedom* of the system. We shall consider only holonomic systems.

> In a nonholonomic system the coordinates cannot all vary independently; that is, the number of degrees of freedom is less than the minimum number of coordinates needed to specify the configuration. (An example of a nonholonomic system is a sphere constrained to roll on a perfectly rough plane. Five coordinates are required to specify the configuration — two for the position of the center of the sphere and three for its orientation. But the coordinates cannot all vary independently, for, if the sphere rolls, at least two coordinates must change.)

If the system is a single particle, the Cartesian coordinates are expressible as functions of the generalized coordinates:

$x = x(q_1, q_2)$
   (two degrees of freedom — motion in a plane)
$y = y(q_1, q_2)$

$x = x(q_1, q_2, q_3)$

$y = y(q_1, q_2, q_3)$ (three degrees of freedom)

$z = z(q_1, q_2, q_3)$

Suppose that the q's change from initial values $(q_1, q_2, \cdots)$ to the neighboring values $(q_1 + \delta q_1, q_2 + \delta q_2, \cdots)$. The corresponding changes in the Cartesian coordinates are given by

$$\delta x = \frac{\partial x}{\partial q_1} \delta q_1 + \frac{\partial x}{\partial q_2} \delta q_2 + \cdots$$

$$\delta y = \frac{\partial y}{\partial q_1} \delta q_1 + \frac{\partial y}{\partial q_2} \delta q_2 + \cdots$$

(10.1)

etc. The partial derivatives $\partial x / \partial q_1$, etc., are functions of the q's. As a specific example, consider the motion of a particle in a plane. Let us choose polar coordinates

$$q_1 = r \qquad q_2 = \theta$$

Then

$$x = x(r, \theta) = r \cos \theta$$

$$y = y(r, \theta) = r \sin \theta$$

and

$$\delta x = \frac{\partial x}{\partial r} \delta r + \frac{\partial x}{\partial \theta} \delta\theta = \cos\theta \, \delta r - r \sin\theta \, \delta\theta$$

$$\delta y = \frac{\partial y}{\partial r} \delta r + \frac{\partial y}{\partial \theta} \delta\theta = \sin\theta \, \delta r + r \cos\theta \, \delta\theta$$

giving the changes in x and y that correspond to small changes in r and θ.

Consider now a system consisting of a large number of particles. Let the system have n degrees of freedom and generalized coordinates

$$q_1, q_2, \ldots q_n$$

Then, in a change from the configuration $(q_1, q_2, \ldots q_n)$, to the neighboring configuration $(q_1 + \delta q_1, \ldots q_n + \delta q_n)$, a representative particle i moves from the point (x_i, y_i, z_i) to the neighboring point $(x_i + \delta x_i, y_i + \delta y_i, z_i + \delta z_i)$ where

$$\delta x_i = \sum_{k=1}^{n} \frac{\partial x_i}{\partial q_k} \delta q_k$$

$$\delta y_i = \sum_{k=1}^{n} \frac{\partial y_i}{\partial q_k} \delta q_k \qquad (10.2)$$

$$\delta z_i = \sum_{k=1}^{n} \frac{\partial z_i}{\partial q_k} \delta q_k$$

The partial derivatives are again functions of the q's.

10.2   Generalized Forces

If a particle undergoes a displacement $\delta\mathbf{r}$ under the action of a force $\mathbf{F}$, then we know that the work δW done by the force is given by

$$\delta W = \mathbf{F} \cdot \delta\mathbf{r} = X \, \delta x + Y \, \delta y + Z \, \delta z \qquad (10.3)$$

where X, Y, and Z are the rectangular components of $\mathbf{F}$. If we express the increments δx, δy, and δy in terms of the generalized coordinates q_k, we see, from Eqs. (10.2) and (10.3), that

$$\delta W = \sum_{k=1}^{n} \left(X \frac{\partial x}{\partial q_k} + Y \frac{\partial y}{\partial q_k} + Z \frac{\partial z}{\partial q_k} \right) \delta q_k = \sum_{k=1}^{n} Q_k \, \delta q_k \qquad (10.4)$$

where

$$Q_k = X \frac{\partial x}{\partial q_k} + Y \frac{\partial y}{\partial q_k} + Z \frac{\partial z}{\partial q_k} \qquad (10.5)$$

The quantity Q_k defined by the above equation is called the *generalized force* associated with the coordinate q_k. Since the product $Q_k \, \delta q_k$ has the dimensions of work, then Q_k has the dimensions of force if q_k is a distance, and the dimensions of torque if q_k is an angle.

For a system of N particles we have for the total work δW done by all the forces $\mathbf{F}_i (i = 1,2,\ldots N)$ in a displacement of the system

$$\delta W = \sum_{i=1}^{N} \mathbf{F}_i \cdot \delta \mathbf{r}_i = \sum_{i=1}^{N} (X_i \, \delta x_i + Y_i \, \delta y_i + Z_i \, \delta z_i) \qquad (10.6)$$

Again let us express the increments δx_i, etc., in terms of the generalized coordinates [Eqs. (10.2)]. We find

$$\delta W = \sum_{i=1}^{N} \left[\sum_{k=1}^{n} \left(X_i \frac{\partial x_i}{\partial q_k} + Y_i \frac{\partial y_i}{\partial q_k} + Z_i \frac{\partial z_i}{\partial q_k} \right) \delta q_k \right] \qquad (10.7)$$

Upon reversing the order of summation we can write

$$\delta W = \sum_{k=1}^{n} \left[\sum_{i=1}^{N} \left(X_i \frac{\partial x_i}{\partial q_k} + Y_i \frac{\partial y_i}{\partial q_k} + Z_i \frac{\partial z_i}{\partial q_k} \right) \right] \delta q_k = \sum_{k=1}^{n} Q_k \, \delta q_k \qquad (10.8)$$

where

$$Q_k = \sum_{i=1}^{N} \left(X_i \frac{\partial x_i}{\partial q_k} + Y_i \frac{\partial y_i}{\partial q_k} + Z_i \frac{\partial z_i}{\partial q_k} \right) \qquad (10.9)$$

is the generalized force associated with the coordinate q_k.

It is usually unnecessary, and even impractical, to use Eq. (10.9) to calculate the actual value of Q_k; rather, each generalized force Q_k can be found directly from the fact that $Q_k \, \delta q_k$ is the work done on the system by the external forces when the coordinate q_k changes by the amount δq_k (the other generalized coordinates remaining constant). For example, if the system is a rigid body, the work done by the external forces when the body turns through an angle $\delta\theta$ about a given axis is $L_\theta \, \delta\theta$, where L_θ is the magnitude of the total moment of all the forces about the axis. In this case L_θ is the generalized force associated with the coordinate θ.

Generalized Forces for Conservative Systems. We have seen (Sec. 4.5) that the rectangular components of the force acting on a particle in a conservative field of force are given by

$$X = -\frac{\partial V}{\partial x} \qquad Y = -\frac{\partial V}{\partial y} \qquad Z = -\frac{\partial V}{\partial z}$$

where $V(x,y,z)$ is the potential energy. The generalized force Q_k [Eq. (10.5)] can then be expressed as

$$Q_k = -\left(\frac{\partial V}{\partial x}\frac{\partial x}{\partial q_k} + \frac{\partial V}{\partial y}\frac{\partial y}{\partial q_k} + \frac{\partial V}{\partial z}\frac{\partial z}{\partial q_k}\right) \tag{10.10}$$

Now the expression in parentheses is just the partial derivative of the function V with respect to q_k. Hence

$$Q_k = -\frac{\partial V}{\partial q_k} \tag{10.11}$$

For example, if we use polar coordinates $q_1 = r$, $q_2 = \theta$, then the generalized forces are $Q_r = -\partial V/\partial r$; $Q_\theta = -\partial V/\partial \theta$. If V is a function of r alone (central force), then $Q_\theta = 0$.

For a conservative system of N particles, we can write Eq. (10.9) in the form

$$Q_k = -\sum_{i=1}^{N}\left(\frac{\partial V}{\partial x_i}\frac{\partial x_i}{\partial q_k} + \frac{\partial V}{\partial y_i}\frac{\partial y_i}{\partial q_k} + \frac{\partial V}{\partial z_i}\frac{\partial z_i}{\partial q_k}\right) = -\frac{\partial V}{\partial q_k} \tag{10.12}$$

10.3. Lagrange's Equations for a Particle

In order to find the differential equations of motion of a single particle in terms of the generalized coordinates q_k, we could start with the equation

$$\mathbf{F} = m\mathbf{a}$$

and try to write its components directly in terms of the q's. It turns out, however, to be simpler to use a different approach. We shall first calculate the kinetic energy T in terms of Cartesian coordinates and shall then express it as a function of the generalized coordinates and their time derivatives. We have

$$T = \frac{1}{2}m(\dot{x}^2 + \dot{y}^2 + \dot{z}^2)$$

Since

$$x = x(q_1, q_2, \ldots q_n) = x(q)$$

we have

$$\dot{x} = \sum_{k=1}^{n}\frac{\partial x}{\partial q_k}\frac{\partial q_k}{\partial t} = \sum_{k=1}^{n}\frac{\partial x}{\partial q_k}\dot{q}_k = \dot{x}(q,\dot{q}) \tag{10.13}$$

with similar equations for $\dot{y}$ and $\dot{z}$. (Remember that n is the number of generalized coordinates used — either 1, 2, or 3 for a single particle, depending on the type of constraints.) The kinetic energy is therefore expressible as a quadratic function of the $\dot{q}$'s:

$$T = \frac{1}{2}m[\dot{x}^2(q,\dot{q}) + \dot{y}^2(q,\dot{q}) + \dot{z}^2(q,\dot{q})] \qquad (10.14)$$

Thus

$$\frac{\partial T}{\partial \dot{q}_k} = m\left(\dot{x}\, \frac{\partial \dot{x}}{\partial \dot{q}_k} + \dot{y}\, \frac{\partial \dot{y}}{\partial \dot{q}_k} + \dot{z}\, \frac{\partial \dot{z}}{\partial \dot{q}_k} \right) \qquad (10.15)$$

Now, from Eq. (10.13) we see that $\partial x/\partial q_k$ is the coefficient of $\dot{q}_k$ in the expansion of $\dot{x}$. Accordingly,

$$\frac{\partial \dot{x}}{\partial \dot{q}_k} = \frac{\partial x}{\partial q_k} \qquad (10.16)$$

and therefore

$$\frac{\partial T}{\partial \dot{q}_k} = m\left(\dot{x}\, \frac{\partial x}{\partial q_k} + \dot{y}\, \frac{\partial y}{\partial q_k} + \dot{z}\, \frac{\partial z}{\partial q_k} \right) \qquad (10.17)$$

Differentiating with respect to the time t, we find

$$\frac{d}{dt}\frac{\partial T}{\partial \dot{q}_k} = m\ddot{x}\, \frac{\partial x}{\partial q_k} + m\ddot{y}\, \frac{\partial y}{\partial q_k} + m\ddot{z}\, \frac{\partial z}{\partial q_k} + m\dot{x}\, \frac{d}{dt}\frac{\partial x}{\partial q_k} + m\dot{y}\, \frac{d}{dt}\frac{\partial y}{\partial q_k} + m\dot{z}\, \frac{d}{dt}\frac{\partial z}{\partial q_k}$$
$$(10.18)$$

Now, to digress, for any function $f(q_1, q_2, \ldots q_n)$, we have

$$\frac{d}{dt}f(q_1, q_2, \ldots q_n) = \frac{\partial f}{\partial q_1}\dot{q}_1 + \frac{\partial f}{\partial q_2}\dot{q}_2 + \cdots \qquad (10.19)$$

Hence, letting $f = \partial x/\partial q_k$, we find

$$\frac{d}{dt}\frac{\partial x}{\partial q_k} = \frac{\partial^2 x}{\partial q_1\, \partial q_k}\dot{q}_1 + \frac{\partial^2 x}{\partial q_2\, \partial q_k}\dot{q}_2 + \cdots + \frac{\partial^2 x}{\partial q_n\, \partial q_k} \qquad (10.20)$$

But

$$\dot{x} = \frac{\partial x}{\partial q_1}\dot{q}_1 + \frac{\partial x}{\partial q_2}\dot{q}_2 + \cdots + \frac{\partial x}{\partial q_n}\dot{q}_n \qquad (10.21)$$

Therefore

$$\frac{d}{dt}\frac{\partial x}{\partial q_k} = \frac{\partial \dot{x}}{\partial q_k} \qquad (10.22)$$

with similar equations for y and for z.

The above result means that the operators d/dt and $\partial/\partial q_k$ can be interchanged. Thus

$$m\dot{x}\frac{d}{dt}\frac{\partial x}{\partial q_k} = m\dot{x}\frac{\partial \dot{x}}{\partial q_k} = \frac{\partial}{\partial q_k}\left(\frac{m}{2}\dot{x}^2\right) \tag{10.23}$$

We can now write Eq. (10.18) in the following way:

$$\frac{d}{dt}\frac{\partial T}{\partial \dot{q}_k} = X\frac{\partial x}{\partial q_k} + Y\frac{\partial y}{\partial q_k} + Z\frac{\partial z}{\partial q_k} + \frac{\partial}{\partial q_k}\left[\frac{m}{2}(\dot{x}^2 + \dot{y}^2 + \dot{z}^2)\right] \tag{10.24}$$

or, from the definition of the generalized force Q_k [Eq. (10.5)],

$$\frac{d}{dt}\frac{\partial T}{\partial \dot{q}_k} = Q_k + \frac{\partial T}{\partial q_k} \tag{10.25}$$

These are the differential equations of motion in the generalized coordinates. They are known as *Lagrange's equations of motion for a particle.*

In case the motion is conservative so that the Q's are given by Eq. (10.11), then Lagrange's equations can be written

$$\frac{d}{dt}\frac{\partial T}{\partial \dot{q}_k} = \frac{\partial T}{\partial q_k} - \frac{\partial V}{\partial q_k} \tag{10.26}$$

The equations can be written even more compactly by defining a function L, known as the *Lagrangian function*, such that

$$L = T - V \tag{10.27}$$

where it is understood that T and V are expressed in terms of the generalized coordinates. Thus, since $V = V(q)$ and $\partial V/\partial \dot{q} = 0$, we have

$$\frac{\partial L}{\partial \dot{q}_k} = \frac{\partial T}{\partial \dot{q}_k} \quad \text{and} \quad \frac{\partial L}{\partial q_k} = \frac{\partial T}{\partial q_k} - \frac{\partial V}{\partial q_k}$$

Equation (10.26) can then be written

$$\frac{d}{dt}\frac{\partial L}{\partial \dot{q}_k} = \frac{\partial L}{\partial q_k} \tag{10.28}$$

Thus the differential equations of motion for a particle in any conservative field are readily obtained if we know the Lagrangian function in terms of an appropriate set of coordinates.

EXAMPLE

Let us find Lagrange's equations of motion for a particle moving in a plane under a central force. We shall choose polar coordinates $q_1 = r$, $q_2 = \theta$. Then

$$T = \frac{1}{2}mv^2 = \frac{1}{2}m(\dot{r}^2 + r^2\dot{\theta}^2)$$

$$V = V(r)$$

$$L = \frac{1}{2}m(\dot{r}^2 + r^2\dot{\theta}^2) - V(r)$$

The relevant partial derivatives are as follows:

$$\frac{\partial L}{\partial \dot{r}} = m\dot{r} \qquad \frac{\partial L}{\partial r} = mr\dot{\theta}^2 - \frac{\partial V}{\partial r} = mr\dot{\theta}^2 + F_r$$

$$\frac{\partial L}{\partial \dot{\theta}} = 0 \qquad \frac{\partial L}{\partial \theta} = mr^2\dot{\theta}$$

The equations of motion Eq. (10.28), are therefore

$$m\ddot{r} = mr\dot{\theta}^2 + F_r \qquad \frac{d}{dt}(mr^2\dot{\theta}) = 0$$

These are identical to the equations found in Sec. 6.6 for the motion of a particle in a central field.

10.4. Lagrange's Equations for a General System

Before we begin with the derivation of Lagrange's equations for a general system, we are going to introduce a new notation: we shall let the symbol x_i represent any Cartesian coordinate. For example, the kinetic energy T of a system of N particles, which we have previously expressed as

$$T = \sum_{i=1}^{N} \left[\frac{1}{2}m_i(\dot{x}_i^2 + \dot{y}_i^2 + \dot{z}_i^2) \right]$$

will now be written simply

$$T = \sum_{i=1}^{3N} \frac{1}{2}m_i\dot{x}_i^2 \tag{10.29}$$

The Cartesian coordinates x_i are functions of the generalized coordinates q_k. For generality, we shall also include the possibility that the functional relationship between x_i and q_k may also involve the time t explicitly. This would be the case if there were moving constraints, for example, a particle constrained to move on a surface which itself is moving in some prescribed manner. We can write

$$x_i = x_i(q_1, q_2, \ldots, q_n, t) = x_i(q, t)$$

Thus

$$\dot{x}_i = \sum_k \frac{\partial x_i}{\partial q_k} \dot{q}_k + \frac{\partial x_i}{\partial t} \tag{10.30}$$

In the above equation and in all that follows, unless stated to the contrary, we shall assume that the range of i is $1, 2, \ldots 3N$, where N is the number of particles in the system, and the range of k is $1, 2, \ldots n$, where n is the number of generalized coordinates (degrees of freedom) of the system.

By virtue of Eqs. (10.30) we can regard T as a function of the generalized coordinates, their time derivatives, and possibly the time:

$$T = T(q, \dot{q}, t)$$

We have then

$$\frac{\partial T}{\partial \dot{q}_k} = \sum_i \frac{\partial}{\partial \dot{q}_k} \left(\frac{1}{2} m_i \dot{x}_i^2 \right) = \sum_i \left(m_i \dot{x}_i \frac{\partial \dot{x}_i}{\partial \dot{q}_k} \right) \tag{10.31}$$

But, from Eq. (10.30),

$$\frac{\partial \dot{x}_i}{\partial \dot{q}_k} = \frac{\partial x_i}{\partial q_k} \tag{10.32}$$

Therefore

$$\frac{\partial T}{\partial \dot{q}_k} = \sum_i m_i \dot{x}_i \frac{\partial x_i}{\partial q_k} \tag{10.33}$$

Differentiating with respect to t, we have

$$\frac{d}{dt} \frac{\partial T}{\partial \dot{q}_k} = \sum_i m_i \ddot{x}_i \frac{\partial x_i}{\partial q_k} + \sum_i m_i \dot{x}_i \frac{d}{dt} \frac{\partial x_i}{\partial q_k} \tag{10.34}$$

Now the generalized force Q_k, from Eq. (10.9), is expressed in our new notation as

$$Q_k = \sum_i X_i \frac{\partial x_i}{\partial q_k} \tag{10.35}$$

Also, in the same way that we established Eq. (10.23), it is easy to show that

$$\sum_i m_i \dot{x}_i \frac{d}{dt} \frac{\partial x_i}{\partial q_k} = \sum_i \frac{\partial}{\partial q_k} \left(\frac{1}{2} m_i \dot{x}_i^2 \right) = \frac{\partial T}{\partial q_k} \tag{10.36}$$

We can therefore write Eq. (10.34) in the form

$$\frac{d}{dt}\frac{\partial T}{\partial \dot{q}_k} = Q_k + \frac{\partial T}{\partial q_k} \qquad (k = 1,2,\ldots n) \quad (10.37)$$

These are Lagrange's equations for a system. They are identical in form to those for a single particle. The number of equations is equal to the number of degrees of freedom n of the system.

If the system is conservative so that

$$Q_k = -\frac{\partial V}{\partial q_k}$$

then we can again define a Lagrangian function $L = T - V$, and the equations of motion can be written

$$\frac{d}{dt}\frac{\partial L}{\partial \dot{q}_k} = \frac{\partial L}{\partial q_k} \qquad (k = 1,2,\ldots n) \quad (10.38)$$

If part of the generalized forces are not conservative, say Q'_k, and part are derivable from a potential function V, we can write

$$Q_k = Q'_k - \frac{\partial V}{\partial q_k} \qquad (10.39)$$

We can then also define a Lagrangian function $L = T - V$, and write the differential equations of motion in the form

$$\frac{d}{dt}\frac{\partial L}{\partial \dot{q}_k} = Q'_k + \frac{\partial L}{\partial q_k} \qquad (k = 1,2,\ldots n) \quad (10.40)$$

The above form is a convenient one to use, for example, when frictional forces are present. (The above equation is, of course, also applicable to the motion of a single particle.)

10.5.   Some Applications of Lagrange's Equations

In this section we shall illustrate the remarkable versatility of Lagrange's equations by applying them to a number of specific cases. The general procedure for finding the differential equations of motion for a system is as follows:

(1) Select a suitable set of coordinates to represent the configuration of the system.

(2) Obtain the kinetic energy T as a function of these coordinates and their time derivatives.

(3) If the system is conservative, find the potential energy V as a function of the coordinates, or, if the system is not conservative, find the generalized forces Q_k.

(4) The differential equations of motion are then given by Eq. (10.37) or Eq. (10.38).

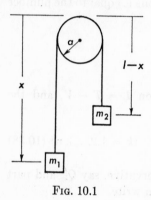

FIG. 10.1

Atwood's machine. A mechanical system known as Atwood's machine consists of two weights of mass m_1 and m_2, respectively, connected by a light inextensible cord of length l which passes over a pulley (Fig. 10.1). The system has one degree of freedom. We shall let the variable x represent the configuration of the system, where x is the vertical distance from the pulley to m_1, as shown. The angular speed of the pulley is clearly $\dot{x}/a$, where a is the radius. The kinetic energy of the system is therefore given by

$$T = \frac{1}{2}m_1\dot{x}^2 + \frac{1}{2}m_2\dot{x}^2 + \frac{1}{2}I\frac{\dot{x}^2}{a^2}$$

where I is the moment of inertia of the pulley, and the potential energy is given by

$$V = -m_1gx - m_2g(l - x)$$

Assuming that there is no friction, we have

$$L = \frac{1}{2}\left(m_1 + m_2 + \frac{I}{a^2}\right)\dot{x}^2 + g(m_1 - m_2)x + m_2gl \qquad (10.41)$$

and Lagrange's equation

$$\frac{d}{dt}\frac{\partial L}{\partial \dot{x}} = \frac{\partial L}{\partial x}$$

then reads

$$\left(m_1 + m_2 + \frac{I}{a^2}\right)\ddot{x} = g(m_1 - m_2)$$

or

$$\ddot{x} = g\frac{m_1 - m_2}{m_1 + m_2 + I/a^2} \qquad (10.42)$$

We see that if $m_1 > m_2$, then m_1 descends with constant acceleration, whereas if $m_1 < m_2$, then m_1 ascends with constant acceleration. The inertial effect of the pulley shows up in the term I/a^2 in the denominator.

The double Atwood machine. Consider the system shown in Fig. 10.2. Here we have replaced one of the weights in the simple Atwood

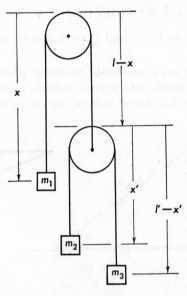

FIG. 10.2

machine by another pulley supporting two weights connected by another cord. The system now has two degrees of freedom. We shall specify its configuration by the two coordinates x and x', as shown. For simplicity, let us neglect the masses of the pulleys in this case. We have

$$T = \frac{1}{2}m_1\dot{x}^2 + \frac{1}{2}m_2(-\dot{x} + \dot{x}')^2 + \frac{1}{2}m_3(-\dot{x} - \dot{x}')^2$$

$$V = -m_1gx - m_2g(l - x + x') - m_3g(l - x + l' - x')$$

where m_1, m_2, and m_3 are the three masses, and l and l' are the lengths of the two connecting cords. Then

$$L = \frac{1}{2}m_1x_1^2 + \frac{1}{2}m_2(-\dot{x} + \dot{x}')^2 + \frac{1}{2}m_3(\dot{x} + \dot{x}')^2$$
$$+ g(m_1 - m_2 - m_3)x + g(m_2 - m_3)x' + \text{constant} \quad (10.43)$$

The equations of motion

$$\frac{d}{dt}\frac{\partial L}{\partial \dot{x}} = \frac{\partial L}{\partial x} \qquad \frac{d}{dt}\frac{\partial L}{\partial \dot{x}'} = \frac{\partial L}{\partial x'}$$

read

$$m_1\ddot{x} + m_2(\ddot{x} - \ddot{x}') + m_3(\ddot{x} + \ddot{x}') = g(m_1 - m_2 - m_3)$$
$$m_2(-\ddot{x} + \ddot{x}') + m_3(\ddot{x} + \ddot{x}') = g(m_2 - m_3) \tag{10.44}$$

from which the accelerations $\ddot{x}$ and $\ddot{x}'$ are found by simple algebra.

Particle sliding on a movable inclined plane. Let us consider the case of a particle sliding on a smooth inclined plane which, itself, is free to slide on a smooth horizontal surface, as shown in Fig. 10.3. In this

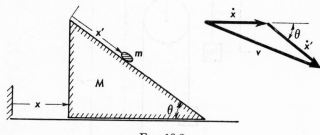

FIG. 10.3

problem there are two degrees of freedom, so we need two coordinates to specify the configuration. We shall choose the coordinates x and x', the horizontal displacement of the plane from some reference point and the displacement of the particle from some reference point on the plane, respectively, as shown.

From a study of the velocity diagram, shown to the right of the figure, we see that the square of the speed of the particle is given by the law of cosines

$$v^2 = \dot{x}^2 + \dot{x}'^2 + 2\dot{x}\dot{x}' \cos \theta$$

Hence the kinetic energy T of the system is given by

$$T = \frac{1}{2}mv^2 + \frac{1}{2}M\dot{x}^2 = \frac{1}{2}m(\dot{x}^2 + \dot{x}'^2 + 2\dot{x}\dot{x}' \cos \theta) + \frac{1}{2}M\dot{x}^2$$

where M is the mass of the inclined plane, θ is the wedge angle as shown, and m is the mass of the particle. The potential energy of the system does not involve x, since the plane is on a horizontal surface. Hence we can write

$$V = -mgx' \sin \theta + \text{constant}$$

and

$$L = \frac{1}{2}m(\dot{x}^2 + \dot{x}'^2 + 2\dot{x}\dot{x}' \cos \theta) + \frac{1}{2}M\dot{x}^2 + mgx' \sin \theta + \text{constant}$$

$$(10.45)$$

The equations of motion

$$\frac{d}{dt}\frac{\partial L}{\partial \dot{x}} = \frac{\partial L}{\partial x} \qquad \frac{d}{dt}\frac{\partial L}{\partial \dot{x}'} = \frac{\partial L}{\partial x'}$$

then become

$$m(\ddot{x} + 2\ddot{x}' \cos \theta) + M\ddot{x} = 0 \qquad m(\ddot{x}' + 2\ddot{x} \cos \theta) = mg \sin \theta$$

$$(10.46)$$

Solving for $\ddot{x}$ and $\ddot{x}'$ we find

$$\ddot{x} = \frac{-g \sin \theta \cos \theta}{\dfrac{m + M}{m} - \cos \theta} \qquad \ddot{x}' = \frac{g \sin \theta}{1 - \dfrac{m \cos \theta}{m + M}} \qquad (10.47)$$

The above result can be obtained by analyzing the forces and reactions involved, but that method is much more tedious than the above method of using Lagrange's equations.

Derivation of Euler's equations for the free rotation of a rigid body. Lagrange's method can be used to derive Euler's equations for the motion of a rigid body. In this section we shall consider the case of a rigid body rotating under no torques.

We have seen that the kinetic energy of a rigid body is given by

$$T = \frac{1}{2}(I_x\omega_x^2 + I_y\omega_y^2 + I_z\omega_z^2)$$

where the ω's are referred to principal axes of the body. Let us refer to Fig. 9.13 which shows the Eulerian angles φ, ψ, and θ. From a study of the figure we see that the relations between the ω's and the Eulerian angles and their time derivatives are as follows:

$$\omega_x = \dot{\theta} \cos \psi + \dot{\varphi} \sin \theta \sin \psi$$

$$\omega_y = -\dot{\theta} \sin \psi + \dot{\varphi} \sin \theta \cos \psi \qquad (10.48)$$

$$\omega_z = \dot{\psi} + \dot{\varphi} \cos \theta$$

Regarding the Eulerian angles as the generalized coordinates, the equations of motion are

$$\frac{d}{dt}\frac{\partial T}{\partial \dot\theta} = \frac{\partial T}{\partial \theta}$$

$$\frac{d}{dt}\frac{\partial T}{\partial \dot\varphi} = \frac{\partial T}{\partial \varphi}$$

$$\frac{d}{dt}\frac{\partial T}{\partial \dot\psi} = \frac{\partial T}{\partial \psi}$$

because the Q's (the generalized forces) are all zero. Now, by the chain rule,

$$\frac{\partial T}{\partial \dot\psi} = I_z\omega_z\frac{\partial \omega_z}{\partial \dot\psi} = I_z\omega_z \qquad \text{so} \qquad \frac{d}{dt}\frac{\partial T}{\partial \dot\psi} = I_z\dot\omega_z \qquad (10.49)$$

Similarly

$$\frac{\partial T}{\partial \psi} = I_x\omega_x\frac{\partial \omega_x}{\partial \psi} + I_y\omega_y\frac{\partial \omega_y}{\partial \psi}$$

$$= I_x\omega_x(-\dot\theta \sin \psi + \dot\varphi \sin \theta \cos \psi) + I_y\omega_y(-\dot\theta \cos \psi - \dot\varphi \sin \theta \sin \psi)$$

$$= I_x\omega_x\omega_y - I_y\omega_y\omega_x \qquad (10.50)$$

From Eqs. (10.49) and (10.50), the ψ equation becomes

$$I_z\dot\omega_z + \omega_x\omega_y(I_y - I_x) = 0$$

which, as we have previously shown (Sec. 9.7), is one of Euler's equations for the motion of a rigid body under no torques. The other two equations can be obtained in a similar way.

10.6. Generalized Momenta. Ignorable Coordinates

Consider the motion of a single particle moving in a straight line (rectilinear motion). The kinetic energy is

$$T = \frac{1}{2}m\dot x^2$$

where m is the mass of the particle, and x is its positional coordinate. Now, rather than define the momentum p of the particle as the product $m\dot x$, we could define p as the quantity $\partial T/\partial \dot x$, namely,

$$p = \frac{\partial T}{\partial \dot x} = m\dot x$$

In the case of a system described by generalized coordinates $q_1, q_2, \ldots q_k, \ldots q_n$, the quantities p_k defined by

$$p_k = \frac{\partial L}{\partial \dot{q}_k} \qquad (k = 1, 2, \ldots n) \ (10.51)$$

are called the *generalized momenta*.* Lagrange's equations for a conservative system can then be written

$$\dot{p}_k = \frac{\partial L}{\partial q_k} \qquad (k = 1, 2, \ldots n) \ (10.52)$$

Suppose, in particular, that one of the coordinates, say q_λ, is not explicitly contained in L. Then

$$\dot{p}_\lambda = \frac{\partial L}{\partial q} = 0 \qquad (10.53)$$

and

$$p_\lambda = \text{constant} = c_\lambda \qquad (10.54)$$

The coordinate q_λ is said to be *ignorable* in this case. The generalized momentum associated with an ignorable coordinate is therefore a constant of the motion of the system.

For example, in the problem of the particle sliding on the smooth inclined plane (treated in the previous section), we found that the coordinate x, the position of the plane, was not contained in the Lagrangian function L [Eq. (10.45)]. Thus x is an ignorable coordinate in this case, and

$$p_x = \frac{\partial L}{\partial \dot{x}} = (M + m)\dot{x} + m\dot{x}' \cos \theta = \text{constant}$$

We can see, as a matter of fact, that p_x is the total horizontal component of the linear momentum of the system, and, since there is no external horizontal force acting on the system, the horizontal component of the linear momentum must be constant.

Another example of an ignorable coordinate is found in the case of the motion of a particle in a central field. In polar coordinates

$$L = \frac{1}{2}m(\dot{r}^2 + r^2\dot{\theta}^2) - V(r)$$

*If the potential-energy function V does not explicitly involve the $\dot{q}$'s, then $p_k = \partial L/\partial \dot{q}_k = \partial T/\partial \dot{q}_k$.

as shown in the example in Sec. 10.3. In this case θ is an ignorable coordinate, and

$$p_\theta = \frac{\partial L}{\partial \theta} = mr^2\dot{\theta} = \text{constant}$$

Here p_θ is just the magnitude J of the angular momentum.

★10.7. Lagrange's Equations for Impulsive Forces

Suppose we have a dynamic system, described by generalized coordinates q_k, in which all the acting generalized forces Q_k are zero except for a short interval of time τ. We can integrate Lagrange's equations as follows:

$$\frac{d}{dt}\frac{\partial T}{\partial \dot{q}_k} = \frac{\partial T}{\partial q_k} + Q_k$$

$$\int_0^\tau d\left(\frac{\partial T}{\partial \dot{q}_k}\right) = \int_0^\tau \frac{\partial T}{\partial q_k}\,dt + \int_0^\tau Q_k\,dt \tag{10.55}$$

Now if Q_k tends to infinity in such way that

$$\lim_{\tau \to 0} \int_0^\tau Q_k\,dt = \hat{Q}_k \tag{10.56}$$

exists and is finite, then the integral $\displaystyle\int_0^\tau (\partial T/\partial q_k)\,dt$ tends to zero, because the quantity $\partial T/\partial q_k$ remains finite. We can therefore write

$$\Delta\left(\frac{\partial T}{\partial \dot{q}_k}\right) = \hat{Q}_k \qquad (k = 1,2,\cdots n) \tag{10.57}$$

for the changes in the quantities $\partial T/\partial \dot{q}_k$ following the application of a generalized impulse force* (or forces) $\hat{Q}_k$ to the system. For systems in which the potential function V does not involve the $\dot{q}$'s explicitly, so that $\partial T/\partial \dot{q}_k = \partial L/\partial \dot{q}_k = p_k$, we can write Eq. (10.57) as

$$\Delta p_k = \hat{Q}_k \qquad (k = 1,2,\cdots n) \tag{10.58}$$

where p_k is the generalized momentum associated with the generalized coordinate q_k.

The generalized impulsive forces $\hat{Q}_k$ are most easily found by calculating the *impulsive work* $\delta\hat{W}^*$ which is given by

$$\delta\hat{W} = \hat{\mathbf{P}}_a\cdot\delta\mathbf{s}_a + \cdots = \hat{Q}_1\,\delta q_1 + \hat{Q}_2\delta q_2 + \cdots = \sum_k \hat{Q}_k\,\delta q_k \tag{10.59}$$

---

*Notice that the generalized impulsive forces $\hat{Q}_k$, defined by Eq. (10.56), are not actually forces, but are time-integrals of forces. They are dimensionally equal to products of generalized force and time.

where $\hat{\mathbf{P}}_a \cdots$ are the applied impulses, and $\delta \mathbf{s}_a \cdots$ are arbitrary small displacements through which the applied impulsive forces act (subject to the constraints of the system).

EXAMPLE

Two rods AB and BC, each of length $2a$ and mass m, are smoothly joined at B and lie at rest on a smooth horizontal table, the points A, B, and C being colinear. Find the motion immediately after an impulse $\hat{\mathbf{P}}$ is applied at point A, as shown in Fig. 10.4.

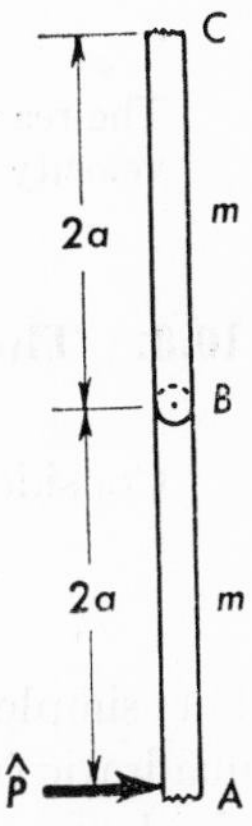

Let us choose generalized coordinates x, y, θ_1, and θ_2 where x and y are the positional coordinates of the joint B, and θ_1 and θ_2 are the respective angles which the two rods make with the initial line ABC. The kinetic energy T, for the initial values $\theta_1 = \theta_2 = 0$, is given by

$$T = \frac{1}{2}m(\dot{x} + a\dot{\theta})^2 + \frac{1}{2}I_c\dot{\theta}_1^2 + \frac{1}{2}m(\dot{x} + a\dot{\theta}_2)^2 + \frac{1}{2}I_c\dot{\theta}_2^2 + m\dot{y}^2$$

where I_c is the moment of inertia of either rod about its center of mass. Now the impulsive work is equal to $\hat{P}\,\delta s$ where

$$\delta s = \delta x + 2a\,\delta\theta_1$$

Thus

$$\delta\hat{W} = \hat{P}\,\delta s = \hat{P}\,(\delta x + 2a\,\delta\theta_1)$$

But for a general displacement of the system we have

$$\delta\hat{W} = \hat{Q}_x\,\delta x + \hat{Q}_y\,\delta y + \hat{Q}_{\theta_1}\,\delta\theta_1 + \hat{Q}_{\theta_2}\,\delta\theta_2$$

Therefore, in our case,

$$\hat{Q}_x = \hat{P} \qquad \hat{Q}_y = 0 \qquad \hat{Q}_{\theta_1} = 2a\hat{P} \qquad \hat{Q}_{\theta_2} = 0$$

The initial motion of the system is then given by Eqs. (10.57):

$$\Delta\left(\frac{\partial T}{\partial \dot{x}}\right) = \hat{Q}_x \; : m(\dot{x} + a\dot{\theta}_1) + m(\dot{x} + a\dot{\theta}_2) = \hat{P}$$

$$\Delta\left(\frac{\partial T}{\partial \dot{\theta}_1}\right) = \hat{Q}_{\theta_1} \; : ma(\dot{x} + a\dot{\theta}_1) + I_c\dot{\theta}_1 = 2a\hat{P}$$

$$\Delta\left(\frac{\partial T}{\partial \dot{\theta}_2}\right) = \hat{Q}_{\theta_2} \; : ma(\dot{x} + a\dot{\theta}_2) + I_c\dot{\theta}_2 = 0$$

$$\Delta\left(\frac{\partial T}{\partial \dot{y}}\right) = \hat{Q}_y \; : m\dot{y} = 0$$

FIG. 10.4

Putting $I_c = \frac{1}{2}ma^2$ and solving for the velocities, we finally obtain

$$\dot{x} = -\frac{\hat{P}}{m} \qquad \dot{y} = 0$$

$$\dot{\theta}_1 = \frac{9}{4}\frac{\hat{P}}{am} \qquad \dot{\theta}_2 = \frac{3}{4}\frac{\hat{P}}{am}$$

The reader should verify that the above result gives $\mathbf{v}_c = \hat{\mathbf{P}}/m$, where $\mathbf{v}_c$ is the velocity of the center of mass of the system.

10.8. The Hamiltonian Function. Hamilton's Equations

Consider the following function of the generalized coordinates:

$$H = \sum_k \dot{q}_k p_k - L \tag{10.60}$$

For simple dynamic systems the kinetic energy T is a homogeneous quadratic function of the $\dot{q}$'s, and the potential energy V is a function of the q's alone, so that

$$L = T(q,\dot{q}) - V(q)$$

Now, from Euler's theorem for homogeneous functions,* we have

$$\sum_k \dot{q}_k p_k = \sum_k \dot{q}_k \frac{\partial L}{\partial \dot{q}_k} = \sum_k \dot{q}_k \frac{\partial T}{\partial \dot{q}_k} = 2T \tag{10.61}$$

Therefore

$$H = \sum_k \dot{q}_k p_k - L = 2T - (T - V) = T + V \tag{10.62}$$

That is, the function H is equal to the total energy for the type of systems we are considering.

Suppose we regard the n equations

$$p_k = \frac{\partial L}{\partial \dot{q}_k} \qquad\qquad (k = 1,2,\ldots n)$$

as solved for the $\dot{q}$'s in terms of the p's and the q's:

$$\dot{q}_k = \dot{q}_k(p,q)$$

*Euler's theorem states that for a homogeneous function f of degree n in the variables $x_1, x_2, \cdots x_r$

$$x_1 \frac{\partial f}{\partial x_1} + x_2 \frac{\partial f}{\partial x_2} \cdots + x_r \frac{\partial f}{\partial x_r} = nf$$

With these equations we can then express H as a function of the p's and the q's:

$$H(p,q) = \sum_k p_k \dot{q}_k(p,q) - L \qquad (10.63)$$

Let us calculate the variation of the function H corresponding to a variation δp_k, δq_k. We have

$$\delta H = \sum_k \left[p_k\, \delta \dot{q}_k + \dot{q}_k\, \delta p_k - \frac{\partial L}{\partial \dot{q}_k} \delta \dot{q}_k - \frac{\partial L}{\partial q_k} \delta q_k \right] \qquad (10.64)$$

The first and third terms in the brackets cancel, because $p_k = \partial L/\partial \dot{q}_k$ by definition. Also, since Lagrange's equations can be written as $\dot{p}_k = \partial L/\partial q_k$, Eq. (10.64) becomes

$$\delta H = \sum_k [\dot{q}_k\, \delta p_k - \dot{p}_k\, \delta q_k] \qquad (10.65)$$

Now the variation of H must be given by the equation

$$\delta H = \sum_k \left[\frac{\partial H}{\partial p_k} \delta p_k + \frac{\partial H}{\partial q_k} \delta q_k \right]$$

It follows that

$$\frac{\partial H}{\partial p_k} = \dot{q}_k \qquad \frac{\partial H}{\partial q_k} = -\dot{p}_k \quad (k = 1,2, \ldots n) \quad (10.66)$$

These are known as *Hamilton's canonical equations of motion*. They consist of $2n$ first-order differential equations, whereas Lagrange's equations consist of n second-order equations. We have derived Hamilton's equations for simple conservative systems. It can be shown that Eqs. (10.66) also hold for more general systems, for example, nonconservative systems, systems in which the potential-energy function involves the $\dot{q}$'s, and for systems in which L involves the time explicitly, but in these cases the total energy is no longer necessarily equal to H.

Hamilton's equations will be encountered by the student when he studies quantum mechanics (the fundamental theory of atomic phenomena). Hamilton's equations also find application in celestial mechanics.

EXAMPLE

Let us obtain Hamilton's equations of motion for a one-dimensional harmonic oscillator. We have

$$T = \frac{1}{2}m\dot{x}^2 \qquad V = \frac{1}{2}kx^2$$

$$p = \frac{\partial T}{\partial \dot{x}} = m\dot{x} \qquad \dot{x} = \frac{p}{m}$$

Hence

$$H = T + V = \frac{1}{2m}p^2 + \frac{k}{2}x^2$$

The equations of motion

$$\frac{\partial H}{\partial p} = \dot{x} \qquad \frac{\partial H}{\partial x} = -\dot{p}$$

then read

$$\frac{p}{m} = \dot{x} \qquad kx = -\dot{p}$$

The first equation merely amounts to a restatement of the momentum-velocity relationship in this case. Using the first equation, the second can be written

$$kx = -\frac{d}{dt}(m\dot{x})$$

or, upon rearranging terms,

$$m\ddot{x} + kx = 0$$

which is the familiar equation of the harmonic oscillator.

PROBLEMS

Lagrange's method should be used in solving the following problems, unless stated otherwise.

1. Find the acceleration of a solid uniform sphere rolling down a perfectly rough plane, the plane being fixed and inclined at an angle θ with the horizontal.
2. A ball of mass m rolls down a movable wedge of mass M. The angle of the wedge is θ, and it is free to slide on a smooth horizontal surface. The contact between the ball and the wedge is perfectly rough. Find the acceleration of the wedge.
3. A particle slides on a smooth inclined plane whose inclination θ is increasing at a constant rate ω. If $\theta = 0$ at time $t = 0$, at which time the particle starts from rest, find the subsequent motion of the particle.
4. Two blocks of equal mass m are connected by a light inextensible cord. One block is placed on a smooth horizontal table, the other block hangs over the edge of the table. Find the acceleration of the system.
5. Solve Prob. 4 for the case in which the cord is heavy, of mass m'.
6. A homogeneous sphere of radius b is balanced on top of a perfectly rough fixed sphere of radius a. If slightly disturbed, find the subsequent motion of the movable sphere and find where it will leave the fixed sphere.
7. Set up the equations of motion of a "double-double" Atwood machine consisting of one Atwood machine (with masses m_1 and m_2) connected by means of a light cord passing over a pulley to a second Atwood machine with masses

m_3 and m_4. Neglect the masses of all pulleys. Find the actual accelerations for the case $m_1 = m$, $m_2 = 4m$, $m_3 = 2m$, and $m_4 = 3m$.

8. Show that Lagrange's method automatically yields the correct equations of motion [component equations of Eq. (5.11)] for a particle moving in a plane in a rotating coordinate system Oxy. HINT: $T = \frac{1}{2}m\mathbf{v}\cdot\mathbf{v}$, where $\mathbf{v} = \mathbf{i}(\dot{x} - \omega y) + \mathbf{j}(\dot{y} + \omega x)$, and $F_x = -\partial V/\partial x$, $F_y = -\partial V/\partial y$.

9. Find the differential equations of motion for a particle in spherical coordinates.

10. Find the differential equations for the spherical pendulum in spherical coordinates.

11. Find the differential equations of motion for a particle constrained to move on a smooth right-circular cone, the axis of the cone being vertical. Show that the particle, given an initial motion, will always remain between two horizontal circles on the cone.

12. The point of support of a simple pendulum of length l is being elevated at a constant acceleration a. Find the period.

13. Two identical rods AB and BC, each of mass m and length $2a$, are joined smoothly at B. The rods lie at rest on a smooth horizontal table and are initially at right angles to each other. An impulse P is applied at A lengthwise to the rod AB. Find the motion of the system immediately after the application of the impulse.

14. Show that the Lagrangian function

$$L = \frac{1}{2}mv^2 - q\varphi + \mathbf{v}\cdot\mathbf{A}$$

yields the correct equation of motion for a particle in an electromagnetic field, namely,

$$m\ddot{\mathbf{r}} = q(\mathbf{E} + \mathbf{v}\times\mathbf{B})$$

where

$$\mathbf{E} = -\nabla\varphi \quad \text{and} \quad \mathbf{B} = \nabla\times\mathbf{A}$$

(The vector quantity $\mathbf{A}$ is called the *vector potential*, and the scalar quantity φ is called the *scalar*, or *electrostatic*, *potential*.)

15. Find (a) the generalized momenta, and (b) the Hamiltonian function H for the Lagrangian function given in Prob. 14.

16. Find and solve Hamilton's canonical equations for (a) A projectile in two dimensions (b) A simple pendulum.

11

Theory of Vibrations

Simple cases of systems that can undergo oscillations about a configuration of equilibrium include a simple pendulum, a particle suspended on an elastic spring, a physical pendulum, etc., all being cases of one degree of freedom. When we consider more complicated systems — systems with several degrees of freedom — we shall find that not one but several different frequencies of oscillation are possible. In our analysis of oscillating systems, we shall find it very convenient to use generalized coordinates and to employ Lagrange's method for finding the equations of motion in terms of those coordinates.

11.1 Potential Energy and Equilibrium. Stability

Before we take up the study of the motion of a system about an equilibrium configuration, let us examine briefly the equilibrium itself. Consider a system with n degrees of freedom, and let the generalized coordinates $q_1, q_2, \ldots q_n$ specify the configuration. We shall assume that the system is conservative and that the potential energy V is a function of the q's alone:

$$V = V(q_1, q_2, \ldots q_n)$$

Now we have shown that the generalized forces Q_k are given by

$$Q_k = -\frac{\partial V}{\partial q_k} \quad (k = 1, 2, \ldots n) \tag{11.1}$$

An equilibrium configuration is defined as a configuration for which all of the generalized forces vanish, namely,

$$Q_k = -\frac{\partial V}{\partial q_k} = 0 \quad (k = 1, 2, \ldots n) \tag{11.2}$$

These equations constitute a necessary condition for the system to remain at rest if, initially, it is at rest. If the system is given a small displacement, however, it may or may not return to equilibrium. If a system always tends to return to equilibrium, given a sufficiently small displacement, the equilibrium is *stable;* otherwise, the equilibrium is *unstable.* (If the system has no tendency to move either toward or away from equilibrium, the equilibrium is said to be *neutral.*)

A ball placed (1) at the bottom of a spherical bowl, (2) on top of a spherical cap, and (3) on a plane horizontal surface are examples of stable, unstable, and neutral equilibrium, respectively.

Let us see how the potential-energy function V enters the picture. Consider the motion of a system subsequent to the application of a small impulse that leaves the system in motion while it is at an equilibrium configuration. Since the total energy is constant, we can write

$$T + V = T_o + V_o$$

or

$$T - T_o = -(V - V_o) \tag{11.3}$$

where T_o is the kinetic energy the system has at the equilibrium configuration (as a result of the impulse), and V_o is the potential energy at the equilibrium configuration. Now if the potential energy is maximum at equilibrium, then $V - V_o$ is negative, and, consequently $T - T_o$ is positive; that is, T increases as the system moves away from equilibrium. This is clearly an unstable situation. On the other hand, if the equilibrium configuration is one of minimum potential energy, then $V - V_o$ is positive, and $T - T_o$ is negative; that is, T decreases. But T can never be negative, consequently T decreases to zero at some limiting configuration close to equilibrium, provided, of course, that T_o is small enough. The equilibrium is stable in this case. Thus the criterion for stable equilibrium is that the potential energy is a minimum.

For a system with one degree of freedom, we have

$$V = V(q) \tag{11.4}$$

and, at equilibrium

$$\frac{dV}{dq} = 0 \tag{11.5}$$

The stability is then expressed as follows:

$$\frac{d^2V}{dq^2} > 0 \text{ (stable)} \tag{11.6}$$

$$\frac{d^2V}{dq^2} < 0 \text{ (unstable)} \tag{11.7}$$

If $d^2V/dq^2 = 0$, we must examine the higher-order derivatives. Although it will not be proved here, it can be shown that if the first nonvanishing derivative is of odd order, the equilibrium is unstable, and if the first non-vanishing derivative is of even order, the equilibrium is stable or unstable, depending on whether the value of the derivative is greater than or less than zero, respectively. In Fig. 11.1 is shown a graph of a hypothetical potential function. The point A corresponds to a position of stable equilibrium, and points B and C correspond to positions of unstable equilibrium.

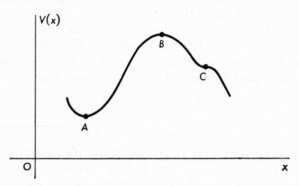

Fɪɢ. 11.1

Eꭓᴀᴍᴘʟꜰ

Let us examine the equilibrium of a body having a rounded (spherical or cylindrical) base which is balanced on a plane horizontal surface. Let a be the radius of curvature of the base, and let the center of mass C be a distance b from the initial point of contact, as shown in Fig. 11.2(a). In Fig. 11.2(b) the body is shown in a displaced position, where θ is the angle

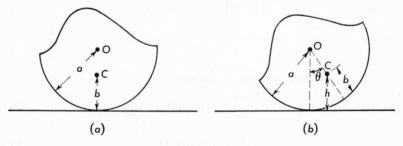

Fɪɢ. 11.2

between the vertical and the line OC (O being the center of curvature), as shown. Let h denote the distance from the plane to the center of mass. Then the potential energy is given by

$$V = mgh = mg[a - (a - b)\cos\theta]$$

where m is the mass of the body. We have

$$\frac{dV}{d\theta} = mg(a - b)\sin\theta$$

so

$$\frac{dV}{d\theta} = 0 \quad \text{for} \quad \theta = 0$$

Thus $\theta = 0$ is a position of equilibrium. Furthermore

$$\frac{d^2V}{d\theta^2} = mg(a - b)\cos\theta$$

and

$$\frac{d^2V}{d\theta^2} = mg(a - b) \quad \text{for} \quad \theta = 0$$

Hence the equilibrium is stable if $a > b$, that is, if the center of mass lies below the center of curvature.

11.2.   Expansion of the Potential-Energy Function in a Power Series

Let us consider first a system having one degree of freedom. Suppose we expand the potential-energy function $V(q)$ as a power series about the point $q = a$. We have

$$V(q) = \kappa_o + \kappa_1(q - a) + \frac{1}{2!}\kappa_2(q - a)^2 + \cdots + \frac{1}{r!}\kappa_r(q - a)^r + \cdots$$

where

$$\kappa_r = \left(\frac{d^r V}{dq^r}\right)_{q=a}$$

Now if the point $q = a$ is a position of equilibrium, then $\kappa_1 = (dV/dq)_{q=a}$ $= 0$, and

$$V(q) = \kappa_o + \frac{1}{2!}\kappa_2(q - a)^2 + \cdots \tag{11.8}$$

The stability at $q = a$ then depends on the sign of κ_2. If κ_2 is positive, the equilibrium is stable, but if κ_2 is negative, the equilibrium is unstable. If κ_2 is zero, then the stability depends on the sign of the first nonvanishing coefficient.

If we transform the origin to the point $q = a$, and arbitrarily set $V(0) = 0$, then we can write

$$V(q) = \frac{1}{2}\kappa_2 q^2 \tag{11.9}$$

if we neglect higher powers of q.

Similarly, for the case of a system with several degrees of freedom, we can effect a linear transformation so that $q_1 = q_2 = \cdots = q_n = 0$ is a configuration of equilibrium, if an equilibrium configuration exists. The potential-energy function can then be expanded in the form

$$V(q_1, q_2, \ldots q_n) = \frac{1}{2}(\kappa_{11}q_1^2 + 2\kappa_{12}q_1 q_2 + \kappa_{22}q_2^2 + \cdots) + \text{higher terms} \tag{11.10}$$

where

$$\kappa_{11} = \left(\frac{\partial^2 V}{\partial q_1^2}\right)_{q_1 = q_2 = \cdots = q_n = 0}$$

$$\kappa_{12} = \left(\frac{\partial^2 V}{\partial q_1\, \partial q_2}\right)_{q_1 = q_2 = \cdots = q_n = 0}$$

etc. We have arbitrarily set $V(0,0,\ldots 0) = 0$. The linear terms in expansion [Eq. 11.10)] are absent because the expansion is about an equilibrium configuration. [See Eq. (11.2).]

The expression in parentheses in Eq. (11.10) is known as a *quadratic form*. If this quadratic form is positive definite,* that is, either zero or positive for all values of the q's then the equilibrium configuration $q_1 = q_2 = \cdots = q_n = 0$ is stable.

---

*The necessary and sufficient conditions that the quadratic form in Eq. (11.10) be positive definite are

$$\kappa_{11} > 0 \qquad \begin{vmatrix} \kappa_{11} & \kappa_{12} \\ \kappa_{21} & \kappa_{22} \end{vmatrix} > 0 \qquad \begin{vmatrix} \kappa_{11} & \kappa_{12} & \kappa_{13} \\ \kappa_{21} & \kappa_{22} & \kappa_{23} \\ \kappa_{31} & \kappa_{32} & \kappa_{33} \end{vmatrix} > 0 \quad \text{etc.}$$

11.3. Oscillations of a System with One Degree of Freedom

If a system has one degree of freedom, the kinetic energy T may be expressed

$$T = \frac{1}{2}\mu\dot{q}^2 \tag{11.11}$$

according to Eq. (10.14). Here the coefficient μ may be a constant, or it may be a function of the generalized coordinate q. In any case we can expand μ as a power series in q and write

$$\mu = \mu(0) + \left(\frac{d\mu}{dq}\right)_{q=0} q + \cdots \tag{11.12}$$

If $q = 0$ is a position of equilibrium, we shall consider q as small enough so that

$$\mu = \mu(0) = \text{constant} \tag{11.13}$$

is a valid approximation. From Eq. (11.9) we see that the Lagrangian function L can be expressed as follows:

$$L = T - V = \frac{1}{2}\mu\dot{q}^2 - \frac{1}{2}\kappa\, q^2 \tag{11.14}$$

where $\kappa = \kappa_2 = (d^2 V/dq^2)_{q=0}$. Lagrange's equation of motion

$$\frac{d}{dt}\frac{\partial L}{\partial \dot{q}} = \frac{\partial L}{\partial q}$$

is then

$$\mu\ddot{q} + \kappa q = 0 \tag{11.15}$$

Thus if $q = 0$ is a position of stable equilibrium, that is, if $\kappa > 0$, then q oscillates harmonically about the equilibrium position with angular frequency

$$\omega = \sqrt{\kappa/\mu} \tag{11.16}$$

and

$$q = q_0 \cos(\omega t + \epsilon) \tag{11.17}$$

where q_0 is the amplitude of the oscillation, and ϵ is a phase angle.

EXAMPLE

Consider the motion of the round-bottomed object discussed in the example of the preceding section (Fig. 11.2). If the contact is perfectly rough, we have pure rolling, and the speed of the center of mass is approximately $b\dot\theta$ for small θ. The kinetic energy T is accordingly given by

$$T = \frac{1}{2}m(b\dot\theta)^2 + \frac{1}{2}I_c\dot\theta^2$$

where I_c is the moment of inertia about the center of mass. Also, we can express the potential-energy function V as follows:

$$V(\theta) = mg[a - (a - b)\cos\theta]$$

$$= mg\left[a - (a - b)\left(1 - \frac{\theta^2}{2!} + \frac{\theta^4}{4!} - \cdots\right)\right]$$

$$= \frac{1}{2}mg(a - b)\theta^2 + \text{constant} + \text{higher terms}$$

We can then write

$$L = \frac{1}{2}(mb^2 + I_c)\dot\theta^2 - \frac{1}{2}mg(a - b)\theta^2 \qquad (11.18)$$

neglecting constants and higher terms. Comparing with Eqs. (11.14) and (11.15), we see that

$$\mu = mb^2 + I_c \qquad \kappa = mg(a - b)$$

The motion about the equilibrium position $\theta = 0$ is therefore approximately simple harmonic with angular frequency

$$\omega = \sqrt{\frac{mg(a - b)}{mb^2 + I_c}} \qquad (11.19)$$

11.4. Two Coupled Harmonic Oscillators

Prior to developing the general theory of oscillating systems with any number of degrees of freedom, we shall study a specific example, namely a system consisting of two identical harmonic oscillators coupled together. As shown in Fig. 11.3, we have two particles of mass m where each particle is connected to a light spring of stiffness k. The particles are also coupled together by a third spring of stiffness k'. We shall assume that the particles are restricted to move in a straight line (the x direction, as shown). The system therefore has two degrees of freedom. We shall choose co-

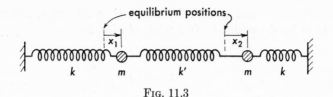

equilibrium positions

$$F_{IG}.\ 11.3$$

ordinates x_1 and x_2, the displacements of the particles from their respective equilibrium positions, to represent the configuration of the system.

The kinetic energy

$$T = \frac{1}{2}m\dot{x}_1^2 + \frac{1}{2}m\dot{x}_2^2 \qquad (11.20)$$

and the potential energy

$$V = \frac{1}{2}kx_1^2 + \frac{1}{2}k'(x_1 - x_2)^2 + \frac{1}{2}kx_2^2 \qquad (11.21)$$

Hence the Lagrangian function L is given by

$$L = \frac{1}{2}m\dot{x}_1^2 + \frac{1}{2}m\dot{x}_2^2 - \frac{1}{2}kx_1^2 - \frac{1}{2}k'(x_1 - x_2)^2 - \frac{1}{2}kx_2^2 \qquad (11.22)$$

The differential equations of motion

$$\frac{d}{dt}\frac{\partial L}{\partial \dot{x}_1} = \frac{\partial L}{\partial x_1} \qquad \frac{d}{dt}\frac{\partial L}{\partial \dot{x}_2} = \frac{\partial L}{\partial x_2}$$

then read

$$m\ddot{x}_1 = -kx_1 - k'(x_1 - x_2)$$
$$m\ddot{x}_2 = -kx_2 - k'(x_2 - x_1) \qquad (11.23)$$

or

$$\ddot{x}_1 + \frac{k}{m}x_1 + \frac{k'}{m}(x_1 - x_2) = 0$$
$$\ddot{x}_2 + \frac{k}{m}x_2 + \frac{k'}{m}(x_2 - x_1) = 0 \qquad (11.24)$$

If it were not for the coupling spring k', the two equations would be separated, and each particle would move independently with simple harmonic motion of frequency $\sqrt{k/m}$. It is reasonable, therefore, to try a solution for which x_1 and x_2 both depend on time through a factor $\cos \omega t$, where ω is to be determined. Our trial solution is

$$x_1 = A_1 \cos \omega t$$
$$x_2 = A_2 \cos \omega t$$

(11.25)

By direct substitution into Eq. (11.24), we find

$$-\omega^2 A_1 \cos \omega t + \frac{k}{m} A_1 \cos \omega t + \frac{k'}{m}(A_1 - A_2) \cos \omega t = 0$$

$$-\omega^2 A_2 \cos \omega t + \frac{k}{m} A_2 \cos \omega t + \frac{k'}{m}(A_2 - A_1) \cos \omega t = 0$$

Canceling the common factor $\cos \omega t$ and collecting terms, we get

$$\left(\frac{k + k'}{m} - \omega^2\right)A_1 - \frac{k'}{m}A_2 = 0$$
$$-\frac{k'}{m}A_1 + \left(\frac{k + k'}{m} - \omega^2\right)A_2 = 0$$

(11.26)

These are the conditions imposed on the coefficients A_1 and A_2 if our trial solution [Eq. (11.25)] is actually a solution. Thus either $A_1 = A_2 = 0$, or else the determinant of the coefficients must vanish:

$$\begin{vmatrix} \dfrac{k + k'}{m} - \omega^2 & -\dfrac{k'}{m} \\[2ex] -\dfrac{k'}{m} & \dfrac{k + k'}{m} - \omega^2 \end{vmatrix} = 0$$

(11.27)

This is known as the *secular* equation.

The above secular equation can be written

$$\left(\frac{k + k'}{m} - \omega^2\right)^2 - \left(\frac{k'}{m}\right)^2 = 0$$

which is a quadratic equation in ω^2. We can further write

$$\frac{k + k'}{m} - \omega^2 = \pm\frac{k'}{m}$$

The two roots, which we shall denote by ω_+ and ω_-, are therefore given by

$$\omega_+^2 = \frac{k}{m} \qquad \omega_-^2 = \frac{k + 2k'}{m}$$

(11.28)

The two frequencies ω_+ and ω_- are called the *normal* frequencies. We have, then, two possible solutions:

$$x_1 = A_1 \cos \omega_+ t \qquad x_2 = A_2 \cos \omega_+ t \tag{11.29}$$

and

$$x_1 = A_1' \cos \omega_- t \qquad x_2 = A_2' \cos \omega_- t \tag{11.30}$$

[Notice that the negative roots of the secular equation, $-\omega_+$ and $-\omega_-$, do not give different solutions, since $\cos \omega t = \cos (-\omega t)$]. The A's are not independent in Eqs. (11.29) and (11.30), however, for, if we substitute the values of ω_2 given by Eq. (11.28) back into either of Eqs. (11.26), we find

(1) for $\omega = \omega_+$

$$\left(\frac{k + k'}{m} - \frac{k}{m}\right)A_1 - \frac{k'}{m}A_2 = 0$$

which reduces, upon cancellation, to

$$A_1 = A_2 \tag{11.31}$$

(2) for $\omega = \omega_-$

$$\left(\frac{k + k'}{m} - \frac{k + 2k'}{m}\right)A_1 - \frac{k'}{m}A_2 = 0$$

which reduces to

$$A_1' = -A_2' \tag{11.32}$$

Thus our solutions [Eqs. (11.29) and (11.30)] can be expressed

$$x_1 = A \cos \omega_+ t \qquad x_2 = A \cos \omega_+ t \tag{11.33}$$

$$x_1 = A' \cos \omega_- t \qquad x_2 = -A' \cos \omega_- t \tag{11.34}$$

The subscripts on the A's are no longer necessary. The oscillations represented by the above solutions are called *normal modes*. The normal modes are characterized by the condition that all coordinates oscillate with the same frequency. In our case the oscillation at the frequency ω_+ is such that

$$x_1 = x_2$$

This is called the *symmetric* mode. The oscillation at the frequency ω_- is such that

$$x_1 = -x_2$$

This is known as the *antisymmetric* mode. Graphs illustrating the two normal modes are shown in Fig. 11.4.

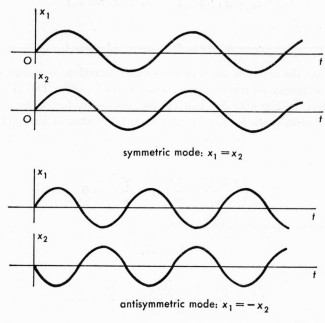

symmetric mode: $x_1 = x_2$

antisymmetric mode: $x_1 = -x_2$

FIG. 11.4

The complete solution. Let us go back now and consider the original differential equations of motion, Eq. (11.24). We can easily see that a trial solution in which the x's depend on time through a factor $\sin \omega t$ rather than $\cos \omega t$ would have yielded essentially the same results as those we have already obtained — we would have found the same normal frequencies and the same normal modes. That is,

$$x_1 = B \sin \omega_+ t \qquad x_2 = B \sin \omega_+ t \qquad (11.35)$$

$$x_1 = B' \sin \omega_- t \qquad x_2 = -B' \sin \omega_- t \qquad (11.36)$$

are also solutions. Now, since the differential equations are linear, we know that solutions may be added together to yield another solution. Hence we can write the complete solution in the form

$$x_1 = A \cos \omega_+ t + B \sin \omega_+ t + A' \cos \omega_- t + B' \sin \omega_- t$$

$$x_2 = A \cos \omega_+ t + B \sin \omega_- t - A' \cos \omega_- t - B' \sin \omega_- t \qquad (11.37)$$

or, equivalently,

$$x_1 = A_o \cos (\omega_+ t + \epsilon_+) + A'_o \cos (\omega_- t + \epsilon_-)$$
$$x_2 = A_o \cos (\omega_+ t + \epsilon_+) - A'_o \cos (\omega_- t + \epsilon_-)$$

[11.37(a)]

The constants of integration, A, A', B, and B' (or A_o, A'_o, ϵ_+, and ϵ_-) are determined from the initial conditions.

Thus at time $t = 0$ we have

$$x_1(0) = A + A' \qquad x_2(0) = A - A' \tag{11.38}$$

Also, differentiating Eq. (11.37) with respect to t to find $\dot{x}_1$ and $\dot{x}_2$ and setting $t = 0$, we find

$$\dot{x}_1(0) = B\omega_+ - B'\omega_- \qquad \dot{x}_2(0) = B\omega_+ + B'\omega_- \tag{11.39}$$

Solving for A, A', B, and B' yields

$$A = \frac{1}{2}[x_1(0) + x_2(0)] \qquad A' = \frac{1}{2}[x_1(0) - x_2(0)]$$

$$B = \frac{1}{2\omega_+}[\dot{x}_1(0) + \dot{x}_2(0)] \qquad B' = \frac{1}{2\omega_-}[-\dot{x}_1(0) + \dot{x}_2(0)] \tag{11.40}$$

Suppose, for example, that initially the two particles are pulled from their equilibrium positions by equal amounts in the same direction and released so that the initial conditions are $x_1(0) = x_2(0)$, $\dot{x}_1(0) = \dot{x}_2(0) = 0$. The result is that the symmetric mode alone is excited, since all the constants except A vanish. On the other hand, if the motion is started by pulling the two particles equally in opposite directions and releasing them, the initial conditions are $x_1(0) = -x_2(0)$, $\dot{x}_1(0) = \dot{x}_2(0) = 0$. In this case all constants except A' are zero, so the antisymmetric alone is excited. In general, the oscillation of the system consists of a mixture of the two modes.

11.5. Normal Coordinates

In the motion of the two coupled harmonic oscillators, given by Eqs. (11.37) or [11.37(a)], let us introduce a new set of coordinates $\bar{x}_1$ and $\bar{x}_2$ defined as follows:

$$\bar{x}_1 = x_1 + x_2$$
$$\bar{x}_2 = x_1 - x_2 \tag{11.41}$$

From Eqs. (11.37) and [11.37(a)] we have

$$\bar{x}_1 = 2A \cos \omega_+ t + 2B \sin \omega_+ t = 2A_o \cos (\omega_+ t + \epsilon_+)$$
$$\bar{x}_2 = 2A' \cos \omega_- t + 2B' \sin \omega_- t = 2A'_o \cos (\omega_- t + \epsilon_-) \tag{11.42}$$

Thus, for any initial conditions, the coordinate $\bar{x}_1$ *always* oscillates with the frequency ω_+, and the coordinate x_2 likewise *always* oscillates with the frequency ω_-. The quantities $\bar{x}_1$ and $\bar{x}_2$ are called *normal coordinates.*

In the general case, a normal coordinate $\bar{q}_r$ is a linear combination of the generalized coordinates $q_1, q_2, \cdots q_n$ such that $\bar{q}_r$ involves only one normal frequency ω_r.

The normal modes of an oscillating system are characterized by the presence of just one of the normal frequencies and the corresponding normal coordinate, all the remaining normal coordinates being equal to zero. In the case of the two coupled oscillators, we have

(1) $\bar{x}_1$ active $\bar{x}_2 = 0$ $x_1 = x_2$: symmetric mode

(2) $\bar{x}_2$ active $\bar{x}_1 = 0$ $x_1 = -x_2$: antisymmetric mode

Differential Equations of Motion in Normal Coordinates.   Let us express the Lagrangian function for the problem of the two coupled oscillators in terms of the normal coordinates $\bar{x}_1$ and $\bar{x}_2$. From Eqs. (11.41) we have

$$x_1 = \frac{1}{2}(\bar{x}_1 + \bar{x}_2)$$

$$x_2 = \frac{1}{2}(\bar{x}_1 - \bar{x}_2)$$

(11.43)

From Eqs. (11.20), (11.21), and (11.22) we obtain

$$T = \frac{m}{2}\left(\frac{\dot{\bar{x}}_1 + \dot{\bar{x}}_2}{2}\right)^2 + \frac{m}{2}\left(\frac{\dot{\bar{x}}_1 - \dot{\bar{x}}_2}{2}\right)^2 = \frac{m}{2}\left(\frac{\dot{\bar{x}}_1}{2}\right)^2 + \frac{m}{2}\left(\frac{\dot{\bar{x}}_2}{2}\right)^2$$

$$V = \frac{k}{2}\left(\frac{\bar{x}_1 + \bar{x}_2}{2}\right)^2 + \frac{k'}{2}\bar{x}_2^2 + \frac{k}{2}\left(\frac{\bar{x}_1 - \bar{x}_2}{2}\right)^2 = \frac{k}{2}\left(\frac{\bar{x}_1^2}{2}\right) + \frac{k''}{2}\left(\frac{\bar{x}_2^2}{2}\right)$$

$$L = \frac{m}{4}\dot{\bar{x}}_1^2 + \frac{m}{4}\dot{\bar{x}}_2^2 - \frac{k}{4}\bar{x}_1^2 - \frac{k''}{4}\bar{x}_2^2$$

(11.44)

where $k'' = k + 2k'$.

We see that there are no cross terms in T, V, or L. The equations of motion

$$\frac{d}{dt}\frac{\partial L}{\partial \dot{\bar{x}}_1} = \frac{\partial L}{\partial \bar{x}_1} \qquad \frac{d}{dt}\frac{\partial L}{\partial \dot{\bar{x}}_2} = \frac{\partial L}{\partial \bar{x}_2}$$

become

$$\frac{m}{2}\ddot{\bar{x}}_1 = -\frac{k}{2}\bar{x}_1 \qquad \frac{m}{2}\ddot{\bar{x}}_2 = -\frac{k''}{2}\bar{x}_2$$

or

$$\ddot{x}_1 + \frac{k}{m}\bar{x}_1 = 0 \qquad \ddot{x}_2 + \frac{k''}{m}\bar{x}_2 \qquad\qquad (11.45)$$

The equations are already separated. The solutions are clearly given by Eqs. (11.42) where

$$\omega_+ = \sqrt{\frac{k}{m}} \qquad \omega_- = \sqrt{\frac{k''}{m}} = \sqrt{\frac{k + 2k'}{m}} \qquad\qquad (11.46)$$

in agreement with our previous results.

It is a characteristic feature of normal coordinates that the differential equations of motion are automatically separated, there being one differential equation for each normal coordinate. This results from the fact that there are no cross terms in the expressions for the kinetic and the potential energy when these are expressed in terms of normal coordinates.

★11.6.   General Theory of Vibrating Systems

Turning now to a general system with n degrees of freedom, we have shown in the last chapter (Sec. 10.4) that the kinetic energy T is a homogeneous quadratic function of the generalized velocities, namely,

$$T = \frac{1}{2}\mu_{11}\dot{q}_1^2 + \mu_{12}\dot{q}_1\dot{q}_2 + \frac{1}{2}\mu_{22}\dot{q}_2^2 + \cdots = \sum_{j,k} \frac{1}{2}\mu_{jk}\dot{q}_j\dot{q}_k \qquad\qquad (11.47)$$

provided there are no moving constraints. Since we are concerned with motion about an equilibrium configuration, we shall assume, as in Sec. 11.3, Eq. (11.13), that the μ's are constant and equal to their values at the equilibrium configuration. We shall further assume that a linear transformation has been introduced so that the equilibrium configuration is given by

$$q_1 = q_2 = \cdots = q_n = 0$$

Accordingly, the potential energy V, from Eq. (11.10), is given by

$$V = \frac{1}{2}\kappa_{11}q_1^2 + \kappa_{12}q_1q_2 + \frac{1}{2}\kappa_{22}q_2^2 + \cdots = \sum_{j,k} \frac{1}{2}\kappa_{jk}q_jq_k \qquad\qquad (11.48)$$

The Lagrangian function then assumes the form

$$L = \sum_{j,k} \frac{1}{2}(\mu_{jk}\dot{q}_j\dot{q}_k - \kappa_{jk}q_jq_k) \qquad\qquad (11.49)$$

and the equations of motion

$$\frac{d}{dt}\frac{\partial L}{\partial \dot{q}_k} - \frac{\partial L}{\partial q_k} = 0$$

then read

$$\sum_j (\mu_{jk}\ddot{q}_j + \kappa_{jk}q_j) = 0 \qquad (k = 1,2, \cdots n) \ (11.50)$$

If a solution of the form

$$q_k = A_k \cos \omega t \qquad (k = 1,2, \cdots n) \ (11.51)$$

exists, then, by direct substitution the following equations must be satisfied:

$$\sum_j (-\mu_{jk}\omega^2 + k_{jk})A_j = 0 \qquad (k = 1,2, \cdots n) \ (11.52)$$

A nontrivial solution requires that the determinant of the coefficients of the A's vanish:

$$\begin{vmatrix} -\mu_{11}\omega^2 + k_{11} & -\mu_{12}\omega^2 + k_{12} & \cdots \\ -\mu_{21}\omega^2 + k_{21} & -\mu_{22}\omega^2 + k_{22} & \cdots \\ \cdots & \cdots & \cdots \end{vmatrix} = 0 \qquad (11.53)$$

The above secular equation is an equation of the nth degree in ω^2. The n roots are the squares of the normal frequencies of the system.

Existence of normal coordinates. Since the kinetic energy T can never be negative, any representation of T in terms of generalized coordinates [Eq. (11.47)] must be positive definite. There is a fundamental theorem in the theory of linear transformations* which states that if the coefficients of the two quadratic forms

$$\sum_{j,k} a_{jk}x_jx_k \qquad \sum_{j,k} b_{jk}x_jx_k$$

satisfy

$$a_{jk} = a_{kj} \qquad b_{jk} = b_{kj}$$

and if the first is positive definite, then there exists a linear transformation

$$x_k = \sum_j c_{kj}y_j \qquad (k = 1,2, \cdots n)$$

such that the two quadratic forms reduce to sums of squares, namely,

$$\sum_{j,k} a_{jk}x_jx_k = y_1^2 + y_2^2 + \cdots + y_n^2$$

$$\sum_{j,k} b_{jk}x_jx_k = \gamma_1 y_1^2 + \gamma_2 y_2^2 + \cdots + \gamma_n y_n^2$$

*See, for example, L. P. Smith, *Mathematical Methods for Scientists and Engineers*, Prentice-Hall, Englewood Cliffs, N.J., 1953.

The theorem further states that the γ's are given by the roots of the determinantal equation

$$\begin{vmatrix} -\gamma a_{11} + b_{11} & -\gamma a_{12} + b_{12} & \cdots \\ -\gamma a_{21} + b_{21} & -\gamma a_{22} + b_{22} & \cdots \\ \cdots & \cdots & \cdots \end{vmatrix} = 0$$

Applying the theorem to our case of a vibrating system, we see that there exists a set of coordinates $\bar{q}_1, \bar{q}_2, \cdots \bar{q}_n$ and a transformation

$$q_k = \sum_j c_{kj} \bar{q}_j \qquad (k = 1, 2, \cdots n) \ (11.54)$$

which reduces T and V to sums of squares:

$$T = \frac{1}{2}(\dot{\bar{q}}_1^2 + \dot{\bar{q}}_2^2 + \cdots + \dot{\bar{q}}_n^2) \tag{11.55}$$

$$V = \frac{1}{2}(\gamma_1 \bar{q}_1^2 + \gamma_2 \bar{q}_2^2 + \cdots + \gamma_n \bar{q}_n^2) \tag{11.56}$$

Then

$$L = \frac{1}{2}(\dot{\bar{q}}_1^2 - \gamma_1 \bar{q}_1^2 + \dot{\bar{q}}_2^2 - \gamma_2 \bar{q}_2^2 + \cdots + \dot{\bar{q}}_n^2 - \gamma_n \bar{q}_n^2) \tag{11.57}$$

The corresponding equations of motion are

$$\ddot{\bar{q}}_k + \gamma_k \bar{q}_k = 0 \qquad (k = 1, 2, \cdots n) \ (11.58)$$

The solutions are

$$\bar{q}_k = \bar{A}_k \cos(\sqrt{\gamma_k}\, t + \epsilon_k) \qquad (k = 1, 2, \cdots n) \ (11.59)$$

Thus the quantities $\bar{q}_1, \bar{q}_2, \cdots \bar{q}_n$ are the normal coordinates, and $\gamma_1, \gamma_2, \cdots \gamma_n$ are the squares of the normal frequencies. We shall not go into the problem of finding the transformation which yields the normal coordinates for a general system. The normal frequencies are given by the roots of the secular equation Eq. (11.53). This equation can be written down without knowing the normal coordinate transformation.

Motion of a general system when damping forces and external driving forces are present. In the foregoing analysis of the oscillation of a general system, we neglected the presence of any frictional forces. If the system is subject to viscous damping forces proportional to the first powers of the velocities of the particles, we can write Lagrange's equations in the form

$$\frac{d}{dt}\frac{\partial L}{\partial \dot{q}_k} = \frac{\partial L}{\partial q_k} + Q_k' \tag{11.60}$$

where the generalized damping force Q_k' is given by

$$Q_k' = -c_{1k}\dot{q}_1 - c_{2k}\dot{q}_2 - \cdots - c_{nk}\dot{q}_n \tag{11.61}$$

The resulting differential equations of motion are similar to the undamped case [Eqs. (11.50)], except that terms involving the $\dot{q}$'s are present. It is often (but not always) possible in this case to find a normal coordinate transformation such that the resulting differential equations are of the form

$$\bar{\mu}_k \ddot{\bar{q}}_k + \bar{c}_k \dot{\bar{q}}_k + \kappa_k \bar{q}_k = 0 \tag{11.62}$$

so that

$$\bar{q}_k = \bar{A}_k e^{-\lambda_k t} \cos (\omega_k t + \epsilon_k) \tag{11.63}$$

The amplitudes of the normal modes thus die out exponentially with time. There is also the possibility of a nonoscillatory situation analogous to the critically damped or overdamped one-dimensional case.

Finally, for the motion of a system which, in addition to linear restoring forces and dissipative forces, is subject to external driving forces that vary harmonically with time, we can express the situation analytically by including terms of the form $Q_{k \text{ ext}} \cos \omega t$ (or $Q_{k \text{ ext}} e^{i\omega t}$) in each equation of motion, Eq. (11.60). The resulting equations of motion in the normalized coordinates assume the form

$$\bar{\mu}_k \ddot{\bar{q}}_k + \bar{c}_k \dot{\bar{q}}_k + \bar{\kappa}_k \bar{q}_k = \bar{Q}_k e^{i\omega t} \tag{11.64}$$

Thus, for example, if the system is subject to a single driving force varying harmonically at a frequency equal to one of the normal frequencies of the system, then the corresponding normal mode is the one that assumes the largest amplitude in the steady-state condition. In fact, if the damping constants are vanishingly small, then the normal mode whose frequency is equal to the driving frequency is the only one that is excited.

★11.7. Vibrations of a System of Many Particles. The Wave Equation

In this section we shall study the motion of a system composed of n identical particles (each of mass m) connected by a series of elastic springs (each of stiffness K), as shown in Fig. 11.5. Let us label the displacements of the particles from their respective equilibrium positions by $\xi_1, \xi_2, \cdots \xi_n$. We shall assume that the particles move only in the longitudinal, or x direction, as shown in the Fig. 11.5, although the following analysis is easily modified to include the case of transverse motion.

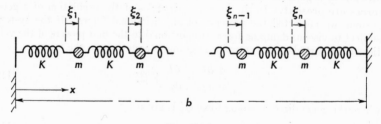

FIG. 11.5

The kinetic energy and the potential energy of the system are given by

$$T = \frac{1}{2}m\dot{\xi}_1^2 + \frac{1}{2}m\dot{\xi}_2^2 + \cdots + \frac{1}{2}m\dot{\xi}_n^2 \tag{11.65}$$

$$V = \frac{1}{2}K\xi_1^2 + \frac{1}{2}K(\xi_2 - \xi_1)^2 + \cdots + \frac{1}{2}K(\xi_n - \xi_{n-1})^2 + \frac{1}{2}K\xi_n^2 \tag{11.66}$$

From the Lagrangian function $L = T - V$, we find that the equations of motion are

$$m\ddot{\xi}_1 = K\xi_1 - K(\xi_2 - \xi_1)$$

$$m\ddot{\xi}_2 = K(\xi_2 - \xi_1) - K(\xi_3 - \xi_2)$$

$$\cdot$$
$$\cdot$$
$$\cdot$$

$$m\ddot{\xi}_r = K(\xi_r - \xi_{r-1}) - K(\xi_{r+1} - \xi_r) \tag{11.67}$$

$$\cdot$$
$$\cdot$$
$$\cdot$$

$$m\ddot{\xi}_n = K\xi_n - K(\xi_{n-1} - \xi_n)$$

Let us use a trial solution in which the ξ's vary harmonically with time:

$$\xi_r = a_r e^{i\omega t} \qquad (r = 1, 2, \ldots n) \tag{11.68}$$

Here a_r is the amplitude of the oscillation of the rth particle. Substituting the above solution into Eqs. (11.67) and canceling the common factor $e^{i\omega t}$ yields the following recursion formula for the a's:

$$-m\omega^2 a_r = K[a_{r+1} - 2a_r + a_{r+1}] \qquad (r = 1, 2, \ldots n) \tag{11.69}$$

The above formula will include the first and the last equations of Eqs. (11.67) if we impose the condition that

$$a_o = a_{n+1} = 0 \tag{11.70}$$

It is possible to obtain an explicit expression for a_r which satisfies the recursion formula by letting

$$a_r^+ = Ae^{i\varphi r} \tag{11.71}$$

so that

$$-m\omega^2 Ae^{i\varphi r} = K[Ae^{i\varphi(r+1)} - 2Ae^{i\varphi r} + Ae^{i\varphi(r-1)}]$$

Dividing by $Ae^{i\varphi r}$ yields

$$-m\omega^2 = K(e^{i\varphi} - 2 + e^{-i\varphi}) = K(2\cos\varphi - 2) = -4K\sin^2\frac{\varphi}{2}$$

Thus

$$\varphi = 2 \sin^{-1} \left(\frac{m\omega^2}{4K} \right)^{1/2} = 2 \sin^{-1} \left(\frac{\omega}{2\omega_o} \right) \tag{11.72}$$

where we have introduced the abbreviation

$$\omega_o^2 = \frac{K}{m} \tag{11.73}$$

Now a_r^+ as given by Eq. (11.71) does not satisfy the boundary conditions of Eq. (11.70). We can, however, easily obtain a formula for the a's which does satisfy the boundary conditions by noting that a_r^- defined by

$$a_r^- = A e^{-i\varphi r} \tag{11.74}$$

also satisfies the recursion formula Eq. (11.69). Hence, if we let

$$a_r = \frac{1}{2}(a_r^+ - a_r^-) = \frac{A}{2}(e^{i\varphi r} - e^{-i\varphi r}) = A \sin \varphi r \tag{11.75}$$

the recursion formula is satisfied and also the boundary condition $a_o = 0$. Furthermore, if we set

$$\varphi(n + 1) = \pi, 2\pi, \ldots n\pi \tag{11.76}$$

then the boundary condition $a_{n+1} = 0$ is met.

The normal frequencies $\omega_1, \omega_2, \cdots \omega_n$ are given by Eqs. (11.72) and (11.76), namely,

$$\omega_1 = 2\omega_o \sin \frac{\pi}{2n + 2}$$

$$\omega_2 = 2\omega_o \sin \frac{2\pi}{2n + 2}$$

$$\cdot$$
$$\cdot$$

$$\omega_s = 2\omega_o \sin \frac{s\pi}{2n + 2} \tag{11.77}$$

$$\cdot$$
$$\cdot$$

$$\omega_n = 2\omega_o \sin \frac{n\pi}{2n + 2}$$

From Eqs. (11.75) and (11.76), the amplitudes a_r are given by

$$a_r = A \sin \frac{rs\pi}{n + 1} \qquad (r, s = 1, 2, \ldots n) \tag{11.78}$$

The subscript s refers to a given mode or normal frequency, and the subscript r refers to a particular particle. The amplitudes a_r for the various modes can thus be represented by means of the sine curve $a_r = A \sin r\varphi$, where $\varphi = s\pi/(n + 1)$. The actual motion of the system when vibrating in a given mode (determined by the integer s) is given by

$$\xi_r = a_r \cos \omega_s t \qquad (11.79)$$

The case $n = 3$ is illustrated in Fig. 11.6.

In Eqs. (11.77), if n is large compared to s, we can replace $\sin [s\pi/(2n + 2)]$ by $s\pi/(2n + 2)$, and so we have approximately

$$\omega_s \cong s\pi\omega_o \qquad (11.80)$$

That is, the normal frequencies are approximately integral multiples of the lowest frequency $\pi\omega_o$.

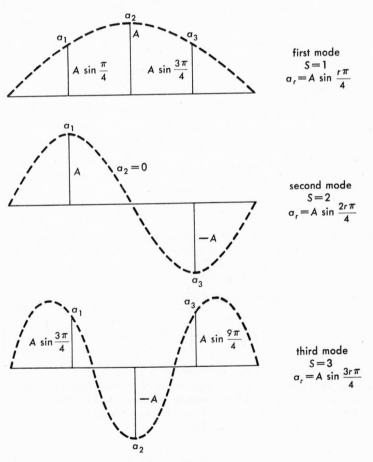

FIG. 11.6

The wave equation.   Let us refer to the equations of motion of our vibrating system of particles [Eqs. (11.67)]. These equations can be written in the form

$$m\ddot{\xi}_r = Kh\left[\frac{\xi_{r+1} - \xi_r}{h} - \frac{\xi_r - \xi_{r-1}}{h}\right] \tag{11.81}$$

where h is the distance (measured along the x direction) between the equilibrium positions of two adjacent particles. If n is very large so that h is very small compared to the total distance between the first and the last particles, then

$$\frac{\xi_{r+1} - \xi_r}{h} \cong \left(\frac{\partial\xi}{\partial x}\right)_{x=rh+h/2} \qquad \frac{\xi_r - \xi_{r-1}}{h} \cong \left(\frac{\partial\xi}{\partial x}\right)_{x=rh-h/2}$$

and

$$\frac{\xi_{r+1} - \xi_r}{h} - \frac{\xi_r - \xi_{r-1}}{h} \cong h\left(\frac{\partial^2\xi}{\partial x^2}\right)_{x=rh} \tag{11.82}$$

The equations of motion, Eq. (11.81), can therefore be written

$$\frac{\partial^2\xi}{\partial t^2} = \frac{Kh^2}{m}\frac{\partial^2\xi}{\partial x^2} \tag{11.83}$$

Now the quantity Kh^2/m has the dimensions of the square of velocity. Let us therefore write the above equation as

$$\frac{\partial^2\xi}{\partial t^2} = v^2\frac{\partial^2\xi}{\partial x^2} \tag{11.84}$$

where $v^2 = Kh^2/m$. This is a well-known equation. It is called the *one-dimensional wave equation*. The wave equation is satisfied by any differentiable function, f, of the argument $x \pm vt$, namely,

$$\xi = f(x + vt) \qquad \xi = f(x - vt)$$

The student should verify that the above solutions satisfy the wave equation. The first solution represents a disturbance moving with speed v in the negative x direction, and the second solution represents a similar disturbance moving with the same speed in the positive x direction.

Of particular importance are the sinusoidal solutions

$$\xi = A\sin\left[\frac{2\pi}{\lambda}(x + vt)\right] \qquad \xi = A\sin\left[\frac{2\pi}{\lambda}(x - vt)\right] \tag{11.85}$$

The constant λ is called the *wavelength*. It is the distance between successive maxima (or minima) of ξ for a fixed value of t. Since the wave equation is linear, we can add any two solutions to obtain a third solution. Let us add the two sinusoidal solutions given above. The result, after use of the appropriate trigonometric identity, is the solution

$$\xi = 2A\sin\frac{2\pi}{\lambda}x\cos\omega t \tag{11.86}$$

where $\omega = 2\pi v/\lambda$. The above solution, obtained from two equal sine waves traveling in opposite directions, is known as a *standing wave*.

Now the standing-wave type of motion represented by Eq. (11.86) will satisfy the boundary conditions of our original problem, namely $\xi = 0$ for $x = 0$ and $x = b = (n + 1)h$, provided the quantity $2\pi b/\lambda$ is an integral multiple of π. Let us then write

$$\frac{2\pi b}{\lambda} = \frac{2\pi(n + 1)h}{\lambda} = s\pi \qquad (s = 1,2,\cdots) \quad (11.87)$$

so that the standing-wave solution takes the form

$$\xi = A \sin \frac{\pi s x}{(n + 1)h} \cos \omega t \qquad (11.88)$$

This agrees with our previous solution, Eq. (11.79), since $x = rh$. According to the above analysis, we can describe the motion of our system of oscillating particles as a set of standing waves, each normal mode corresponding to an integral number s of waves.

PROBLEMS

1. Two identical springs, each of natural length L and stiffness k, have their upper ends fixed a distance $2a$ apart. Their lower ends are tied together and support an object of mass m. Find the position of equilibrium and verify that the equilibrium is stable.

2. A cubical block of side $2a$ is balanced on top of a rough spherical cap of radius b. Show that the equilibrium is stable or unstable, depending on whether a is less than or greater than b, respectively.

3. Investigate the stability of the above situation for the case $a = b$.

4. A solid homogeneous hemisphere of radius a is balanced on top of a rough spherical cap of radius b. Show that equilibrium is stable if a is less than $\frac{3}{5}b$.

5. Find the period of oscillation about the equilibrium configuration in Prob. 1.

6. Do the same for Probs. 2 and 4.

7. A particle of mass m moves in a straight line, the x axis. The potential energy is given by $V(x) = -axe^{-kx}$ where a and k are constants. Find the equilibrium position and the period of small oscillations about the equilibrium position.

8. A rod of length $2a$ and mass m is supported by two springs. One spring is tied to each end of the rod, the springs are vertical, and the rod is horizontal. Find the normal frequencies of oscillation of the system, assuming that the motion is such that the rod remains in a vertical plane.

9. A double pendulum consists of a light inextensible cord of length $2a$ with one end fixed, the other end supporting a particle of mass m, and there is a second particle of mass m at the middle of the cord. Find the normal frequencies for small oscillations about the equilibrium position, assuming that the system remains in a vertical plane.

10. A cord of length a, with one end fixed, supports at the other end a rod of mass m and length b. Find the normal frequencies of the system, assuming that the amplitudes are small and that the system remains in a vertical plane.

11. Find the normal coordinates for the double pendulum (Prob. 9) and verify that the Lagrangian function reduces to sums of squares of the normal coordinates and their time derivatives. Assume that the departure from the equilibrium configuration is small.

12. Verify Eqs. (11.77) for the case $n = 3$ by solving the secular equation for this case.

13. Two identical simple pendulums are coupled together by a very weak force of attraction that varies as the inverse square of the distance between the two particles. (This force might be the gravitational attraction between the two particles, for instance.) Show that, for small departures from the equilibrium configuration, the Lagrangian can be reduced to the same form as that of the two coupled harmonic oscillators [Eq. (11.22)]. Show further that if one pendulum is started oscillating with the other at rest, then eventually the second pendulum will be moving and the first one will be at rest, and so on.

14. A linear triatomic molecule (CO_2, for example) consists of a central atom of mass m and two other atoms, each of mass m', the three atoms being in a straight line. Set up the Lagrangian function for such a molecule, assuming that the motion takes place along a single straight line (the x axis) and find the normal modes and normal frequencies. Assume that the forces between adjacent molecules can be represented by a spring of stiffness k.

15. Illustrate the normal modes for the cases $n = 4$ and $n = 5$, as shown in Fig. 11.6 for $n = 3$.

12

The Special Theory of Relativity

The special theory of relativity, briefly introduced here, is an important development of modern physics and has applications ranging from nuclear dynamics to celestial mechanics, profoundly influencing our ideas of space and time.

12.1. The Michelson-Morley Experiment

The history of the theory of relativity begins with a famous experiment, performed by Michelson and Morley in 1887, to determine the velocity of the earth in space by means of light waves.

A diagram of the optical arrangement of the Michelson-Morley experiment is shown in Fig. 12.1. The apparatus is essentially an optical interferometer. A beam of light from a source S is split into two beams by a half-silvered mirror M. One beam is reflected to a mirror M_1 which reflects the light directly back to M. The other beam (the transmitted beam) goes directly to another mirror M_2 which reflects the light back to M also. The two partial beams then recombine at M, part of the combined light going

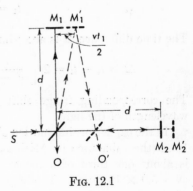

Fig. 12.1

toward an observer O who sees an interference pattern. The interference pattern can be made to shift by one fringe by moving either of the two mirrors M_1 or M_2 a distance equal to one fourth of a wavelength of light.

257

Now suppose that both mirrors M_1 and M_2 are at the same distance d from the mirror M. If the apparatus does not move during the time that the light is being reflected back and forth, then the two waves return to M at the same time and meet in phase at O. Suppose, however, that the apparatus is moving with velocity v in the direction of the initial beam from S. The paths of the beams will then be as shown by the dashed lines in Fig. 12.1. The times taken by the two partial waves in their respective journeys are no longer the same if we assume that light travels with constant speed c through some all-pervading medium (the ether). (The situation is analogous to the case of two swimmers in a stream, one swimmer going upstream and back, the other going across the stream and back.) Thus the wave that is moving toward M_2 travels with speed $c - v$ relative to the apparatus, and, on returning, this wave travels with relative speed $c + v$. The total time t_2 for the round trip is therefore

$$t_2 = \frac{d}{c - v} + \frac{d}{c + v} = \frac{2cd}{c^2 - d^2} \tag{12.1}$$

On the other hand, the wave which is reflected by M_1 travels along the path $MM_1'O'$, as shown. If we call t_1 the total time for the round trip in this case, then the distance MM_1' ($= M_1'O'$) is $(d^2 + \frac{1}{4}v^2 t_1^2)^{1/2}$, so

$$t_1 = \frac{2\left(d^2 + \frac{1}{4}v^2 t_1^2\right)^{1/2}}{c} \tag{12.2}$$

Solving for t_1, we get

$$t_1 = \frac{2d}{(c^2 - v^2)^{1/2}} \tag{12.3}$$

The time difference Δt is accordingly given by

$$\Delta t = t_2 - t_1 = 2d\left[\frac{c}{(c^2 - v^2)} - \frac{1}{(c^2 - v^2)^{1/2}}\right] = \frac{dv^2}{c^3} + \ldots \tag{12.4}$$

The corresponding fringe shift is $c\,\Delta t/\lambda = (d/\lambda)(v/c)^2$, where λ is the wavelength of the light.

In the earth's orbital motion about the sun $v/c \simeq 10^{-4}$, and, if d is about 10 m (the value used by Michelson and Morley), the expected fringe shift is about one third of a fringe using yellow light from a sodium lamp ($\lambda = 5.9 \times 10^{-5}$ cm). The experiment was performed by floating the whole apparatus in mercury and observing the fringes continuously while rotating the apparatus through 90°. No appreciable shift, at least none anywhere near as large as the expected one third of a fringe, was observed. This negative result came as a shock to the scientific world; it was contradictory to the accepted idea concerning electromagnetic radiation, namely, that such radiation must have some medium for its transmission.

Two physicists, Fitzgerald and Lorentz, attempted to explain the negative result of the Michelson-Morley experiment by proposing that a rigid body *contracts* in a direction parallel to its direction of motion (through the ether) in the ratio $(1 - v^2/c^2)^{1/2}$. This postulated shortening, known as the Fitzgerald-Lorentz contraction, would equalize the two light paths, and thus there would be no fringe shift.

Now this *ad hoc* manner of explaining the experimental result is not very satisfactory, for the hypothesis is not capable of direct verification. Any attempt to measure the Fitzgerald-Lorentz contraction by any known means is doomed to failure, since the measuring equipment contracts along with the object to be measured.

12.2. Einstein's Postulates of Special Relativity

In 1905 Albert Einstein resolved the problem of explaining the Michelson-Morley experiment by a radical approach based upon two postulates:

    (1) All physical laws are of the same form in all inertial systems.

    (2) The speed of light is the same in all inertial systems, regardless of the motion of the source.

The first postulate extends our earlier ideas about inertial reference systems, discussed in Sec. 5.2, to include *all* physical laws. This postulate denies the validity of any reference to motion of the coordinate system when stating a physical law. In other words, only *relative* motion has meaning, hence the name *relativity*. The second postulate says that any observer who measures the speed of light will always obtain the same result, regardless of the speed of the source relative to him (or of his speed relative to the source) as long as he uses an inertial reference system for his measurements.*

12.3. The Lorentz Transformation

Let us apply the relativity postulates to the case of two observers A and B who are moving relative to one another with constant velocity v. We shall designate A's coordinate system by $Oxyz$ and B's system by $O'x'y'z'$.

---

*Noninertial reference systems are treated in the *general theory of relativity* which Einstein formulated in 1916. The general theory is largely concerned with gravitational phenomena. A discussion of the general theory is beyond the scope of this book.

For simplicity, we shall assume that the respective axes Ox, $O'x'$, etc., are parallel, and that the relative motion is in the x direction; that is, the primed system is moving in the x direction with speed v relative to the unprimed system (Fig. 12.2).

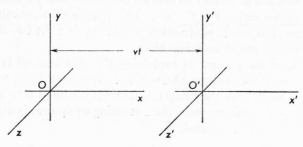

Fig. 12.2

Now if the two origins O and O' are coincident at time $t = 0$, then the distance OO' is equal to vt. The equations of transformation, according to classical or Newtonian kinematics, are then

$$x = x' + vt$$
$$y = y'$$
$$z = z'$$
$$t = t'$$

(12.5)

The equation $t = t'$ expresses the assumed equality of the time scales of the two observers. (They are using identical clocks.) The above transformation is sometimes called the *Galilean transformation*.

Suppose we consider a particular experiment in which a flash of light is sent out from O at the instant $t = 0$ when the two origins O and O' coincide. The light wave will travel outward in all directions with speed c. The front of the light wave can thus be represented as an expanding sphere given by the equation

$$r^2 = x^2 + y^2 + z^2 = c^2t^2$$

(12.6)

According to the transformation [Eq. (12.5)], the equation of the wave front in the primed system is

$$(x' + vt')^2 + y'^2 + z'^2 = c^2t'^2$$

(12.7)

This is the equation of a sphere of radius ct' centered at the point $x' = -vt'$ on the x' axis. Now if the above equation is correct, the wave front is moving with speed $c - v$ in the positive x' direction and with speed $c + v$

in the negative x' direction. This clearly contradicts the second postulate. According to the latter, the wave front must travel at the rate c in *both* coordinate systems. In other words, observer B must also see a wave traveling outward in all directions with speed c. The equation of the wave front in the primed coordinate system must be

$$x'^2 + y'^2 + z'^2 = c^2 t'^2 \tag{12.8}$$

rather than Eq. (12.7), according to the second postulate.

Let us see if we can find a transformation which does yield Eq. (12.8) from Eq. (12.6). We shall assume that $y' = y$ and $z' = z$. Subtracting Eq. (12.6) from Eq. (12.8), we have

$$x'^2 - x^2 = c^2 t'^2 - c^2 t^2$$

or

$$x'^2 - c^2 t'^2 = x^2 - c^2 t^2 \tag{12.9}$$

Now it turns out that a *linear* transformation

$$x' = a_1 x + a_2 t$$
$$t' = b_1 x + b_2 t \tag{12.10}$$

with the proper choice of constants will yield the required result. Substitution of the values of x' and t' given by the above transformation into Eq. (12.9) gives

$$(a_1 x + a_2 t)^2 - c^2 (b_1 x + b_2 t)^2 = x^2 - c^2 t^2 \tag{12.11}$$

This equation is necessarily an identity, since it must hold for all x and t. Expanding and equating coefficients, we find

$$a_1^2 - c^2 b_1^2 = 1 \quad a_1 a_2 - c^2 b_1 b_2 = 0 \quad a_2^2 - c^2 b_2^2 = c^2 \tag{12.12}$$

Now we have only three equations and four unknowns, but we know that the point $x' = 0$ (the origin O') is moving with speed v in the x direction. Hence the equation

$$x' = 0 = a_1 x + a_2 t$$

must reduce to

$$x = vt$$

Thus we have a fourth equation

$$v = -\frac{a_2}{a_1} \tag{12.13}$$

From Eqs. (12.12) and (12.13) we find, after a little algebraic exercise, that

$$a_1 = b_2 = \gamma \quad a_2 = -\gamma v \quad b_1 = -\frac{\gamma v}{c^2} \tag{12.14}$$

where

$$\gamma = \left[1 - \frac{v^2}{c^2}\right]^{-1/2} \tag{12.15}$$

Hence the following transformation satisfies our requirement that the equation of the expanding wave front is the same in both coordinate systems [Eqs. (12.6) and (12.8)]:

$$x' = \gamma(x - vt)$$

$$y' = y$$

$$z' = z \tag{12.16}$$

$$t' = \gamma\left(t - \frac{vx}{c^2}\right)$$

This is known as the *Lorentz transformation*. It is easy to show that the inverse of the above transformation is

$$x = \gamma(x' + vt')$$

$$y = y'$$

$$z = z' \tag{12.17}$$

$$t = \gamma\left(t' + \frac{vx'}{c^2}\right)$$

Notice that if v is very small compared to the speed of light, then γ is very nearly unity, and Eqs. (12.17) reduce to Eq. (12.5).

12.4. Some Consequences of the Lorentz Transformation

There are two immediate and surprising conclusions we can draw if we assume that the Lorentz transformation is valid physically. Consider first the measurement of the length of a rod. Let us suppose that the rod is fixed in the primed coordinate system and that it lies along the $O'x'$ axis. Then the length of the rod, as measured by observer B, is

$$L_o = x_2' - x_1'$$

where x_1' and x_2' are the coordinates of the ends of the rod. Now the quantity $x_2' - x_1'$ transforms, according to the Lorentz transformation, as follows:

$$L_o = x_2' - x_1' = \gamma[(x_2 - vt_2) - (x_1 - vt_1)] = \gamma[L - v(t_2 - t_1)]$$

where $L = x_2 - x_1$. Thus, assuming that observer A measures the positions of the ends of the rod at the same time (to him), that is, $t_2 = t_1$, then

$$L_o = \gamma L$$

or

$$L = \frac{L_o}{\gamma} = \sqrt{1 - \frac{v^2}{c^2}}L_o \tag{12.18}$$

Thus observer A says that the length of the rod is shorter than B says it is. The length of a moving rod appears shortened in the ratio $1/\gamma$. Similarly, a rod fixed in the unprimed system would appear shortened to B. The apparent shortening, expressed by Eq. (12.18), is just the right amount to explain the null result of the Michelson-Morley experiment (the Fitzgerald-Lorentz contraction).

Next let us compare two intervals of time, such as the ticks of a clock, as measured by our two observers. Let us suppose that the clock is at rest in the primed system. The time interval T_o between two consecutive ticks, $t' = t_1'$ and $t' = t_2'$, is

$$T_o = t_2' - t_1'$$

The Lorentz transformation then gives

$$T_o = t_2' - t_1' = \gamma\left[\left(t_2 - \frac{x_2 v}{c^2}\right) - \left(t_1 - \frac{x_1 v}{c^2}\right)\right] = \gamma\left[T - (x_2 - x_1)\frac{v}{c^2}\right]$$

where $T = t_2 - t_1$. Now the clock is moving with speed v in the x direction in the unprimed system, hence $x_2 - x_1 = vT$, and so

$$T_o = \gamma\left[T - (vT)\frac{v}{c^2}\right] = \gamma T\left(1 - \frac{v^2}{c^2}\right) = \frac{T}{\gamma}$$

or

$$T = \gamma T_o = \frac{T_o}{\sqrt{1 - v^2/c^2}} \tag{12.19}$$

Thus the two observers do not agree on the time intervals between ticks. Observer A says that the intervals are longer than B says they are. A moving clock appears to run slow in the ratio γ.

An important consequence, from a philosophical point of view, of the above results is that our intiutive ideas concerning space and time have to be drastically changed. We can no longer think of space and time as distinct entities. They are related in a peculiar way which depends on the motion of the reference system.

In a given reference system, which includes a time clock, a set of values (x,y,z,t) is called an *event*. We can think of events as points in a four-dimensional space, called *space time*. Two simultaneous events (events having the same values of t) in one reference system may not be simultaneous when described in a different reference system.

12.5. Relativistic Kinematics. Transformation of Velocities

From the Lorentz transformation, Eqs. (12.17), by differentiating, we can write

$$dx = \gamma(dx' + v\,dt')$$

$$dt = \gamma\left(dt' + \frac{v}{c^2}\,dx'\right)$$

Dividing the top equation by the bottom one, we have

$$\frac{dx}{dt} = \frac{dx' + v\,dt'}{dt' + \frac{v}{c^2}\,dx'}$$

or

$$\dot{x} = \frac{\dot{x}' + v}{1 + \frac{v\dot{x}'}{c^2}} \tag{12.20}$$

where $\dot{x} = dx/dt$ and $\dot{x}' = dx'/dt'$. We find similarly, from Eqs. (12.16),

$$\dot{x}' = \frac{\dot{x} - v}{1 - \frac{vx}{c^2}} \tag{12.21}$$

An interesting and important consequence of the above equations for the transformation of velocities is that velocities no longer combine in the same way that they do in the Newtonian kinematics. For example, suppose that observer B sees a particle traveling with velocity $\dot{x}' = c/2$ in his (the primed) coordinate system. Furthermore, let us suppose that the primed system is moving with velocity $c/2$ in the x direction relative to the unprimed system (observer A). Then, according to Eq. (12.20), the velocity of the particle in the unprimed system is not c but is given by

$$\dot{x} = \frac{\dfrac{c}{2} + \dfrac{c}{2}}{1 + \dfrac{\left(\dfrac{c}{2}\right)\left(\dfrac{c}{2}\right)}{c^2}} = \frac{c}{1 + 1/4} = \frac{4}{5}c$$

As a second example, we observe that if something moves with a velocity c in one coordinate system, say $\dot{x}' = c$, then

$$\dot{x} = \frac{c + v}{1 + \dfrac{cv}{c^2}} = c$$

that is, it moves with velocity c in the other coordinate system also. This is consistent with the second postulate of special relativity.

12.6. Relativistic Dynamics. The Variation of Mass with Velocity

Let us consider a collision of two identical particles, each of mass m. We shall suppose that the collision is perfectly *inelastic*, so that the particles stick together after colliding. Let the particles be moving with velocities $+v$ and $-v$, respectively, in the x direction before the collision, as measured in the unprimed coordinate system $Oxyz$ [Fig. 12.3(a)].

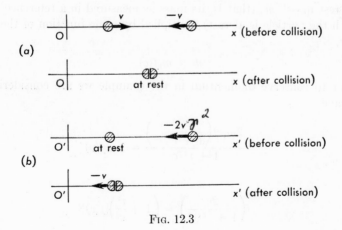

Fig. 12.3

After colliding, both particles are at rest in the unprimed system. The total momentum, in the x direction, is given by

$$mv + (-mv) = 0 \qquad \text{(before collision)}$$

$$2m(0) = 0 \qquad \text{(after collision)}$$

Now suppose we observe the above collision from a coordinate system $O'x'y'z'$ which is moving with velocity v in the x direction relative to the unprimed system [Fig. 12.3(b)]. Before the collision, the first particle is at rest in the primed system, and the second particle has a velocity

$$\dot{x}' = \frac{\dot{x} - v}{1 - (v\dot{x})/c^2} = \frac{-2v}{1 + v^2/c^2}$$

in the primed system, according to the rule for transformation of velocities, Eq. (12.20). After the collision, the two particles are both moving with velocity $\dot{x}' = -v$ in the primed system.

Now if mass is independent of motion, then the total momentum in the x' direction in the primed system is

$$m(0) + m\left(\frac{-2v}{1 + v^2/c^2}\right) \qquad \text{(before collision)}$$

$$2m(-v) \qquad \text{(after collision)}$$

The two quantities are not equal. Thus we are faced with the choice of either giving up the principle of conservation of linear momentum, or else we must assume that the mass of a particle somehow depends on the motion of that particle relative to a given observer. Rather than give up the principle of conservation of momentum, we choose the latter alternative. We shall assume that the mass of a moving particle is equal to the product of its "rest mass" m_o (that is, its mass as measured in a reference system in which the particle is at rest) multiplied by some function of the speed, namely,

$$m = m_o f(v)$$

In order to conserve momentum in the example we are considering, we must have

$$\frac{2m_o v f\left(\dfrac{2v}{1 + v^2/c^2}\right)}{1 + v^2/c^2} = 2mv f(v)$$

or

$$f\left(\frac{2v}{1 + v^2/c^2}\right) = \left(1 + \frac{v^2}{c^2}\right)[f(v)]^2 \qquad (12.22)$$

It is readily verified that

$$f(v) = \frac{1}{\sqrt{1 - v^2/c^2}} \tag{12.23}$$

satisfies the functional equation, Eq. (12.22). Hence, if we write

$$m = \frac{m_o}{\sqrt{1 - v^2/c^2}} \tag{12.24}$$

we have conservation of momentum in the collision we are considering. [It can be shown that the mass-velocity formula, Eq. (12.24), also yields conservation of momentum in general.] According to Eq. (12.24), the mass of a particle increases as the speed increases and approaches infinity as the speed v approaches the speed of light. Equation (12.24) has been verified experimentally for electrons and other particles accelerated to high speeds.

12.7. The Mass-Energy Relation

Let us consider the work W done in accelerating a free particle from rest to a final speed v. If $\mathbf{F}$ is the force acting on the particle, we have

$$\mathbf{F} = \frac{d}{dt}(m\mathbf{v}) = m_o \frac{d}{dt}\left(\frac{\mathbf{v}}{\sqrt{1 - v^2/c^2}}\right)$$

For simplicity, let us consider only motion in a straight line, the x axis in an appropriate coordinate system, so that we can write

$$dW = F\,dx = dx\,\frac{d(m\dot{x})}{dt} = \dot{x}\,d(m\dot{x})$$

and

$$\begin{aligned}
W &= \int_o^v \dot{x}\,d(m\dot{x}) = \left[\dot{x}(m\dot{x})\right]_o^v - \int_o^v m\dot{x}\,d\dot{x} \\
&= mv^2 - m_o \int_o^v \frac{\dot{x}\,d\dot{x}}{\sqrt{1 - \dot{x}^2/c^2}} \\
&= mv^2 + m_oc^2[\sqrt{1 - v^2/c^2} - 1] \\
&= mc^2 - m_oc^2 \tag{12.25}
\end{aligned}$$

Since the total work done on a free particle appears as kinetic energy T of the particle, we have

$$T = mc^2 - m_oc^2 \tag{12.26}$$

The above formula reduces to the usual formula for kinetic energy if v is small compared to c:

$$T = m_o c^2 \left[\left(1 - \frac{v^2}{c^2} \right)^{1/2} - 1 \right] = m_o c^2 \left(1 + \frac{1}{2} \frac{v^2}{c^2} + \ldots - 1 \right)$$

$$= \frac{1}{2} m_o v^2 + \ldots$$

If we write Eq. (12.26) as

$$m = m_o + \frac{T}{c^2} = m_o + m' \qquad (12.27)$$

we can associate with the kinetic energy T an equivalent mass m' where

$$T = m' c^2$$

Einstein generalized this viewpoint by saying that any mass m is equivalent to an amount of energy E where

$$E = mc^2 \qquad (12.28)$$

The principle of conservation of energy should then be modified to include mass as a form of energy.

The above equation has been amply verified experimentally. In the case of nuclear fission, for example, the total mass of the fission fragments is less than that of the original nucleus, the mass difference appearing as energy.

PROBLEMS

1. Fill in the steps leading to Eqs. (12.14).

2. Show that the inverse Lorentz transformation, Eqs. (12.17), follows algebraically from the direct transformation, Eqs. (12.16).

3. A train is 1/2 mile long and travels at a speed of 100 mph. Compute the Lorentz contraction.

4. A cosmic-ray meson has a half-life of 2.2×10^{-6} sec in a system in which the meson is at rest. Compute the half-life of mesons traveling at a speed of 99.9 percent of the speed of light relative to the observer who is measuring the half-life.

5. Two distant galaxies A and B are observed by us on the earth to be receding in opposite directions, the speed of recession of each being $3/4\,c$. Will an observer on A be able to see galaxy B? If so, what will he say that the speed of recession of B is?

6. Show that Eq. (12.22) is satisfied by $f(v)$ defined by Eq. (12.23).

7. Electrons in a linear accelerator are accelerated to a speed of $0.9999c$. What is the ratio of their mass to their rest mass?

8. Show that the rest mass of the electron is equivalent to about 0.531 million electron volts. Compute the kinetic energy in million electron volts of the electrons in Prob. 7.

9. Show that the momentum $p\ (= mv)$ is related to the mass energy E by the relation $E^2 = m_o^2 c^4 + c^2 p^2$.

10. A constant force F acts on a particle of rest mass m_o. Find the distance the particle travels in a time t if it starts from rest.

11. Analyze the two-particle collision of Sec. 12.6 for the case of a perfectly elastic collision. Show that the mass-velocity formula (12.24) gives conservation of linear momentum in this case.

Answers to Odd-numbered Problems

Chapter 1

1. (a) 9
   (c) $9(6)^{-1/2}$

7. $\mathbf{L} = -3\mathbf{i} - 2\mathbf{j} + 5\mathbf{k}, \qquad L = \sqrt{38}$

9. $\left(\dfrac{\sqrt{3} - 3}{2}\right)\mathbf{i}' - \mathbf{j}' + \left(\dfrac{3\sqrt{3} + 1}{2}\right)\mathbf{k}'$

Chapter 2

3. (a) A circle
   (b) A spiral

Chapter 3

1. $\dfrac{13F_o t_1^2}{6m}$

3. $v = v_o - \left(\dfrac{cv_o^{1/2}}{m}\right)t + \left(\dfrac{c^2}{4m^2}\right)t^2$

   $x = v_o t - \left(\dfrac{cv_o^{1/2}}{2m}\right)t^2 + \left(\dfrac{c^2}{12m^2}\right)t^3$

   $\left.\right\}$ *until $v = 0$ which is at $t = \dfrac{2\,m\,v_o^{\frac{1}{2}}}{c}$*

   Yes: $\dfrac{2mv_o^{3/2}}{3c}$

7. $\dfrac{v_o v_t}{\sqrt{v_o^2 + v_t^2}}$ where v_t = terminal speed = $\sqrt{mg/c}$

11. $\dfrac{2\pi}{\sqrt{63.92}}$ sec; about $2\frac{1}{4}$ oscillations

Chapter 4

Part I

3. $m\ddot{x} = -c\dot{x}(\dot{x}^2 + \dot{y}^2)^{1/2}$
   $m\ddot{y} = -mg - c\dot{y}(\dot{x}^2 + \dot{y}^2)^{1/2}$
   No

Part II

1. Range: $\dfrac{v_o^2}{g} - \dfrac{2\sqrt{2}cv_o^2}{3g^2}$
   Drift: $F_o v_o^2 g^2/m$

3. (a) $\mathbf{F} = -\mathbf{i}cy/z - \mathbf{j}cx/z + \mathbf{k}cxy/z^2$

(c) $\mathbf{F} = (\mathbf{i} + \mathbf{j} + \mathbf{k})ace^{c(x + y + z)}$

Part III

1. Tangential component of acceleration: $g(1 + 4\pi^2 a^2 n^2)^{-1/2}$

3. $(2ga)^{1/2}, 3mg$

5. $\ddot{r} - r \sin^2 \alpha \dot{\varphi}^2 = -g \cos \alpha, \qquad \dfrac{d}{dt}(r^2 \dot{\varphi}) = 0$

in spherical coordinates where α is half angle of cone

7. (a) 0.999 sec, 184°

(b) 1.065 sec, 228°

Chapter 5

1. $a + \dfrac{ga^2}{2v_o^2} + \dfrac{v_o^2}{2g}$; from rear of wheel a height ga^2/v_o^2 from center

3. $2\pi L^{1/2}(g^2 + b^2\omega^4)^{-1/4}$

5. 0.7 lb east

7. $\dfrac{4\omega v^3 \cos \lambda}{3g^2}$ west of point of projection

Chapter 6

5. Inverse-cube law of force

7. $r = (ae^{k\theta} + be^{-k\theta})^{-1}, \qquad k^2 = 1 - cm^{-1}k^{-2}$

$r = (a \cos k\theta + b \sin k\theta)^{-1}, \qquad k^2 = -1 + cm^{-1}k^{-2}$

$r = (a\theta + b)^{-1}, \qquad c = m^{-1}k^{-2}$

9. Angle between radius vector $\mathbf{r}_a$ and major axis is

$$\cot^{-1}(\tan \varphi - c \csc 2\varphi)$$

where $c = r_e v_e^2 / r_a v_a^2$

11. (a) 354 years, (b) 0.99, (c) $20v_e$ and $0.05v_e$

13. $\pi\sqrt{1 - ka}$

Chapter 7

1. $[2mE(1 + m/M)]^{1/2} \qquad$ and $\qquad [2ME(1 + M/m)]^{1/2}$

3. $\dfrac{v_o^2}{2\mu g}\left(\dfrac{m}{m + M}\right)^2$

9. $E_b + \dfrac{E_b}{2M}$

11. $m\ddot{y} = cv_e - mg$ where $m = m_o + M - ct$

(a) 4.2×10^6

(b) 44.6

Chapter 8

1. (a) On central line $\dfrac{4a}{3\theta} \sin \dfrac{\theta}{2}$ from center

(b) $x_c = \dfrac{4a}{3\pi}$　$y_c = \dfrac{4b}{3\pi}$

(c) At intersection of medians

(d) $\dfrac{3b}{5}$ from vertex

3. $\dfrac{2a}{5}$ from center

5. $\sin^{-1}(8\mu/3)$

11. $ma^2\left(\dfrac{1}{2} - \dfrac{16}{9\pi^2}\right)$

13. (a) $2\pi\sqrt{\dfrac{2\sqrt{2}a}{3g}}$,　$l' = a\sqrt{2}/6$

(b) $2\pi\sqrt{\dfrac{7\sqrt{2}a}{12g}}$,　$l' = a\sqrt{2}/12$

15. $5g/7$

17. $g\left(\dfrac{m_1 - m_2}{m_1 + m_2 + I/a^2}\right)$

19. (a) Horizontal component: $\frac{3}{4}mg \sin \theta(3 \cos \theta - 2)$

Vertical component: $\frac{1}{4}mg(3 \cos \theta - 1)^2$

(b) Slipping begins when $|3 \sin \theta(3 \cos \theta - 2)| = \mu(3 \cos \theta - 1)^2$; rod slips backward if above equation is satisfied for $\theta < \cos^{-1}(2/3)$, otherwise rod slips forward.

21. A point $a/2$ from center where a is the radius of the disc.

23. $v_{cm1} = -\dfrac{\hat{P}}{4m}$,　$\omega_1 = -\dfrac{3\hat{P}}{2ml}$

$v_{cm2} = \dfrac{5\hat{P}}{4m}$,　$\omega_2 = \dfrac{9\hat{P}}{2ml}$

Velocity of B is $-\hat{P}/m$

Chapter 9

1. (a) $J = \dfrac{Mab\omega}{12}$

Angle between $\mathbf{J}$ and x axis is $\tan^{-1}(a/b)$, whereas that between ω and x axis is $\tan^{-1}(b/a)$.

(b) Same as (a), but should be proved.

3. Kinetic energy in Prob. 1 is $\dfrac{M\omega^2a^2b^2}{24(a^2 + b^2)}$.

5. $\tan \theta = b/a$

7. $\dfrac{a}{b} = \dfrac{1}{3}$

11. $\dfrac{2\pi}{\omega}(1 + 3 \cos^2 \alpha)^{-1/2}$

Chapter 10

1. $\dfrac{5}{7}g \sin \theta$

3. $x = \left(\dfrac{x_o}{2} - \dfrac{g}{4\omega^2}\right)e^{\omega t} + \left(\dfrac{x_o}{2} + \dfrac{g}{4\omega^2}\right)e^{-\omega t} + \dfrac{g}{2\omega^2} \sin \omega t$

5. $g\left(\dfrac{m + m''}{2m + m'}\right)$ where m'' is mass of cord hanging over table

7. m_1: $\dfrac{23}{25}g$ (up)

m_2: $\dfrac{13}{25}g$ (down)

m_3: $\dfrac{1}{25}g$ (down)

m_4: $\dfrac{9}{25}g$ (down)

9. $m[\ddot{r} - r(\dot{\theta}^2 + \sin \theta \dot{\varphi}^2)] = -\dfrac{\partial V}{\partial r}$

$m\left[\dfrac{d}{dt}(r^2\dot{\theta}) - r^2 \sin \theta \cos \theta \dot{\varphi}^2\right] = -\dfrac{\partial V}{\partial \theta}$

$m\dfrac{d}{dt}(r^2 \sin^2 \theta \dot{\varphi}) = -\dfrac{\partial V}{\partial \varphi}$

11. $\ddot{r} - r \sin^2 \alpha \dot{\varphi}^2 = -g \cos \alpha, \qquad \dfrac{d}{dt}(r^2\dot{\varphi}) = 0$

in spherical coordinates where α is the half angle of the cone

13. $v_1 = \dfrac{4\hat{P}}{5m}, \qquad \omega_1 = 0, \qquad v_2 = \dfrac{\hat{P}}{5m}, \qquad \omega_2 = \dfrac{3\hat{P}}{5ma}$

Chapter 11

1. Let l be the stretched length of the spring. Then the equilibrium length l_o is given by

$$2k(l_o^2 - L^2)^{1/2}\left(\dfrac{l_o - L}{l_o}\right) = mg$$

3. Unstable

5. $2\pi\sqrt{\dfrac{m}{2k\left(1 - \dfrac{La^2}{l_o^3}\right)}}$

7. $x = k^{-1}, \qquad T = 2\pi\sqrt{\dfrac{m}{ka}}$

9. Antisymmetric mode: $\omega_+ = \sqrt{\dfrac{g}{a}}\sqrt{2 + \sqrt{2}}$

Symmetric mode: $\omega_- = \sqrt{\dfrac{g}{a}}\sqrt{2 - \sqrt{2}}$

11. $\bar{q}_1 = \sqrt{2}\,\theta + \varphi,\ \bar{q}_2 = \sqrt{2}\,\theta - \varphi$ where θ and φ are the inclinations to the vertical of the upper and lower halves of the cord, respectively.

Chapter 12

3. 0.004 inch
5. Yes; 0.96c
7. 70.7

Index